The Water Crisis

The
Water
Crisis

SENATOR FRANK E. MOSS

FOREWORD BY

Paul H. Douglas

FREDERICK A. PRAEGER, *Publishers*
New York • Washington • London

FREDERICK A. PRAEGER, PUBLISHERS
111 Fourth Avenue, New York, N.Y. 10003, U.S.A.
77-79 Charlotte Street, London W.1, England

Published in the United States of America in 1967
by Frederick A. Praeger, Inc., Publishers

Second printing, 1968

Library of Congress Catalog Card Number: 67-20490

Printed in the United States of America

To those Utah pioneers whose first act in building
a western empire was to divert a mountain stream
to water their arid lands

Foreword

Senator Frank E. Moss of Utah is competent in many fields, but perhaps most of all in the problems connected with water. He was reared in a state whose prosperity has been inseparably linked to the wise use of water. The Mormon pioneers who settled Utah were the first English-speaking Americans to use irrigation.

Since entering the Senate in 1959, Frank Moss has worked unceasingly on water legislation and investigations, gaining a wide knowledge of the water needs of every part of the nation.

He is a member of the Senate Committee on Interior and Insular Affairs, to which are referred all bills authorizing projects built by the Bureau of Reclamation, as well as legislation on water research, planning, and conservation. For two years, he served as chairman of the Subcommittee on Irrigation and Reclamation. He is a member of the Committee on Public Works, to which legislation is referred authorizing water pollution control measures, and all projects built by the U.S. Army Corps of Engineers.

Under his chairmanship, a subcommittee on Western Water Development supervised a staff study of proposals to transport water from the Arctic to western Canada and the American West and Midwest. He served on the Senate Select Committee on National Water Resources, which investigated the capability of our water resources to meet expanding demand.

Senator Moss is a man of great competence and sterling integrity. I have seen him stand firm against many pressures and temptations. It was once said of George Norris that he could not be flattered, fooled, or frightened and that no one could buy or bully him. This is equally true of Frank Moss. Like Sir Thomas More, he is a man for all seasons.

Out of his wealth of experience comes this book's analysis of the pressures that have brought about the water crisis facing the United States. It is an outstanding contribution to an enlarged public understanding that is so essential to the subject. His recommendations are of great significance and will have considerable influence on the course of public policy in the years ahead.

PAUL H. DOUGLAS

Preface

FOR THE NEXT GENERATION of Americans, I believe it is not an exaggeration to say that water—its competing uses and the conflicts that arise out of those uses—may be the most critical national problem.

The amount of water available to the nation is fixed, but the number of persons using it increases every day. And the uses of water multiply with technological growth. How do we share fairly the water that too many people need for too many purposes? How do we use it wisely, and maintain it?

Already, the struggle for water plagues numerous citizens in their daily lives. Already, many in government and many citizens' groups are turning their attention to the need for defining our water problems and working out equitable solutions as rapidly as possible. Already, the conflicts among competitive users—and their organized spokesmen—are great in number and often very bitter.

In our fervor to claim what seems to be our God-given right to water —whether as individuals, as towns or cities or states, as industrial corporations, as government agencies charged with responsibilities for conservation or health or defense—we too frequently downgrade or altogether disregard the rights of other users to the same water. And we dishonor the water itself, our heritage from a simpler world, through shocking misuse and mismanagement.

This book has been written in the hope that it will contribute to the definition and solution of the water crisis. For the most part, it contains what I have learned about the water needs of the United States during eight years in the Congress—and what I believe should be done.

Water problems are closely interrelated; therefore, if they are to be classified, it must be on a somewhat arbitrary basis. The first section of this book treats the history and politics of water use in the United States and, against that background, divides U. S. water problems into five categories. Pollution is discussed in Chapter V. Three other problems, shortage, variability, and depletion, are taken up in Chapters VI, VII, and VIII, respectively. The fifth problem is waste, which includes inefficient use of all kinds, unused runoff, and such water losses as those caused by "water-stealing" vegetation and evaporation from reservoirs. These topics are discussed in various chapters, with problems and solutions alike emphasized, particularly in Chapters XIII and XIV.

In general, the second part of the book is devoted almost entirely to solutions for water problems—projects accomplished and programs "in the works," in various stages of research and development, or proposed.

In the third section, I have outlined my proposals for reorganization of our water management activities and for a fundamental *national* water policy.

Information for the book has been drawn from many sources, of course, but the most extensive source is the work of the Senate Select Committee on National Water Resources, on which I served. Although all final judgments are my own, many persons have assisted in the book's preparation. Significant work in drafting and research was done by Oscar Jager, a free-lance writer with considerable experience in the natural resources field, and by my Administrative Assistant, Grant W. Midgley. Much reliance has been placed on the knowledge of Theodore M. Schad of the Library of Congress. All members of my personal staff have helped a great deal. Those on the staffs of the Senate committees on which I serve and many individuals in federal agencies and private industry have provided valuable material.

FRANK E. MOSS

March 1, 1967

Contents

MAPS, CHARTS, AND ILLUSTRATIONS

PART ONE

Into The Vortex

CHAPTER I

The Heritage Abused

As a nation, we Americans are guilty of abusing our natural heritage. An earlier generation bears the responsibility for the raids on the forests of the United States. Our generation is raiding the rivers and lakes, attacking the estuaries, and threatening the bays and seas that touch our land.

It is easy to see why. The demand for water is truly prodigious. Every year, we must find larger amounts to supply the kitchens and bathrooms of our sprawling cities and suburbs, to water parks and crops in our drier states, to accommodate boating and water skiing, and, most important, to supply a tremendously successful and voracious industrial machine. Today, whole regions of the country compete with one another for the flow of rivers and lakes as intensely as early settlers of the West fought for water holes.

Excessive pressure on water supply is not, of course, confined to the United States. It is a phenomenon common to areas of large population and to all industrialized nations. In the 1850's, Michael Faraday wrote a letter to *The Times* of London deploring contamination of the Thames. This century has seen a growing European concern for the sickness of some of that continent's famed lakes, and rivers. Writing in a company publication in 1965, an executive of a firm whose international business includes dyes, plastics, and pharmaceuticals said that, as a Swiss, he was thinking primarily of Switzerland, but that, to many countries, "the protection of our water has now become a matter of life and death."

Although we seldom think about it, we know how essential water is to all life. Primitive organisms were nurtured in the warm seas of the Paleozoic era more than 500 million years ago. One of the remarkable facts about human existence is the similarity of blood to sea water. Our bodies are two-thirds water. The distribution of fresh water over the globe has been a determining factor in the activities of man and in the location of the earth's centers of influence. Yet the deterioration of America's waters has taken place in the face of our understanding of their importance.

Nor is water the only natural resource to suffer deterioration. Our entire environment shares the same fate. Basically, the problem is usually thought of as one of overpopulation. U.S. figures show projections for births, deaths, and immigration indicating a population rise from 192 million in the early 1960's to 245 million by 1980, and perhaps to 350 million by the year 2000. Increases around the globe are comparable. Because of our ability to choke out plants and animals, conservationist Wallace Stegner has compared modern mankind to a weed. Building on the knowledge acquired by past generations, we cultivate a food supply, extinguish natural enemies, and use energy stored in the earth to do our work. A life form successful beyond all others, man is overrunning the earth, crushing the very environment that gives him life.

It is true that, if our population increase were less explosive, the pressure on our waters would have come more slowly, and the crisis we now face might have been postponed. But there is another—and perhaps even more powerful—force that increases water demand. Western civilization has produced the richest society the world has known. As our homes get bigger, our automobiles more numerous, and our vacation trips longer, we eat up more resources of all kinds—land, metals, energy fuels, farm products, building materials. And we use more water. In addition, our rising standard of living has spawned another condition—urbanization—that cuts water supply even as our affluence increases demand. When we take farm and meadowland to build subdivisions, we injure the water-holding capacity of an area. Bricks and concrete not only hold heat and intensify evaporation but also block and, thereby, reduce infiltration into the underground water reserves.

The real reason for our water crisis is failure to husband our resources. Although we have known how rapidly the population has been increasing and have known that a higher standard of living requires more water, political and social action—as almost always happens—have lagged behind technological change. Our activities as industrialists, scientists, and engineers have outrun our activities as citizens.

In an address to the Royal National Society in Athens in 1966, Vice-Admiral Hyman Rickover warned that human liberty itself could be extinguished if we permit a pattern of life to develop wherein technology, rather than man, becomes central to society's purpose. Admiral Rickover said:

> Much more thought should be given to technological interference with the balance of nature and its consequences for man, present and future. There is need of wider recognition that government has as much a duty to protect the land, the air, the water, the natural environment against technological damage, as it has to protect the country against foreign enemies and the individual against criminals.

Doubtless, some of our apathy has been due to the faith of Americans in the ability of science to solve the water problem. Scientific marvels surround us. Are we not on the way to the moon? Have we not produced enough nuclear bombs to blow up the earth? Has not more scientific knowledge been accumulated in our lifetimes than in all the ages before?

Science *can* solve our water problems, given the opportunity, insofar as the solutions can be purely scientific. We have long known how to take salt out of seawater. In limited instances, we have made rain. We regularly purify waste water. Recirculation systems have been built, cutting drastically the amount of water needed to make a ton of product. But science cannot solve the political and legal problems that often must be dealt with first.

To reach the moon, we have given a single agency—the National Aeronautics and Space Administration—the authority to build and operate space vehicles, and Congress allots it $5 billion every year. In defense of our country, we have deployed hundreds of Minuteman missiles in reinforced concrete bunkers. We have sent nuclear-powered Polaris submarines around the world under water. We cannot do such things without the knowledge provided by science. But we also give the Department of Defense the authority to build and maintain these weapons systems, and we allocate to the department every year (for all purposes) a sum equal to one-tenth of the gross national product.

Who has the authority to manage the nation's waters? Where is the money to clean them up?

The water problem confronting the United States in the 1960's can be seen clearly through the eyes of an informed Canadian, Jack Davis, Member of Parliament, and Parliamentary Secretary to the Minister of Mines and Technical Surveys of the Dominion of Canada, who has compared the water resources of the two countries in these words:

> Obviously we [Canadians] are well off. . . . The total amount of water flowing in our rivers is greater than that flowing in all the rivers and streams in the United States and Alaska. Meanwhile our natural storage capacity is many times that of the U.S.A. Taking both these factors into account, and allowing for the much greater population of the United States, it can be seen that we are at least ten times better off than our neighbors to the south.

That estimate relates to the total volume of U.S. waters. But the capability of these waters to meet our needs has been impaired by pollution. Moreover, that capability varies widely according to region.

Many factors have contributed to the deterioration of our waters: the heedless use of rivers as waste dumps; the desire to put water to single-purpose uses; the difficulty of bringing about cooperation among the states; and the Balkanization of federal water-management agencies. If our waters are to be restored, we must cut through the accretion of interest groups, agenices, and laws in order to establish a comprehensive water management program.

The states must replace the present anarchy in water use with river-basin authorities, empowered to fix and enforce water quality standards. The federal government must give up its hodgepodge of water resource agencies and establish one department with the responsibility and the mandate to prepare a long-range plan for water and to continue expansion of sewage treatment programs. Industry must recognize the maintenance of clean water as a cost of doing business. The taxpayers must realize that we have been living off the capital of our waters and that this principal must now be restored.

The consumer must understand that the prices he has been paying for manufactured goods—paper, for example—have reflected widespread use of waterways for waste disposal and have not included the cost of proper treatment. The stockholder must realize that some of his dividends represent free use of streams by the corporations in which he has invested. The nation's officials must make basic decisions on the amount of irrigation water to be supplied—and for what crops. Every user of water must understand that we need to know much more about the nature of this precious resource, and that we must greatly increase our technical capability to handle it.

All of us must recognize that there is enough water for all uses *only if it is wisely managed.* The United States is not less dependent on water than earlier civilizations, many of which perished from inability to deal with water problems. Already, we are torn by controversies arising out of conflicting uses of water and disturbed by the tremendous political pressures from various interest groups.

My eyes were opened to the national scope of our water crisis in 1959, the year that I came to the Senate. Having been reared in an arid state and having served as a public official, I have always had a basic concern about water. Like many Americans, I was aware of water pollution. However, my interest had centered not on pollution but on short supply.

One of my assignments was on the Committee on Public Works, which considers water-pollution control bills. I will never forget my amazement as I listened to witnesses tell of the rising contamination pouring into our streams and came to the realization that the United States was polluting its water resources at a faster rate every year. In that year, the committee recorded that "pollution is increasing rapidly" —at the same time control efforts were "actually falling behind." Within two years, as precipitation began to decline in the Northeast, the menace of pollution was intensified by drought.

That year, the Senate Select Committee on National Water Resources was appointed. Its task was to assess the nation's water supplies in relation to anticipated demand through the year 1980. In

WATER RESOURCE REGIONS,
MAINLAND UNITED STATES

NEW ENGLAND

DELAWARE & HUDSON RIVERS

CUMBERLAND RIVER

CHESAPEAKE BAY

WESTERN GREAT LAKES

EAST. GREAT LAKES

OHIO RIVER

TENN. RIVER

SOUTHEAST

UPPER MISSISSIPPI RIVER

LOWER MISSISSIPPI RIVER

LOWER ARK.-RED & WHITE RIVERS

UPPER MISSOURI RIVER

LOWER MISSOURI RIVER

UPPER ARKANSAS-RED RIVERS

WESTERN GULF

PECOS RIVER

UPPER RIO GRANDE AND

PACIFIC NORTHWEST

GREAT BASIN

COLORADO RIVER

SO. PACIFIC

CENTRAL PACIFIC

Senate Select Committee on National Water Resources

January, 1961, it issued a 147-page report and thirty-two "committee prints" (studies of individual aspects of the over-all water problem).

Although we speak of a "national water problem," it is, in reality, a jigsaw puzzle of the problems of river basins, each having unique characteristics in terms of supply and demand. To take a basin-by-basin look, the committee divided the nation into twenty-two water resource regions. Of these, it found that five would be using all available water supplies by or before 1980: the South Pacific, Colorado River, Great Basin, Upper Rio Grande–Pecos River, and Upper Missouri River regions. Waters of three more, it estimated, would be in full use by the year 2000: the Upper Arkansas–Red Rivers, Western Great Lakes, and Western Gulf.

Most of the others—whose rainfall is adequate—already have polluted their lakes and streams to the point where many communities face shortages of water of acceptable quality. These regions include New England, the Delaware and Hudson, the Chesapeake Bay, the Southeast, Eastern Great Lakes, Western Great Lakes, Ohio, Cumberland, Lower Mississippi, and Lower Missouri.

Only one river basin—the Tennessee—has been developed with the objective of using the resource fully. The Pacific Northwest region, served by the Columbia River, enjoys a plentiful water supply—but suffers from haphazard development and some pollution. The Central Pacific, another region of plentiful supply, is now being tapped for use in southern California. Even such a well-watered region as the Upper Mississippi has gone from extreme drought to severe flooding in less than a decade.

Almost every river basin in the United States faces difficult water problems; for most basins, the problems are critical. They are not, however, beyond solution. The same wealth and skill that enable us to build great strip cities with astonishing speed can enable us to clean up our waters. We have proven our ability to control flood. We can develop new sources of sweet water. We can stop wasting the water we have. But we can do these things only if we make a major effort to install a national water management program.

What will such an effort entail?

The Select Committee divided water management into five principal categories. The first is regulating streamflow, which includes protecting the soil of our watersheds and constructing surface reservoirs. The second category is improving water quality, which means purifying sewage and keeping all damaging wastes out of rivers and lakes. The third category is increasing water use efficiency, which means recirculation—using water more than once—and reduction of all wasteful practices. The fourth category is expanding the use of underground storage. The fifth is expanding natural water yield which includes desalting, weather modification, and reduction of evaporation losses.

Since the report was issued, a sixth category of water management has gained prominence. This is redistribution—transporting water from river basins that have a surplus to areas of shortage. Already, some redistribution is being done on a limited scale. For example, the Central Utah Project will transfer water from the Colorado Basin into the Great Basin—where, in the valleys to the west of the Wasatch Mountains, most of Utah's people live. Under discussion are diversions from both Canadian and American sources into the Great Lakes, and continent-long diversions that would bring water from Arctic regions of Canada and Alaska to Canada's prairie provinces, the western United States, and—possibly—Mexico.

If America's dishonored water resources are to be restored, we must have a comprehensive program applying those six water management essentials to each of the nation's river basins.

Many writers and speakers have emphasized the need for citizens working to support better water management. There is widespread recognition of the need. However, it bears repeating that to get an effective nation-wide program going, we must have a citizenry aware of the several kinds of water problems, alert to the politics of water use, and determined to solve the conflicts and correct the abuses that have led to crisis.

CHAPTER II

The Politics of Water

THE LONGEST ORAL ARGUMENT made before the U.S. Supreme Court in this century did not come in any of the cases concerning the great social issues, or subversion, or the rights of accused persons. That distinction went to *Arizona v. California*—a water case.

In the average case, the court hears about an hour of oral argument. The offshore oil cases involving Texas and Louisiana were allotted more than sixteen hours. *Arizona v. California* was allotted twenty-two hours. Before the argument was heard, a Special Master (an officer of the court who is skilled as a trial examiner) was appointed. The first appointed master died, and a second was chosen. In total, their work took eight years. They heard 340 witnesses, reviewed 25,000 pages of testimony, and reported findings in a volume of 433 pages. The final decree of the court was handed down in 1964. Arizona won, and obtained the right to 2.8 million acre-feet* of water from the Colorado River.

---

* An acre-foot is the measure of the volume of water sufficient to cover an acre of ground to a depth of one foot, or 325,851 gallons.

Arizona v. *California* symbolizes the mounting struggle to get water
for competing uses and rival regions. It is true that the West has
always fought over water, while, to most of the nation, water has
been—like air—there for the taking. But five years of drought in the
Northeast and a rising tide of pollution have made the nation aware at
last of the incalculable value of this resource.

Increasingly, the control of water becomes the key to prosperity,
growth, and political and economic power in the United States.

To put water resources to use, the people of the United States have
invested a tremendous $180 billion in facilities—dams, hydroelectric in-
stallations, treatment plants and sewers, irrigation works and reservoirs,
dikes and levees. In 1961, the Senate Select Committee on National
Water Resources estimated that by 1980 some $230 billion more would
have to be spent.

Investments of this magnitude—plus the advantages that regions and
industries gain from use of the water—have generated massive political
pressures involving cities, states, big business, trade and service associations, farmers, conservationists, the many federal agencies concerned
with water, and the Congress.

Enactment of the Water Quality Act of 1965 stirred a hornet's nest.
Big industry, faced with the possibility of having to clean up the nation's waterways, registered strong opposition at the National Water
Conference sponsored by the U.S. Chamber of Commerce in December
of the same year. The federal government was pilloried by an array
of executives who favored local standards and controls. Their speeches
were part of the politics of water, intended to warn Congress and the
new Water Pollution Control Administration to tread lightly lest industry's wrath be incurred.

The Washington *Evening Star,* often a spokesman for business enterprise, took issue with the philosophy emanating from the U.S. Chamber meeting. An editorial said:

> The National Water Quality Act was passed in October. By now, indus-
> tries affected by the law—paper mills, oil refineries and chemical plants—
> should be aware of their responsibilities in cleaning up the nation's
> streams. But judging from remarks made at the national water confer-
> ence . . . they have yet to get the message.

The message had been presented courteously but clearly by James
M. Quigley, Assistant Secretary of Health, Education, and Welfare,

who shortly thereafter was named Acting Commissioner of the new Water Pollution Control Administration. Mr. Quigley stated that the task of his agency was to prevent, as well as abate, pollution. He apparently parted company with his audience when he told the business leaders: "You must accept and act on the principle that the cost of pollution control from now on is part of the cost of doing business."

But Governor Henry L. Bellmon of Oklahoma asserted that the object of pollution abatement programs must be the attainment and preservation of usable waters and "not the elimination of waste discharges." He proclaimed that one of the unavoidable multipurposes of our streams is to serve as a receptacle for waste. If what appears to be the Bellmon philosophy were to prevail, the nation's water could be polluted beyond redemption. It may be necessary to dump waste into rivers, but it is highly undesirable to do so. If dumping is to continue without destroying the waters, the waste must be purified to reduce as much as possible its deleterious effect downstream.

In favoring state and local—rather than national—standards, the U.S. Chamber and its audience had good, self-serving reasons. Speaker after speaker called for local controls and self-regulation. John O. Logan, executive vice president of Olin-Mathieson Chemical Corporation, helped to set the stage for a new round in the politics of water. Mr. Logan called for federal tax concessions or other incentives to induce industry to clean up the nation's streams, saying:

> The chemical industry believes in a positive attitude and maximum self-regulation as the best means of providing solutions to its water resources problems. It does also support appropriate control programs and control agencies at the regional, state and local level, with emphasis on the lowest level *capable of doing the job*. Where Federal participation is desirable, the chemical industry will cooperate. It will support research-oriented public programs.

Herbert S. Richey, president of the Valley Camp Coal Company of Cleveland, admitted that industrial water users have not been "fully responsive" to their obligations. Nonetheless, he equated the Water Quality Act with "the *threat* of dictatorial Federal control."

According to George Olmstead, president of S.D. Warren Company, a Boston-based paper manufacturer, any truly comprehensive pollution abatement program involved a "social cost" to be borne by the public regardless of the source. And, in Mr. Olmstead's view, need existed for "really realistic" time schedules to perform a task that he estimated would cost a billion dollars for his industry alone. Whether or not Mr. Olmstead feared federal control, he was quite ready to have the federal government pay "a substantial part of the capital expenditures for waste treatment facilities"—through fast tax write-offs, investment credits, other special subsidies from the taxpayer, or all three.

Dayton H. Clewell, senior vice president of Socony-Mobil Oil, told of efforts of his industry to end pollution from petrochemicals. He correctly stated that no single sector of the population was free of blame for the condition of our waters.

Industry's point of view—at least as represented by the Chamber—was summed up by Robert P. Gerholz, a Flint, Michigan, real estate developer and president of the Chamber, who warned the corporation executives to seek state regulation to head off federal "coercion." Mr Gerholz said:

> I submit that there is no national problem. I do not believe that the problem can best be met in a national context . . .
>
> I submit that better results will emanate from voluntary and cooperative efforts of industry, municipalities, and state governments to conserve and redeem water resources than from programs handled by Washington's many agencies.

An opposite stand was taken by *The New York Times* in its editorial of December 16, 1965, which stressed:

> There is no inherent right to pollute water. A businessman who pours untreated filth or acids or chemicals or chemical wastes into a river is, often without realizing it, an enemy of the public good.
>
> The American people know that the day of the unrestrained polluter is fast drawing to a close, although not fast enough in our view. Recognizing this, some manufacturers hope merely to shift the burden of cleaning up their own operations from their stockholders to the general public. They ask either Government subsidies or fast tax write-offs to pay for pollution control facilities for their plants.
>
> We see no justification for either direct or indirect subsidies. To grant additional subsidies to major polluters would, in effect, be to penalize unfairly the businessmen who have installed in the past or who now are in the process of installing the necessary equipment on their own initiative and at their own expense.

The nature of the Water Quality Act of 1965 was itself determined by the politics of water—and these considerations, in turn, determine the usefulness of the law. Commissioner Quigley has declared that its aim is "to encourage the states to establish their own water quality standards for the parts of interstate waterways which flow within their boundaries." The law gave the HEW Secretary no authority until June 30, 1967. Then he could act only in the cases of states that fail to submit satisfactory standards. If, at that time, the Secretary could impose a minimum standard, the act might perform its hoped-for task. But, said Mr. Quigley:

> The entire process of establishing and enforcing standards is surrounded by safeguards [for industry].
> The Secretary's authority is not arbitrary. A conference of affected parties must be held before Federal standards are set. There is a provision for a hearing board, on which each affected state is represented, and on which there is to be a balance of interest. The board has authority to make findings as to whether the standards set by the Secretary shall be approved or modified. And in setting standards, the Secretary must be mindful that the standards must meet tests of "physical and economic feasibility" in the courts, should their violation trigger an enforcement action.

Much as water seeks its own level, it appeared that pollution control might be the lowest standard that HEW would accept with the threat of prolonged court action to face. Almost certainly, lobbying activities in state legislatures could be expected to be intense. One hope was that a greater federal presence in water quality enforcement of itself would result in diminished pollution. At least, both industry and municipalities understood that federal intervention could expand if local log-rolling resulted in continued stalemate.

Pollution is but one sector of the battlefront. The politics of water extends far beyond questions of who will enforce quality and who will pay the bill for abatement. With a federal investment alone of $50 billion in water projects, it would be naïve to expect otherwise. Flood control, hydroelectric power, regional economic growth and decay—all these depend upon Congressional authorizations and appropriations. So do payrolls and business profits; so do the operations of many federal agencies.

Conflict of Use

The genesis of the politics of water is *conflict of use*—the difficulty of making a fixed supply of water stretch to meet all demands. Before looking further at the pressures and power structures, it is necessary to examine briefly the uses of water.

Men require water for five basic needs: personal use, industrial use, agricultural use, transportation, and electric power generation.

Personal use means drinking, bathing, maintaining the home, and maintaining the city. It includes all uses of water for recreation—boating, swimming, fishing, and hunting waterfowl—and the care of lakes, streams, and fountains to maintain their beauty.

Industrial use means every use for processing, cooling, or the disposal of waterborne wastes of manufacturing and processing plants. In 1965, there were 150,000 such establishments in the United States using water in their operations.

Water for agriculture means all use for food and fiber production.

Transportation includes use of waterways to move goods or to move passengers for hire. Every year, more than a billion tons of shipping move on the inland waterways of the United States.

Water is used two different ways to generate electric power. One is the damming of streams to produce hydroelectric power. The other is production in steam plants. Tremendous quantities of cooling water are required for the latter.

To classify the uses of water is, of course, to oversimplify. For example, although commercial fishing is an industrial use, its water requirements are entirely different from those for manufacturing and processing. Recreation includes sport fishing and duck hunting; yet the need for water to support wildlife habitat is not limited to the sport it affords. Not being a "use" of water, floods cannot be put into one of the classifications; yet control of flooding is part of water management.

No one of the five uses can be said to be, singly, the most important. In theory, radical adjustments might be made in the amounts of water utilized for different purposes. Last to be given up would be water for drinking and for essential health needs. But for survival as the world's leading industrial nation, we must have ample water for all purposes.

A complicating factor in defining water uses is the differing degrees to which they are "consumptive." For consumptive use, in the definition generally accepted, water must be diverted from its natural channels. Thus, city water is taken from streams or lakes and channeled through a water system for consumption, and it is then returned to a water course in a degraded form and usually in a different place. Similarly, industrial uses and irrigation both require diversion; irrigation water not consumed by plants returns to water courses only some time later, mostly through the ground.

In contrast to these consumptive uses on the part of municipalities, industries, and agriculture, most other uses require quantities of water "in place." Any substantial alteration, either to the physical character of a water course or to its quality, affects its value to fish and wildlife and may change its suitability for recreation and its esthetic value. Power generation requires construction on river beds, but seldom alters water quality. (A storage reservoir may even improve quality by permitting silt to settle and the water to change in color from a dirty brown to a clear blue.) Dikes and levees for flood control may complicate the use of the water that flows in the channel.

The national interest requires water for all uses, but regions and economic groups seek to control water resources for their own—often conflicting—purposes. What is it they seek?

As already noted, industry wants to use rivers and lakes as cheap facilities for the disposal of wastes. Industry also wants large quantities of water for cooling and processing and for the inexpensive barge transportation that developed waterways afford. In addition, it is advantageous for industry to be close to markets, and large concentrations of population are found around major rivers.

Cities—many of them—also want to use waterways as inexpensive receptacles for human and industrial wastes. The citizens of the cities want low charges for water and for sewer service. At the same time, millions of citizens want extensive clean waters on which to sail and water ski, and in which to swim. They want large areas of rivers, lakes, and wetlands for fishing and waterfowl hunting.

Western farmers want large quantities of inexpensive irrigation water. They get much of it at 2 cents per 1,000 gallons. Water from federal reclamation projects is sold to irrigators according to the portions of dam construction costs allocated to irrigation, which are repaid in fifty years, but without interest.

The shipping industry wants well-regulated waterways and protected

TWO MAJOR USES OF STREAMS

Principal Hydroelectric Projects Developed and Under Construction January 1, 1967

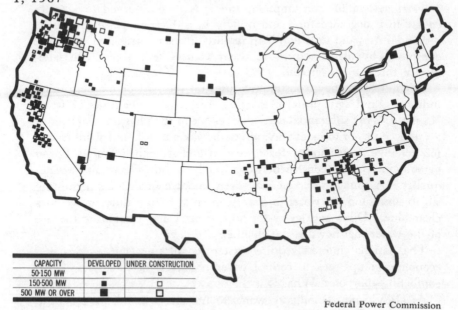

CAPACITY	DEVELOPED	UNDER CONSTRUCTION
50-150 MW	■	□
150-500 MW	■	□
500 MW OR OVER	■	□

Federal Power Commission

Irrigated Cropland In Relation to Farmed Acreage

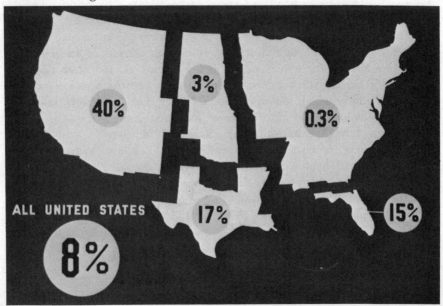

Senate Select Committee on National Water Resources

ocean harbors. It wants permission to use them to dispose of its human and machine wastes.

Both "investor-owned" and "consumer-owned" power companies want the right to dam streams to generate electricity, often with no thought of providing such other benefits as flood control, storage, recreation, and water supply.

A Man's Own Choices

Competition for water touches many Americans in a personal way— affecting their living conditions and pocketbooks.

In Kentucky, an employee of an automobile manufacturer works in a plant on the Ohio River. The plant was located there to take advantage of low-cost water transportation. The worker's wages are good, and he likes his job. But his plant and others upstream pollute the river; its wastes are unpleasant and must be highly treated for use in his home.

In New Jersey, an executive builds a new country home in a fashionable section reclaimed from marshland. Formerly, the swamp was a stop for waterfowl migrating on the Eastern Flyway. But the migrants now pass over the area, and the homeowner must travel farther than he once did to enjoy duck hunting.

In Buffalo, a salesman of business systems enjoys good commissions from sales to industrial plants located along the Great Lakes. But the plants pollute the lakes; contamination of Lake Erie has closed his family's favorite beach. In Nashua, New Hampshire, a woman who owns real estate avoids a tax increase when a bond issue to build a sewage treatment plant is voted down. But on warm summer nights, she has to endure disagreeable odors from the Nashua River. In Idaho, a dairy operator must sell choice bottom land and move his plant because the location will be flooded when a federal reclamation project is completed. But the area will gain irrigation water and a population increase, and the demand for his dairy products will go up.

As such competition for water control affects more and more persons, the great conflicts between regions and economic groups are generated or exacerbated.

At the height of the 1965 water shortage in the Northeast, Mayor Robert F. Wagner of New York told a "crisis team" dispatched to the city by President Johnson that New York would not indefinitely release 200 million gallons daily from its watershed reservoirs to prevent salt-water intrusion in the Delaware River up to Philadelphia's intake pipes. This warning came despite a Supreme Court decision, handed down years ago, requiring New York to release at least that amount.

Calling a "war over water the ultimate absurdity," *The New York Times* asked settlement "across the conference table or in the courts." A compromise was reached satisfying the interests of both cities. It provided that New York would no longer release the 200 million gallons a day into the Delaware. Instead, the water would be "banked" in three reservoirs available alternately to New York and Philadelphia on an emergency basis. To keep salt out of Philadelphia's water supply, four temporary intake pipes were mounted on barges farther up the river.

Will Chicago take another 750,000 gallons of Lake Michigan water a day to flush waste down the Illinois River, or will the water continue to go over Niagara Falls, generating electric power?

Will a federal dam be built on the Nez Perce site on the Snake River, with a large reservoir to provide storage and recreation in addition to power generation, or will a private power company build a "run-of-the-river" dam at the High Mountain Sheep site to produce power and pay taxes?

Will Northern States Power Company build a steam generating plant on land it owns along the St. Croix River, or will a Wisconsin-Minnesota joint commission work out a solution satisfying advocates of a wild-rivers concept?

Questions like these come oftener and with more insistence as we press harder to divide up our waters for more uses.

Of all politico-economic pressures, none is more intense than the struggle "to bring in new industry." Every governor of every state works for industrial development, and every candidate for governor promises to try harder. Promoting new industry is a principal occupation of chambers of commerce. Most states have industrial commissions, which, financed by tax money, run advertisements and organize conferences to inform business leaders of the area's advantages. Business and political leaders alike relish announcing the establishment of a new business or the securing of a new government contract for an existing plant.

The productivity of labor in relation to cost is a powerful inducement to locating an enterprise. So are climate, a congenial atmosphere for employees, and, of course, water: water for use and water to carry off wastes. The community with a river to pollute has a powerful argument for the location of a big plant. The one with water restrictions is not "encouraging" industry.

The availability of water is a prime consideration in the location of virtually every industrial development.

In a 1961 discussion of water problems of industrial nations, the managing director of a Swiss dye manufacturer told how his firm and a number of others, who together had been operating a chemical works in Cincinnati, looked toward modernization following World War II. He said they found it "impractical to continue operating," let alone expand, because "the possibility of treating waste water had become too slim, while adequate supplies of the water we required to run the plant were no longer to be had." The operation was relocated in New Jersey.

In 1965, a multimillion dollar mine-mouth coal-burning electric power plant was projected by three southwestern private utility corporations. They wished to use coal from the Kaiparowitts Plateau in south-central Utah, and new long-line transmission techniques, to generate and transport electricity to load centers in Arizona and southern California. The first concrete step, they said, was to secure "an assured water right." A contract was signed under which they would receive 102,000 acre-feet of Utah's share of Colorado River water each year for fifty years.

The development of processes utilizing southern pine to make paper brought a great new industry to the South. Between the late 1920's and 1966, more than a hundred such plants were located along southern rivers, enormously increasing their pollution load.

The politics of water extends to big and small communities. Both fear costs of clean-up and loss of industry. In 1965, Detroit had only primary treatment of municipal sewage; this treatment removes only 40 per cent of impurities. Municipal and industrial wastes discharged by Detroit accounted for half the fearful pollution of Lake Erie. City officials' answers to questions concerning cleaner water are not much different from those given by spokesmen of Detroit industry. Municipal water experts have countered the U.S. Public Health Service figures on the daily flow into the Detroit River of "more than 1.6 billion gallons of waste water . . . 1.1 billion from industry and 540 million from municipal sewage" by saying, "We do not . . . disagree with their data, only that in their evaluation thereof they accentuated the negative, not the positive."

Detroit points out that the city and the surrounding counties have spent $266 million for water pollution control over a decade. Agreeing that progress has been slow, city officials claim nonetheless that they are following a well-founded plan. As part of this city's water politics, the National Sanitation Foundation was hired to study the problems and suggest remedies. The Foundation reported that present treatment "will remain sufficient for some time to come."

Politics or Policy?

In the absence of a national water policy, water will continue to be allocated—and abused—according to the strengths of the present water-political organizations and the effectiveness of their campaigns.

Perhaps the most celebrated demonstration of the power of the water interests lies in the fact that the most extensive recommendation of both Hoover Commissions *not* put into effect was that calling for re-organization of the agencies that manage water.

It would be difficult to describe the late President Herbert Hoover as anything but a highly prudent man. Yet the first commission on government reorganization that he headed ran into a buzz saw when it recommended steps that would have radically altered the functions of the U.S. Army Corps of Engineers. In 1949, the first Hoover Commission proposed creation within the Department of the Interior of the Water Development and Use Service to take over the Corps' water functions and the work of the Bureau of Reclamation.

A motion to exempt the Corps from future governmental reorganization was defeated on the House floor. But a motion to take the Corps out of water resources development died in Senate committee. President Harry S. Truman, who had backed reorganization as logical and essential, was forced to abandon the program. Commenting editorially, *The New York Times* said: "The Army Corps of Engineers . . . have strong ties in Congress as the result of their virtual control of local rivers and harbors projects, which are plums that members fight for on behalf of constituents."

There is a historical basis for the *Times'* observation. The Army Engineers are the oldest engineering organization in America and one of the most competent in the world. Adoption of the reorganization program would have made it possible to apply the capability of the Corps to a broader range of problems and to use the national interest as the guide to selection of the "plums."

A booklet issued by the National Rivers and Harbors Congress in 1965 announced that the organization's projects committee "consisting of many waterway leaders from each of the nation's (read Corps of Engineers) engineering divisions . . . carefully screens worthy projects." The congress is a private organization without legislative standing, but its stamp of approval is eagerly sought as a "stepping stone toward authorization and construction."

In 1965, the six national vice-presidents of the National Rivers and Harbors Congress were three U.S. Senators and three members of the House. Four were Democrats and two Republicans. The "togetherness" of the Corps of Engineers and some members of the congress was reflected in a leaflet, issued by the latter group, saying: "We believe in . . . a full scale survey by the Army Engineers of municipal and industrial water supply and future needs."

One of the controversies between the Corps of Engineers and its opponents has been over damming the Potomac River. To build a dam across the Potomac at Seneca, Maryland, has long been an ambition of the Corps—for which it initially sought $120 million. President Lyndon B. Johnson's call for a swimmable Potomac caused the Corps to retreat from this project. Plans for a dam were dropped—or so it seemed. Instead, the Potomac River Basin Advisory Committee developed a program with dams excluded at least for this and the next generation. In December, 1965, the committee announced an interim plan but said that final details would require more time. Then, on December 23, a group of federal planners issued a separate report calling for an $80 million dam at Seneca. The initial Corps of Engineers dam was held necessary to ensure water supply for Washington and to "flush out" the lower Potomac. The substitute dam was held essential to trap sediment. In either case the Corps would do the building. However, Assistant Secretary of the Interior Kenneth Holum, in charge of the Potomac development project, ruled out the dam. By August, 1966, it again appeared that the Corps had agreed to put the proposal on the shelf.

When President Truman proposed the Columbia Valley Authority in 1949, he ran into a maelstrom of water politics. A CVA meant an independent agency with broad power for river valley development. It also meant elimination of the Corps of Engineers from future developments. It meant public power on a massive scale in the Northwest.

The proposed CVA was violently opposed by the National Association of Electric Companies, a group of private utilities. It was opposed by the National Rivers and Harbors Congress, an organization that includes in its ranks high officers of the Corps of Engineers, members of Congress, private contractors who build under contract with the Corps, state and local officials, and certain waterway organization spokesmen. Also opposed were the National Association of Manufacturers, the U.S. Chamber of Commerce, the National Wildlife Federation, a number of Republican governors of northwestern states, and the Pacific Northwest Development Association, a group financed by private utilities. This powerful combination defeated the Columbia Valley Authority, which never got past the hearing stage. A similar combination defeated a 1949 proposal for a Missouri Valley Authority.

The politics of water cuts across both party lines and political philosophies, producing not only strange bedfellows, but also arguments that are gems of inconsistency. Thus, during the 1964 Presidential campaign, Barry Goldwater alienated tens of thousands of voters by proposing to sell TVA to private industry, even though, back home in Arizona, the Senator actively fought for every possible federal dollar for the proposed Central Arizona Project. Water is politics in Arizona, and the big question is not whether federal dollars will stifle local initiative but how to get more dollars and water through federal intervention.

(In my own state of Utah, water is always a political but seldom a partisan issue. Ultraconservatives, who deplore expenditure of federal money on welfare, readily campaign for more for water projects. Without such developments as the Central Utah Project, which will utilize water from the Colorado River system, the state would stagnate. Obviously, I support optimum federal water development in my state and am highly responsive to its water needs.)

His election as governor of California may require former actor Ronald Reagan to do some fast backtracking on the issue of federal support. Like other states, California is the recipient of large amounts of federal dam and other water-works construction. Yet, at the time he was making television appearances under the sponsorship of General Electric Company (which sells equipment to public power groups as well as to private power companies) Mr. Reagan's conservative speeches included demands that federal participation in hydroelectric power development be ended.*

California and Arizona were once locked in a desperate struggle over the sharing of the waters of the lower Colorado. But water politics is as fluid as water itself. The states soon drew closer together in their determination to transfer water from surplus areas. A press release on that subject brought no national headlines, but it spoke volumes concerning the politics of water. It announced the formation of a new information service called "Water for the West," with a Washington office in the National Press Building—where the local lobbyist for the Colorado River Association is also housed.

The new organization was termed a "joint cooperative effort" of the Central Arizona Project Association and the Colorado River Association, two erstwhile rivals. Other organizations were expected to join. Among other things, the release deplored "extravagant, baseless charges against Western resource development" by individuals and organizations, whom it termed "private preservationists posing as conservationists."

The Central Arizona Project Association is dedicated to diversion of Colorado River water for a last proposed massive lower basin irrigation project. The Colorado River Association is dedicated to more water for southern California, and its largest and most important member is the Metropolitan Water Board of Southern California. Instead of fighting each other for the diminishing supply of the Colorado, the associations have joined hands to push for Bridge and Marble Canyon dams—opposed by the preservationists—and inter-basin transfer.

Much as the Corps of Engineers gains support from the National Rivers and Harbors Congress, the Bureau of Reclamation has its own private lobby in the National Reclamation Association, which seeks to promote reclamation in the seventeen western states in which it operates. The association supports "the principle of integrated multiple-use development of our water resources under repayment terms consistent with sound business principles" and works for the encouragement of in-

---

* General Electric states that Mr. Reagan was the host and sometimes star of "General Electric Theater" and that statements made during personal appearances were expressions of personal opinion, not company policy.

dividual initiative and responsibility. It is also for the right of people "with or without the federal government to develop their water and power resources in accordance with interstate compacts and water laws of the respective states."

Representative Wayne Aspinall of Colorado, Chairman of the House Interior Committee, warned the association at its 1964 meeting not to expect routine Congressional approval of water projects proposed by federal agencies. He said:

> Unless agency ambitions, competition, and conflicts are put aside, unless there is a willingness to adopt uniform policies and procedures, unless there is the fullest cooperation and coordination, unless there is also a willingness to cooperate and compromise in sectional disputes, unless partisan politics is removed from project consideration and projects are considered on the basis of merit and feasibility and, most important, unless decisions are based upon one basic measure—the public interest— then surely we will not succeed in making the maximum and best use of our limited resources.

The Soil Conservation Service has a host of friends in the members of the soil conservation districts. If the President's budget requests a cut in appropriations for the service or its programs, a flood of letters flows to members of Congress.

The overseer of the spending of such appropriations—the Bureau of the Budget—has been called the nation's invisible government, and it is a powerful factor in the politics of water. If a project construction measure fails to win its favor, it may be killed by an "unfavorable report" to Congress—a letter informing the committee that the bill under consideration lacks the administration's approval.

The Bureau of the Budget was created by Congress in 1921 to permit the President to centralize fiscal control by revising, reducing, or increasing budget estimates of all departments and agencies. Nothing in the Congressional mandate gave the bureau policy-making power, but it has assumed more and more on the grounds of fiscal containment. It has become an unofficial planning agency and policy-making body that must be reckoned with in water development as well as in virtually every other federal program.

The Budget Bureau's most notorious attempt to make resources policy came in the Dixon-Yates case in 1953, following the inauguration of

President Dwight D. Eisenhower. Seeking to diminish the public power concept represented by the Tennessee Valley Authority, the bureau rejected its requests for funds to expand facilities. Instead, the bureau sought to force TVA to permit a private power company to build a thermal plant to supply electricity to an Atomic Energy Commission installation in the TVA area. President Eisenhower canceled the contract after investigation revealed that a Budget Bureau consultant working closely on the proposal was an official of an investment banking firm that was to supply financing to the private utility concerned.

The lobby and pressure groups concerned with water seem endless in number. They are not confined to organizations supporting or defending a particular federal agency. Just as the Chamber of Commerce helps industry define its position for Congressional pressure purposes, so the National Association of Manufacturers battles the "federal presence" and legislation that might require responsibility for water quality by NAM members. The National Parks Association wants no tampering with water resources within the parks, and it wants more water-based parks. The Wilderness Society wants to keep virgin forests forever unspoiled. The Izaak Walton League seeks water pure enough for fishing; the Sports Fishing Institute wants to "shorten the time between bites." The Sierra Club wants to keep nature wild and untamed. The Trustees for Conservation, the National Audubon Society, and the Citizens Committee for Natural Resources have similar concerns.

If the private power companies are highly successful lobbyists, much the same must be said for public power groups. The National Rural Electric Cooperative Association has successfully defended the Rural Electrification Agency and the 2 per cent interest rate for REA projects. The American Public Power Association has won the respect of the private companies, if not their love. Both the NRECA and APPA endorse comprehensive multipurpose projects, particularly if a large public power component is included. Sometimes, however, they have supported public power projects without regard to maximum multipurpose use.

Organized labor, individual unions, the National Grange, and the Farmers Union have generally supported multipurpose development. The Auto Workers, in a move diametrically opposed to that of the U.S. Chamber of Commerce, held an antipollution conference in Detroit to emphasize union interest in cleaning up the Great Lakes. The Farm

Bureau Federation, an outgrowth of the U.S. Chamber of Commerce, has usually followed industry's position on water clean-up, conservation, development, and power.

Some organizations—notably the League of Women Voters—have supported beneficial legislation from the standpoint of the national interest. *The Big Water Fight*, a book compiled by the league's Education Fund and published in 1966, contains case histories of citizen action campaigns. Many of these campaigns resulted in the solution of state and local water problems (for instance, in numerous localities, they forced construction of sewage treatment plants). In addition, this local action provided strong backing for federal water resources legislation.

Water lobbying will not, of course, be ended however beneficial may be the changes in the nation's water management methods. The views of individuals and organizations are necessary to the American legislative and political process, and these views will always be expressed on existing operations as well as proposed changes.

But the critical condition of the nation's water resources in the early 1960's reflected the activities of groups organized to promote limited interests, often in the context of the less intensive use of natural resources decades ago. Today, the need these groups have for a share of America's waters cannot be met unless our waters are restored and preserved.

CHAPTER III

The Vital Quantity

BODIES OF WATER may be destroyed by drought or by pollution—but water itself is one of the few indestructible commodities used by man. Its form may be changed, by boiling into steam or freezing into ice. Its quality can be drastically altered. Some water is "consumed" by plants, and vegetation tends to break water down into its component elements, oxygen and hydrogen. But most water moves continuously in the eternal hydrologic, or rain, cycle. For all practical purposes, as much water is now held by the seas, rivers, lakes, ponds, and swamps, by the ground and the atmosphere, as when the earth was created.

The water cycle has no beginning and no end. It is a massive system operating on the land, on the seas, and in the skies. The greatest influence on the cycle is exerted by the action of the sun on the seas, which cover three-fourths of the globe. Water from the oceans' surfaces evaporates into the earth's atmosphere. That which condenses over the land falls as precipitation—rain, snow, dew, sleet, or hail. As determined by atmospheric conditions, some water falls in torrents that run off rapidly

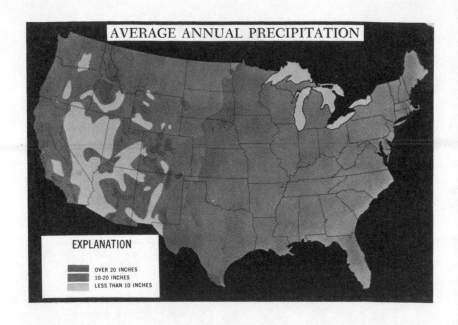

AVERAGE ANNUAL PRECIPITATION

EXPLANATION

OVER 20 INCHES
10-20 INCHES
LESS THAN 10 INCHES

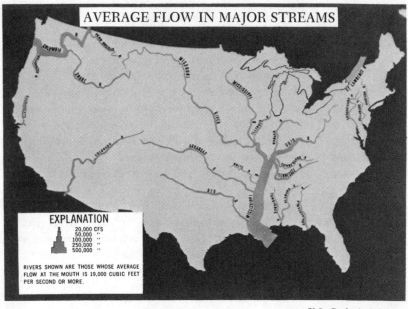

AVERAGE FLOW IN MAJOR STREAMS

EXPLANATION

20,000 CFS
50,000 "
100,000 "
250,000 "
500,000 "

RIVERS SHOWN ARE THOSE WHOSE AVERAGE
FLOW AT THE MOUTH IS 19,000 CUBIC FEET
PER SECOND OR MORE.

U.S. Geological Survey

and cause flooding. In other cases, there comes the gentle rain, beloved by man, that sinks into the soil to nurture growing plants. The plants take a share of the precipitation, and a major part is returned to the atmosphere by evaporation. The remainder penetrates deeper into the earth to become ground water or finds it way into lakes and streams. The streams, in turn, carry the water to the sea, where most of it originated.

Hydrologists estimate that 80,000 cubic miles of water are evaporated from the seas each year. Another 15,000 cubic miles are drawn from the lakes, rivers, land surfaces, and—most important—transpired from the surfaces of the leaves of living plants. This entire process is known as evapotranspiration. Total evapotranspiration equals total precipitation, but most of the moisture falls into the seas. About 24,000 cubic miles of precipitation fall upon the land each year—an amount equivalent to a lake the size of Texas and 475 feet deep in every part.

In a consideration of the vast quantities of water on the earth, it must be kept in mind that the figures we are given are approximations. To a lesser degree, the same holds true for the water resources of the United States. At times, it appears that authorities differ widely in their estimates. But what we are looking at are evaluations of relative quantities—not exact measurements.

Of the more than 300 million cubic miles of water on this planet, about 97 per cent is in the oceans. Of the remaining 3 per cent, two-thirds is in the freezing Arctic and Antarctic regions, leaving only 1 per cent of the earth's water that is fresh and readily accessible to man. One estimate of the distribution of fresh water on the earth puts it (in cubic miles) as follows: glaciers and ice caps, 7 million; ground water, 2.016 million; lakes, 20,000; streams, 300.

In estimating quantities of ground water, hydrologists frequently distinguish between water below the surface down to a half-mile (or 2,000 feet) and deeper deposits. This is because the water below a half-mile is difficult and expensive to pump out. Writing in *Natural History* in 1964, Raymond L. Nace, research scientist of the U.S. Geological Survey, had this to say about ground-water quantities:

> The volume of ground water in the upper half-mile of the continental crust is about 3,600 times greater than the volume of water in all rivers at any one time, and nearly 20 times greater than the combined instan-

taneous volume of water in all rivers and lakes. It is easy to see, therefore, that ground-water reservoirs have tremendous importance as equalizers of streamflow.

The Soviet Union is the richest water nation, with about 27 per cent of the world's accessible supply. Canada is second with 24 per cent. Portions of both nations suffer periodic droughts, however, because most of their water lies in the north and flows into the Arctic seas.

Our average mean rainfall of 29 inches gives the United States about 3 per cent of the earth's accessible fresh water supply. United States rainfall produces 4.4 trillion gallons of water daily. About three-fourths of this is returned to the atmosphere by evapotranspiration, leaving about 1.1 trillion gallons for daily use. Thus is our supply of water fixed.

Inland fresh surface waters in our 48 contiguous states cover some 95,500 square miles—an area equal to that of the state of Oregon—or 61.12 million acres. The U.S. portion of the Great Lakes contains 58 per cent of this great reserve. In addition, Alaska has 12.4 million acres and Hawaii 4,640 acres of surface fresh waters.

Bays, sounds, and tidal areas of the coastal rivers, collectively called estuaries, are estimated at between 20 and 30 million acres. This is not fresh water, of course, but it is a water resource of great value and is profoundly affected by the flow and quality of the rivers.

Nace has called North American lakes "a major element in the earth's water balance." Including the Great Lakes, lakes in North America hold about 7,800 cubic miles of water—26 per cent of all liquid fresh surface water in existence.

The Great Lakes contain about one-fifth of the earth's fresh water supply, exclusive of that locked up in the polar ice caps. Their area is so great that Ohio, New York, and New Jersey could all be submerged under their waters. Even then, there would be sizable lakes left around the edges. The huge water mass is 1,333 feet deep not far off Lake Superior's shore at Munising, in the Michigan Upper Peninsula.

The lakes are the result of massive glacial assaults, which four times gouged out huge valleys in the basin. As the glaciers retreated, they left behind part of their icy fingers. Narrow bodies of water collected between the retreating ice and that left behind. With each new glacial plunge southward and each subsequent retreat, the volume of the waters became greater. The lakes took their present shape in about 2000 B.C.

Initially, Great Lakes waters drained southward into the Illinois and Wabash rivers and into thousands of smaller streams. The present drainage system was born when glacial ice gave way to the St. Lawrence River below Niagara Falls. Today, 214,000 cubic feet of water thunder over the falls each second to be delivered by the St. Lawrence to the Atlantic.

No great rivers feed the Great Lakes. They depend on the plentiful rains and snowfall of the basin for their new waters. These yield an average of 21 trillion cubic feet of water annually. Average annual precipitation over the 296,000 square miles of drainage area is 31.9 inches. Of the lakes' annual water intake, 6.5 trillion cubic feet flow out through the St. Lawrence while most of the remaining 15 trillion cubic feet returns to the atmosphere by evaporation.

The waters of the lakes were originally soft and of high quality but are rapidly becoming hard and polluted. The American Association for the Advancement of Science has reported that Lake Superior alone remains essentially in its original chemical condition. Superior is by far the youngest of the lakes.

The Geological Survey tells us that the world ratio—about 75 per cent ground water to 25 per cent surface water—also holds good for the United States. Usable ground-water supplies in the United States are estimated at 47.5 million acre-feet.

According to Gerald Meyer, assistant chief of the Geological Survey's Ground Water Branch, the most abundant ground-water reserves of the United States are found in five areas. The largest reserve is contained in the Atlantic and Gulf coastal plain. This region also utilizes the most ground water.

Second in importance is a series of alluvial basins in the Far West. This region is dry, but the alluvial deposits are very thick and contain quantities of water left by centuries of recharge. Listed third is the glacial northern part of the nation. This region extends from the Rocky Mountains nearly to the Atlantic Coast and from the Canadian border south to about the Missouri and Ohio rivers.

The fourth and fifth regions are the High Plains, which lie east of the Rockies and extend northward from Texas to South Dakota, and the Columbia Lava Plateau of the Northwest.

Although ground water is everywhere, it is plentiful only in certain water-bearing strata. As a federal publication explains, "Ground water is not just water *under the ground*. It is water held in the rocks by certain forces, replenished by nature according to climate and the local geology, and consequently variable in both amount and quality. No magic means are necessary to locate it—just scientific knowledge and plain common sense."

Hydrologists search for water-bearing rock or earth formations known as aquifers (literally, water-bringers), which can be tapped to create wells. Gravel, sand, sandstone, and limestone formations are the best water-bringers, but constitute only a small fraction of the earth's outer crust. Most formations are tightly packed clay, shale, or various hard rocks quite impermeable to water. Where no better aquifers are to be found, these other formations usually will yield sufficient water for domestic supply.

Aquifers may be only a few feet thick or hundreds of feet in depth. They may exist just beneath the earth's surface or hundreds of feet below. They may carry water only a short distance, or, as in the case of the Dakota sandstone, for hundreds of miles.

Contrary to popular belief, ground water does not exist as an underground lake or river filling deep channels or wide, ghostly caverns. Most ground water accumulates in earth pores and cracks above the bedrock that underlies the permeable surface of the earth and below the "water table." The water table is that level under the ground where atmospheric and water pressures are equal and opposite.

A "zone of aeration" lies between the water table and the land surface. This zone may be saturated after heavy rains and nearly dry during lengthy droughts. Some water is held in the zone by capillary action resulting from the atmospheric pressure. But the moisture within the zone of aeration will not "come to a well" even though it moistens rocks and soils. Drilling within the zone produces no water at the surface. Rock apertures within the zone of aeration contain only air.

A "zone of saturation" lies between the water table and bedrock, and it is this zone to which we look when drilling wells. Where the formations are highly impermeable, wells are recharged very slowly. Wells are useful only if the rate of recharge is consistent with the pace at which water is pumped out.

In the zone of saturation, ground water actually flows. Like a river, it follows the path of least resistance through permeable formations and around those it cannot penetrate. Although it may flow at a rate of thousands of feet daily in highly porous formations of sandstone or sand, in most formations it moves very slowly. Often, it travels miles before emerging as springs or swamps in earth depressions or seeping into rivers or lakes.

Water rises upward under pressure. Natural pressure may occur in artesian wells, which are created by piercing aquifers that lie between layers of impermeable rock or earth. Water rising to the surface spontaneously from such aquifers is said to be under artesian pressure.*

Ground water forms a great natural reserve, which feeds lakes and streams during dry spells when surface waters fall below the water-table level. Conversely, when streams and lakes rise above the water table, they add to ground-water reserves.

Ground water holds salt water from the sea at bay. Near the coastline, sea water intrudes into the ground exactly as it does into a tidal river. When the river's flow drops, the sea water moves farther up the channel. In the same way, ground-water exhaustion leads to salt-water intrusion, sometimes destroying the value of wells. For example, Florida has ground water in plentiful supply but overpumping in some areas has caused serious salination problems.

Hydrologists seeking ground water for development consider such factors as quantity, ability of the water to come to a well, the rate of recharge, and quality. In its normal state, ground water is cleaner and purer than most surface water. Like surface water, it may become saline through contact with mineral salts, and it is subject to the same contaminants. The principal reason that little ground water is taken from below a half-mile is that formations become less porous and harder to penetrate the farther we go below the earth's surface. However, rock formations yielding water have been located more than a mile down.

Ideally, water should not be withdrawn from underground sources at a rate faster than it is recharged, or water tables fall. Even in areas where ground water is plentiful, local wells may go dry if located too close together. The difference between an original water table and a lower one after a period of pumping is called a "drawdown." By deter-

* Artesian wells gets their name from the French town of Artois, near which they were first drilled during the Middle Ages.

mining drawdown and recharge rates, hydrologists can predict future water-table levels.

In some areas of the United States, such as Arizona and the High Plains of Texas, ground water is being mined and the water tables are falling. However, it is the opinion of Gerald Meyer that the total amount of ground water has not changed appreciably from years past. "There is no evidence to support the popular belief that water tables are falling everywhere throughout the country," he has said.

In sharp contrast to our fixed supply of water is our burgeoning demand. America's use of water is increasing at an almost incredible rate. In the early 1960's, we used about 350 billion gallons of water daily— equal to about 30 per cent of total supply. By 1980, we are expected to use 600 billion gallons, or over half the supply. By the year 2000, we are expected to use about 900 billion gallons.

As we have seen, one reason for this rising demand is the population explosion, but the heaviest pressure comes from our affluence. A rising standard of living is not possible without increasing water use.

The average person can get along with 5 or 6 pints of water daily in the temperate zone if he is moderately active. This will replace body losses, but will permit no washing of any kind. Even if 5 gallons were permitted for washing, drinking, and all other personal use, living would be primitive. A modern American city dweller uses 50 gallons a day in his home. It takes 25 gallons of water for a shower, 35 for a tub bath, and 3 to flush a toilet. Washing a car requires 10 gallons, and 1,000 gallons are needed to water the lawn.

But the big users of water are not individuals, although much could be saved if we took pure water less for granted and were more careful in its uses. Municipal withdrawals of water in 1965—including personal use—were 16.7 million gallons daily. By the year 2000, they are expected to rise to 42.2 million.

In our era, the greatest increase in water use has been for industry. Modern industrial processes require tremendous quantities of water. On the average, it takes more than 30,000 gallons to produce a ton of steel, 200 gallons to make a pound of synthetic rubber, 30 to manufacture a pound of paper, and 1 gallon to brew a pint of beer. Projections of water requirements for the chemical industry show it will need nearly five times as much in 1980 as it used in 1954. Such increases in demand must intensify the nation's tug-of-war over water, even though water-use practices are improved.

Industry needs water for many essential purposes. The estimated 5 billion gallons of water used daily by the steel industry are primarily for cooling, but a part of this amount is also employed as a solvent, a catalyst, a conveying medium for the transport of materials and waste, and as a cleaning agent. Water under high pressure—"hydraulic water" —is used to remove scale from steel, to tilt Bessemer converters, and to operate open-hearth doors and various valves and reversing mechanisms on open-hearth furnaces.

Water plays an integral part in leather-making. Hides and skins are first "fresh salted" to prevent decomposition. The hides undergo a preliminary washing in cold water, which has been treated with antiseptic to retard bacterial action in the soaking vats. After the soaking process, the hides are fleshed—that is, the fat is scraped from the dermal tissue— in preparation for dehairing. The skins are then repeatedly submerged, soaked, and drained in vats containing a saturated solution of lime and water to aid the hair-removing operations. The stock is then washed in running water and again soaked in vats to remove lime and protein decomposition before the hides are ready for the chemical conversion to leather, which involves drumming (soaking) in vegetable or mineral solutions.

In making paper, barked and cleaned logs are fed into a machine that reduces them to small chips, which in turn are fed into a digester, where chemicals and steam break them down into cellulose and other wood elements. Chemicals, lignin, and resins are removed, after which the cellulose fibers—called pulp—are cleaned, screened, and bleached. The "furnish"—those dyes, pigments, and resins that provide the desired finish—is added. At this point, the pulp is 99 per cent water and 1 per cent fiber and furnish. It is fed into a Fourdrinier paper machine, which sprays a thin layer onto a rapidly moving endless screen where the water drops away and leaves a mat of fibers. This mat is then rolled, pressed, and dried to produce finished paper.

Altogether, American industry withdrew about 32 billion gallons of water yearly a decade ago. It is expected to require 101 billion gallons by 1980, and 229 billion by the year 2000. Such an increase is most easily understood if we express it as the amount industry uses for *every American every day*. The National Water Institute says that this amounted to 560 gallons in 1950, 849 gallons in 1960, and will be 1,193 gallons by 1975.

Agriculture has been the nation's single biggest user of water, and will be for many years. The quantity of water a plant needs is affected by conditions of temperature, humidity, light, wind, and soil moisture but usually amounts to several hundred times the dry weight of the plant itself during a single growing season. On a warm day, a single tree can dispose of 60 to 80 gallons of water. It requires 4,000 gallons of water to raise a pound of beef, 1,300 to grow a pound of cotton, 500 for a pound of rice, 80 for a pound of potatoes, and 50 for a pound of wheat. American agriculture is expected to use 167 million gallons of water daily by 1980—more than industry's projected use. By the year 2000, it is expected to use 185 million, which will be less than industry is then expected to utilize.

Steam electric-power generating plants require tremendous amounts of water for steam and cooling, whether they burn oil, coal, or gas, or utilize atomic energy. By the end of this century, such plants are expected to be the greatest user of water, requiring 430 million gallons daily.

To use water, of course, does not mean to *consume* it. When we say that industrial use has doubled, we do not mean that only new water is being added; much water is being used over and over again. Agriculture is our greatest consumer, using up, in terms of immediate availability, about two-thirds of the water withdrawn from streamflow or underground. Industry consumes only about 7 per cent of water withdrawn. Municipalities consume about 10 per cent, mines about 20 per cent, and steam generating plants an insignificant fraction.

Most used water goes either directly back into a stream or indirectly through a sewage treatment plant. But water that is consumed is diverted from streamflow and then returns—not to a stream—but to the atmosphere or ground. Eventually, much of it gets back into streams, too, but for a time, it is out of circulation and not available for use.

D. F. Peterson of Utah State University has drawn up a daily "water budget" for the United States. If one thinks of streams as being filled up every morning, instead of by a continuous process, such a budget (in billions of gallons) would look like this:

Streamflow (after filling) 1,260
Pumped from ground water (6 to possibly 10) 10

Available for the day 1,270
Withdrawn from streams 315

Not withdrawn 955
Consumed: irrigation 84
     industry 3
     municipal ... 3
        90
Returned to streams 225

Net streamflow (end of the day) 1,180

Although industry does not consume much water, its use constitutes a major—though different—problem than that of consumption. Pollutants added by industry make much of the water it uses and discharges downstream useless for some distance without expensive treatment. The same, of course, holds true for much of the water used by municipalities and discharged as sewage.

In view of the tremendously larger volume of ground water in relation to surface water, it might be thought that the former could provide an additional supply to meet our rising demand. But, as we have seen, ground and surface water are intimately interrelated, and the depletion or contamination of one can affect the other. For the nation as a whole, ground water is an alternate rather than an additional supply.

Raymond L. Nace in a speech entitled "Are We Running Out of Water?," delivered at the First International Water Quality Symposium, said:

> The total discharge of rivers is an approximate measure of potentially available and manageable liquid water in continental areas. The hydrologic cycle has operated long enough that the large amounts of water stored in lakes and underground are in quasi-equilibrium with water in other parts of the environment. . . . Ground water reservoirs in general, like their surface counterparts, merely permit use of water at a different time and place and with different temperatures and chemical properties than would be possible if dependence were solely on natural flow in rivers and delay in lakes.

For localities, however, ground water can provide a water source where surface supplies are not available or where they are inconvenient or expensive to use.

At least 80 per cent of the water used in the United States comes from surface sources, and the balance from underground. In many countries, the reverse is true. Denmark, Belgium, West Germany, and the Netherlands all use much more water from underground than from the surface. Some areas of the United States, of course, depend heavily on ground water. New Mexico, Arizona, and the High Plains of Texas are examples.

Ground-water use is becoming more important in the United States. Between 1945 and 1960, ground-water use doubled, and by the latter year each of ten states was withdrawing 1 billion gallons or more daily. Some aquifers—in the High Plains for example—permit withdrawal of water at a rate far faster than recharge without serious depletion of the reserve. But such water mining pushes costs up significantly and can force radical alterations in the economy of an area.

The old-fashioned well is disappearing, even in rural America. The electric pump has eliminated the old-fashioned, long-handled, cast-iron hand pump and brought the water tap to the modern farm kitchen. However, wells are still the major source of water supply in rural areas and also supply large quantities of water for irrigation, industry, and municipalities, particularly in the arid West.

The use and consumption figures above, revealing as they are, only begin to tell the story of our need for water. To operate our cities, farms, and factories, we must take water out of its natural channels and use and consume it. But we must also use the bodies of water themselves, and this use is not less significant to an affluent nation.

Our larger rivers are used for navigation, and they support a shipping industry that moves at low cost 457 million tons of freight a year while giving jobs to 80,000 employees. Falling water generates about one-sixth of all the electric power used by the United States. Streams, lakes, and estuaries are essential for boating, swimming, fishing, hunting, and to support wildlife of great value.

The special problems of water for recreation and water for fish and wildlife are discussed in later chapters. Here it must only be emphasized that, although water resources form a supply to be used, they are also a place to live—for man and other creatures. The percentage of streamflow that can be withdrawn and replaced is limited if a favorable environment is to be maintained for various desirable activities. On this point, Nace writes:

Consideration of water problems solely as functions of streamflow and "withdrawal" uses is an evasion of the real situation. Water need per individual in industrial societies is greater than has been supposed, by nearly ten times, and the population that can be supported with acceptable living standards undoubtedly is much smaller than some writers have calculated.

In addition to providing and maintaining tremendous quantities of water when and where needed, we must also see to it that the supply is of adequate quality. It is to this question of quality that we now turn.

CHAPTER IV

The Question of Quality

PRIMITIVE MAN used fresh water for drinking and washing; he traveled on it; the fish and wildlife it nurtured provided him with food. Modern man uses water for the same basic purposes. But the remarkable properties of water have made possible a variety of uses that have contributed greatly to the advance of civilization.

Water flowing downhill can be used to generate electric power, and it can be transported and stored inexpensively. Water is the most nearly universal solvent; therefore, it is indispensable for cleaning, is an efficient carrier of waste, and has many other uses in industry. Water is a very poor conductor of heat; more heat is required to raise its temperature, and more cold required to lower it, than for any other common substance. Consequently, water can absorb and carry off large quantities of heat. A typical blast furnace with iron production capacity of 1,000 tons daily might utilize 11 million gallons of water in 24 hours.

The various uses of water affect its quality. In beet-sugar refining, for instance, water is used for washing the beets, and the sugar is extracted in a process using hot water. Most of the water is taken from streams, and that which goes back—unless sufficiently treated—contains a num-

THE QUESTION OF QUALITY 43

ber of substances not in the water when it went into the plants. Among them are lime, soil, and sugar—and they make the water less suitable for other uses.

Quality can be defined as composition—the volume of the substances dissolved in the water as well as those it may carry undissolved, as a running stream carries silt. Water quality has many aspects—salt and mineral content, acid content, color, turbidity, volume of dissolved oxygen, content of disease-producing bacteria, and, in the water of modern America, content of numerous and sometimes highly complex chemical substances.

Quality can vary widely according to the purpose for which the water is to be used. For example, a service station attendant puts distilled water in your automobile battery. Tap water cannot be used, as the minerals it contains would start chemical reactions and destroy the battery cells. But distilled water—no matter how pure it is—is not satisfying to drink because the absence of minerals makes it taste flat.

Water quality is determined both by nature and man. The natural character of water varies with location, season of the year, and the kinds of soils through which the water moves. Water quality may be affected by silt, wind, water temperatures, bacteria in soils or streams, vegetation, and other environmental factors. Rivers have tremendous erosive powers, grinding up rocks and reacting with soils and plant and animal matter to alter water quality.

Concern with water quality as a factor in public health goes back more than a century, to the bacteriological researches of Louis Pasteur. Prior to the acceptance of Pasteur's theories about waterborne disease, little attempt was made to improve the make-up of water delivered through public supply systems. The Public Health Service Act of 1912 established the agency of that name and authorized investigations of water pollution related to the diseases and impairments of man. However, the promulgation of regulations and enforcement of measures to control disease-bearing waters have been carried out by state, city, and county boards of health.

Except for its effect on public health, most of the nation paid little attention to water quality until after World War II. Concern before that time was with quantity—searching out and storing enough for the needs of cities and industries.

A naturally flowing stream in a healthy, stabilized watershed purifies itself. Part of this purification process is aeration—the process whereby a stream rushing over rocks takes in air. Another part is the settling of "solids," which takes place in pools and in reaches of stream bed where the water runs quietly.

But the most important phase of the purification process is the decomposition of organic wastes by micro-organisms during their life cycle. These organisms are bacteria, which feed on organic materials and require oxygen. Organic materials (carbon compounds) enter streams from four sources: aquatic plants and animals; soils containing humus; human sewage; and industrial plants such as tanneries, meat packers, and paper mills, which use vegetable or animal products.

As the amount of organic material in a stream increases, the bacteria proliferate, decomposing more organic material and using more oxygen. To a point, the oxygen is replaced by a new supply dissolved from the air. Beyond that point, however, it is not replaced fast enough, and the dissolved oxygen content of the stream is reduced. If the content gets low enough, fish die, and, finally, the oxygen-using bacteria are replaced by other strains, which feed on nitrates and phosphates but need no oxygen. Then the water takes on the familiar foul aspect of massive pollution.

In our eagerness to make use of them, we have often forgotten what natural bodies of water are—delicately and marvelously balanced communities that nourish plant and animal life. Some waters—for example, salt-water estuaries and adjoining marsh lands—can be incredibly fertile. It has been said that the Sapelo marshes of Georgia produce six times as much organic material in a given space as an area sown to wheat. Interference with the natural environment, such as tearing the bottom by channel dredging, can destroy fertility as well as degrade water quality.

Lakes have a life cycle that may last hundreds or even thousands of years. Young lakes tend to have little salt in solution, contain abundant oxygen, and are relatively free of vegetation. After many years, dissolved minerals, including plant nutrients, increase in quantity. Algae and other plants begin to proliferate. The once clear lake loses oxygen to the plants, and water quality deteriorates as decomposed matter increases turbidity, fouls the lake bottom, and otherwise pollutes the source. Man-made pollution, as in the case of Lake Erie, speeds up the death process.

Because of the solvent property of water, all natural fresh waters contain varying degrees of dissolved mineral salts. Common salt (sodium chloride) is sometimes present in large quantities in waters that flow in rivers. It has been estimated that some 25,000 tons of salt are discharged daily from saline springs into the otherwise satisfactory waters of the Arkansas and Red rivers.

Salt found in most fresh water is of such small quantity that it is measured in parts per million—one of a number of measurements used by sanitary engineers to rate water quality. A pound of table salt in a million pounds of water yields a salt concentration of one part per million. Salt concentration in our rivers and lakes varies greatly. Lake Tahoe, in Nevada and California, has a salt concentration of only 70 parts per million; Lake Michigan has 170, the Missouri River has 360, the Pecos River, 2,600. Ocean water has about 35,000 parts per million of salt concentration; the Dead Sea, 250,000. During its present period of concentration, Great Salt Lake has averaged 266,000 parts per million, or nearly 27 per cent salt.

Although sodium chloride is the most common salt in the world's waters, other mineral salts—silicates, fluorides, carbonates, nitrates, sulphates—are also found in significant quantity. Most common minerals found in combination with these are calcium and magnesium, although iron, sodium, potassium, and aluminum salts are common enough. Those who use a vaporizer to humidify the air of a room when a member of the family has a cold have seen the scale that collects on the heating element. That scale is a layer of minerals deposited as the pure water goes off as steam. Such mineral-salt content affects the value of water to industry, agriculture, and municipalities. Water containing less than 500 parts per million of dissolved solids (salts in solution) is generally usable for ordinary purposes, and most sources contain significantly less. Water with less than 2,000 parts per million of dissolved solids is generally suitable for irrigation.

Turbidity, or cloudiness, results from siltation, or sedimentation. At Minneapolis, Minnesota, the Mississippi River is relatively free of sediment, measuring only 10 parts per million. At St. Louis, where the "Big Muddy" joins the main stem, turbidity reaches 593 parts per million. At New Orleans, over 1,000 miles farther downstream, turbidity has been reduced to 223 parts per million. Water having a turbidity of more

TYPICAL WATER QUALITY PROBLEMS

THESE TWO ARE NATURAL

Color

Hardness

THESE TWO ARE MAN-MADE

Industrial Wastes

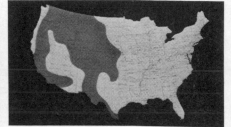

Irrigation Return Flows

U.S. Geological Survey

than 5 parts per million should be treated before being used for drinking.

Water color is the liquid's appearance after sediment has been removed. Color may result from decaying vegetation, sewage, industrial wastes, or other contamination. The U.S. Public Health Service has developed a platinum-cobalt scale to measure water color, and has placed an upper limit of 15 on water used for drinking. A color value of 10 usually passes without notice. The color value of natural swamp water may run as high as 200 to 300.

Water color is an important attribute of quality, both from an aesthetic point of view and because color makes water unsuitable for many industrial processes. An example is the production of photographic and other types of fine papers. Excessive color is particularly objectionable in mill operations where high brightness is required or white or light-colored sheets are being prepared.

Taste and odor may be associated with discoloration, or may exist independently. Generally, bad taste in water results from decaying organic matter, industrial pollution, and the like. Detergents give water a fishy or an oily taste. Water with a high iron content may taste "rusty," while that with other high mineral content may have a medicinal taste.

The pH, or acid-alkaline, balance within a water source is also a determinant of quality. The pH scale runs from 0 to 14, and at either extreme is generally not usable without treatment. Natural fresh waters usually have a pH balance of 6 to 8. A pH balance above 7 makes the water alkaline; below that level it is acid. Sea water is slightly alkaline. Many industrial applications require careful pH control.

Discussed above was the action of oxygen-using bacteria in decomposing organic wastes. The rate at which a bacteria population consumes oxygen is called "biochemical oxygen demand." Dissolved oxygen is present in the pure water of fast flowing streams in about 10 parts per million. The lower limit to support fish life over a sustained period is 3 to 5 parts per million of dissolved oxygen. Together with the biochemical oxygen demand, the amount of dissolved oxygen determines the degree of pollution in a watercourse.

Radioactivity is measured in curies, a rate of disintegration, and roentgens, a measure of energy. Some waters contain natural radioactivity, but these are negligible. Safe limits for radioactivity were first set down by the U.S. Public Health Service in 1962.

The presence of bacteria in water is usually measured by the coliform test. The test measures the concentration of two major groups of bacteria: coliform organisms, originating largely in the intestinal tract of warm-blooded animals, including man; and aerobacter aerogenes, originating in soil, grain, and decaying vegetation. Although coliform bacteria are not harmful themselves, their concentration in the animal system is substantially parallel to that of other dangerous bacteria that are also found in the intestines of warm-blooded animals.

Pesticide and herbicide content of water is measured by the infrared spectrophotometer. The various substances of which the product is composed emit different colors when examined under the instrument, the intensity of color indicating the concentration of the foreign substance.

Concentration of pesticide in water is expressed in parts per million or even parts per billion.

"Hard" water is caused by the presence of certain mineral salts—iron, calcium, magnesium, barium, aluminum—or by the presence of free acid. Calcium salts, in particular, are common in limestone areas, and calcium carbonate—the principal ingredient of limestone—is the most common cause of water hardness. Water with less than 60 parts per million of hardness is "soft"; that with 60–120 causes a few problems in homes and industry; water with 121–180 may require softeners; water with hardness in excess of 180 must be softened before using.

Hard water requires much more soap for lathering, although it does not affect detergent lathering. But even with detergents, hard water roughens the skin, shortens fabric life, and increases fabric costs for the American family. Hard water leaves scale in pipes and boilers. Water softeners are used in many homes, laundries, hospitals, hotels, and industry, to remove the compounds that cause hardness.

Establishing the proper quality for particular uses is an important job of water resource managers. Domestic and industrial water supplies must be of the highest quality. Industries that process food, drugs, or chemicals for human consumption or bodily use must have water of potable quality. However, it is possible to use lower-grade water for many domestic and municipal purposes. Lawns can be watered with water of less than potable standards and streets flushed with still lower quality. Fires can be fought with polluted river waters. Many small in-city factories using municipal supplies could turn to water of lesser purity for cooling and processing.

Industries manufacturing paper, complex chemicals, and products requiring consumption of water require varying degrees of purity. For example, the chemical composition of water is critical in obtaining excellence in leather. Often a tanner with two plants in different locations in the same state finds it difficult to make the same quality leather in both. In tanning, hardness of water is overcome through treatment, while disinfectants are used to maintain microbiological standards.

Water delivered to industry may be of lower grade when cooling is the purpose. But it must be free of corrosive substances and organic matter that fouls cooling equipment. In many cases, water drawn from municipal supplies must be further purified by industry to meet exacting requirements. Water evaporators similar to those used in some desalting plants are used to purify brackish waters before they are fed into boilers.

Water quality maintenance requires aeration to restore oxygen to heated waters, or the use of cooling ponds or tanks to reduce temperatures.

Water for irrigation must be free of bacterial contamination and of concentrated salts. Because water returning to streams from irrigated lands often carries added salts, downstream users suffer as more irrigated acreage puts heavier pressure on waterways. Quality requirements are high for swimming and other water-based recreation. The protection of the entire aquatic environment is necessary to maintain productive fishing waters. The introduction of the internal combustion engine for pleasure craft—the motorboat—has added a source of pollution that must be controlled to keep waters fit for other forms of recreation.

Although pollution may appear to have small effect on navigation, there is a direct connection between navigation and water quality management. During low-flow periods, locks and low dams may intensify water pollution by blocking the flow of wastes. Acid wastes can corrode steel ship hulls and lock gates. Sludge, a product of badly contaminated waters, can foul bottoms and cooling systems, and such water can be beyond the capacity of a ship's internal purification system to disinfect.

Where does the responsibility lie for the maintenance of water quality?

Traditionally, the use and regulation of water resources has been a local undertaking. So long as a limited quantity of foreign matter goes into a stream, natural processes keep the water reasonably clean. When the nation was young, the next town or the next factory was usually small enough and far enough downstream to permit such processes to maintain water quality. Therefore, regulations seldom applied beyond a few miles and almost never beyond state borders, and they were promulgated by city, county, and state governments. Local boards of health assumed responsibility for providing waters free of disease germs.

Growth of the nation and expansion of water use have multiplied quality problems enormously and have forced greater recognition of the interstate nature of streams. We cannot all live upstream; therefore, those who do have a responsibility to maintain the excellence of the waters they use and send downstream. Since 1948, Congress has enacted a number of water quality bills, principally aimed at abating pollution of interstate streams and assisting communities to finance the construction of sewage treatment plants.

Voluntary efforts to improve quality management have had a measure of success. An example is the formation by eight states of the Ohio River Valley Sanitation Commission (ORSANCO) in 1948. When ORSANCO was established, more than 99 per cent of the population along the river discharged raw sewage into it. Lack of treatment of industrial wastes was equally appalling. By 1965, treatment plants were in operation or under construction for 94 per cent of the population, and 1,552 of the 1,730 industrial plants in the area of ORSANCO jurisdiction had installed facilities meeting the commission's basic requirement.

Neither governmental nor voluntary efforts have had the reach or depth to protect our water. Commenting on a Public Health Service report, the Senate Select Committee declared that the nation "has been caught unawares by the huge demands for water resulting from rapid population and economic growth, and is relatively unprepared sociologically, economically, legally, or technically to handle them." The committee added that the "cheapness and plentifulness of water has been oversold," in relation to the need for waste control.

For the future, the maintenance of water quality—and its restoration to vast stretches of waterway—will remain a major part of the problem of providing enough water for all uses. Nothing short of comprehensive quality management on a river-basin basis is likely to prove adequate.

CHAPTER V

Thoreau Would Weep

MORE THAN A CENTURY and a quarter have passed since a youthful Henry David Thoreau and his brother spent a week rowing down the Concord and up the Merrimack rivers above Lowell, Massachusetts.

Even in that long-gone day, the Merrimack's carrying capacity was overtaxed by the wastes of factories spawned along its banks by the nascent industrial revolution, and the human wastes from towns that clustered around the region's industries. Above Lowell, the Merrimack was still a relatively clear stream abounding with sunfish, perch, pickerel, and shiners. But pollution in the lower stream was already taking its toll; salmon and shad were becoming rare. Thoreau wrote of the river, "When at last, it has escaped from under the last of its factories, [it] has a level and unmolested passage to the sea, a mere *waste* water, as it were, bearing little with it but its fame."

Thoreau bemoaned the effect of river pollution on native fish and the consequent destruction of the livelihoods of the local fishermen. He called on the fish to be patient for "a few thousand years," after which they could surely return to their native habitat where "nature will have leveled the Billerica dam and the Lowell factories," and of the fishermen, he wrote that "One might like to know more of that race, now extinct, whose seines lie rotting in the garrets of their children, who openly professed the trade of fisherman, and even fed their townsmen creditably . . ."

Were the philosopher of Walden to look upon today's Merrimack, he would likely weep for the river and the children of this nation's tomorrow. If the Merrimack of today represents the future of American water courses, the time may yet come when nature will indeed have leveled the dams, the factories, and the towns of America. Its long history of pollution makes the famed river an instructive example of how this water sickness spreads.

As rivers go, the Merrimack is not a major stream. Less than 110 miles in length, of which the lower 22 are tidal, it is formed at Franklin, New Hampshire, by the confluence of the Pemigewasset and the Winnepesaukee rivers. The river flows southward into Massachusetts, where it makes a sharp turn eastward and flows for 45 miles into the Atlantic at Newburyport, Massachusetts. Just above Nashua, New Hampshire, it is joined by the Nashua, which rises in Massachusetts and flows northward. What happens downstream along the Merrimack affects the health and welfare of the citizens of Massachusetts. What happens upstream on the Nashua is vital to New Hampshire.

Because it falls 4,600 feet in its short but sharp descent from its headwaters in the White Mountains, the Merrimack early attracted industry. Before Watt's steam engine, rivers powered the waterwheels that turned the mechanical looms of the early textile plants. Today, textile plants are largely gone, but the Merrimack and its thirteen major tributaries now receive even more noxious wastes from chemical plants, paper mills, tanneries, synthetics plants, and dye works, while treated, untreated, and semitreated municipal sewage and wastes pour in from other industrial and public sources.

The Merrimack may not be the most polluted river in the nation, but it is a contender for the dubious honor. During hot weather and low stream flow, the river at some points bubbles hydrogen sulphide gas that permeates the area with the stench of rotten eggs. Even so, in the lower Merrimack, water is withdrawn for drinking purposes. Heavily chlorinated, the water is still potable, although it reportedly tastes of suds and oil and is sometimes discolored by dye and other industrial wastes that cannot always be removed. Cities using Merrimack water include Lawrence and Lowell, which together withdraw supplies for a population of 163,000.

Merrimack Valley housewives in the lower stream area complain that they cannot get their laundry clean. High ammonia concentrations from decomposed industrial and human wastes combine with chlorine to reduce the effectiveness of the disinfecting process. The time could soon come when it will no longer be safe to use the waters of the Merrimack at all for drinking because of high bacterial and virus content.

The spotlight was turned on the modern Merrimack and its tributaries at a Boston conference called by the Secretary of Health, Education, and Welfare in February, 1964. More than forty-four municipalities and fifty-seven industries were involved. Former Governor Endicott Peabody of Massachusetts asked for the conference under terms of the Water Pollution Control Act passed in 1956, which gives primary responsibility for pollution control to the states. A conference can be assembled only at the request of a governor.* The federal authority is limited to recommendations, although the HEW secretary can sue for enforcement if no action follows. The act's lengthy and cumbersome procedures have failed to cut pollution significantly.

The findings of federal water-pollution experts were presented to the Merrimack conference by Herbert H. Pahren, Senior Sanitary Engineer. His presentation was couched in technical language, but a clear picture emerged of the urgent need for a huge clean-up job.

Mr. Pahren reported that in some parts of the lower river, zero dissolved oxygen (DO) readings were obtained, indicating "very serious conditions in the stream for fish life even for very short periods." Indeed, pollution in the Merrimack has all but destroyed the river's once abundant fish life. The shellfish areas at the river's tidal mouth were closed down in 1926 because of excessive pollution. With sufficient reduction of pollution, these areas could be reopened for commercial use and recreation.

Both Massachusetts and New Hampshire have standards for swimming and other recreational use of streams, based upon coliform bacterial presence. Immediately below Lawrence, Massachusetts, the coli-

---

* A later statute (July 20, 1961) permits the secretary to call a conference on his own initiative if pollution from one state is endangering the health or welfare of people in another state.

form bacterial count was some 400 times the maximum used as a guide for water supplies.

Overall, according to engineer Pahren, any bodily contact with the Merrimack River is a hazard from Franklin, New Hampshire, to just above its mouth, a distance of 116 miles. Despite the danger, the Merrimack is still used for boating and water skiing from Lowell to the New Hampshire state line and in the tidewater near the mouth of the river. Yet, according to expert testimony, a drop of water sprayed into the face of a boater or water skier may contain forty-two coliform bacteria at the Tyngsborough Bridge recreation area. Measurements taken in this area revealed a coliform count twenty-six times the Massachusetts limit for safe bathing.

Odorous solids dot the surface of the Merrimack in many areas. The river looks black because of industrial coloration and the sludge that coats its bottom. White suspended matter from paper-mill operations further detracts from the aesthetic values of the river. In June, 1963, organic cyanide compounds were discovered in raw waters pumped into the Lowell water plant.

Fearful of a flight of industry from the Merrimack, some officials and local industry joined to oppose effective clean-up. The state of New Hampshire, in the person of an assistant attorney general, took issue with the constitutionality of the Merrimack conference. The executive secretary of the New England Interstate Water Pollution Control Commission denied the need for federal action on the grounds that state laws are adequate. This official recognized one requirement, however, when he stated that "money is the critical need—not enforcement."

As long ago as 1908, the Massachusetts legislature ordered a study of sanitary conditions on the Merrimack. In 1909, the legislature received a report warning that pollution was rapidly increasing. So, again in 1909, another report was ordered by the legislature. The state Board of Health reported back in 1913 that the objectionable conditions were due to large quantities of wool scourings, other industrial wastes, and the dumping of raw municipal sewage. In 1923, the Board of Health was once more ordered to investigate the river. It reported that the pollution problem could be solved only by building treatment plants or by the construction of a trunk sewer from Lowell to the ocean.

Nothing was done.

Additional reports were made in 1936, 1938, and 1947 by various public and private organizations. All reported serious pollution, and in each case the projected cost of abatement rose considerably. Throughout the next sixteen years, there was more study, and more reports were filed. Finally, in 1963, a Boston engineering firm prepared a report with recommendations and cost estimates for waste-treatment construction to cope with still higher levels of pollution. As expected, costs had again risen. And again, nothing has been done.

If the Merrimack is badly polluted, its tributary, the Nashua, is at least equally in need of abatement and control. Mario J. Vagge, mayor of Nashua, New Hampshire, relating that this town had done about a third of the job required locally, urgently called for federal assistance.

"I feel this way," said the mayor, "the Federal Government spends millions on highways—I want our rivers clean, our water clean, and it has to be clean."

Warning that delay would add to both dangers and costs, Mayor Vagge described conditions on the Nashua, which flows through his city:

> I have gone over to the Nashua River. That is the worst. If you ladies and gentlemen came through Nashua in the dry spell, I'm going to tell you that you will never come to Nashua again.
>
> Right by the Main Street Bridge, there are hundreds and hundreds of dead fish up on the banks, and the river is so black I don't know how you can drown in it. I'm not fooling. I don't know how you can sink in it.
>
> We have taken it and depolluted part of the river, which maybe we shouldn't have done, but we did it to get a head start on it. But the Nashua River that comes into Nashua itself is an awful thing. I know people call me on hot nights and want to know what we are going to do about it . . .

Death Comes to the Lakes

Another classic case of pollution begins with a celebration in Ashtabula, a cozy, small town with a good port on the Ohio shore of Lake Erie. It was a grand occasion. The crowd pressed close to hear the President of the United States. Presidents rarely visit Ashtabula.

"I want to say just one word to you men along the lake shore. I want the people of Ohio, Pennsylvania, and New York to aid in a campaign for pure drinking water from the Lake," Theodore Roosevelt told the audience. "You can't get pure water and put your sewage into the lake," the President added. "I say this on behalf of your children. You know my views on children."

President Roosevelt spoke from the rear platform of a train that had stopped in Ashtabula on August 25, 1910. His words were in vain. Industries and communities along the 8,300 miles of the Great Lakes shoreline have continued to dump their wastes into the convenient waters. With the passage of each day, the condition of the lakes worsens as more pollutants are poured into less water. The sweet, clean waters that delighted the early settlers are changing—and in some areas they are dying.

The lure of the Great Lakes has brought fully one-eighth of all who inhabit North America to live along their shores. Two of the five cities of the United States with populations of a million or more—Chicago and Detroit—and the two largest cities in Canada—Toronto and Montreal—are on the lakes or their outflow, the St. Lawrence River.

From the Great Lakes, 27 million individuals draw fresh water, which is returned filth laden. Paper mills, automobile plants, steel mills, chemical plants, and small towns—as well as the great cities—flagrantly misuse the waters.

Erie, the northern border for much of industrial America, is the sickest of the Great Lakes. Its ills are cancerous. They are repeated in varying degree in lakes Superior, Michigan, and Huron above, and in Lake Ontario below.

Today, about a fourth of Lake Erie is all but dead. This huge expanse encompasses 2,600 square miles in the central basin. It contains almost no oxygen, and no fish swim there; the surface is infested with scum. The natural death cycle to which all lakes are subject has been made to leap ahead by the tremendous quantities of pollution that have been poured in. Usually, a lake's decay is measured in geologic time; in Erie's case, the changes can be measured from year to year. Even if the contamination could be cut off completely, the algae forming the green scum would continue to proliferate—feeding on nitrogen and phosphorus and taking more and more oxygen from the tired waters. Unless the death cycle is reversed, the entire lake will die, and much of northern Ohio could wither with it.

Erie is the shallowest of the Great Lakes and has the smallest volume

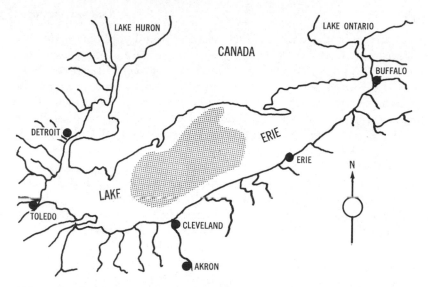

The growth of algae, stimulated by pollution, has driven out the oxygen in the shaded portion of the large central basin of Lake Erie shown above. Here, no fish exist.

Evening Star, Washington, D.C.

of water. These factors have made it particularly vulnerable to degeneration by pollution. Had man been careful during the past century, the lake would still have generations of life before final deterioration. But human and industrial wastes continue to take their fearful toll. Hundreds of companies, producing products ranging from earth-moving equipment to baby bottles, eject their wastes into the lake. Every day, nearly 1.5 million pounds of suspended solids go into Lake Erie from the Detroit River alone. Every day, that river is used as the dumping ground for more than 1.6 billion gallons of processing and cooling water—1.1 billion gallons from industry and 540 million gallons from municipal sewage treatment plants.

Major cities on the lake add tremendous quantities of pollution. Buffalo and Detroit have provided only primary treatment to their billions of gallons of municipal sewage. Cleveland returns almost a billion and a half gallons of inadequately treated sewage daily, plus millions of gallons of industrial waste carried by adjacent rivers. Phosphates from municipal sewage have brought proliferation of ugly algae growth in the lake and along its shores.

A survey by the Cleveland *Plain Dealer* found only one of three of Cleveland's treatment plants adequate. The smallest of the plants, built in 1922, handles 32 million gallons of sewage daily. It removes from the raw sewage only a third of suspended solids and discharges the remainder into the lake. A second plant, which handles much of the wastes of twenty suburbs in addition to local sewage, was seriously overtaxed. Three suburban plants serving a population of 250,000 spew 30 million gallons of treated effluent into the lake daily.

At Euclid, the largest suburban plant treats 14 million gallons of waste daily. Flanking the outflow pipe is a town beach, which has been shut down for six years because of high coliform count.

David Blauschild, an auto dealer, launched a lone fight in 1965 to induce officials to enforce antipollution ordinances against seven companies. Finding his right to sue as a member of the general public challenged by the city's chief attorney, Blauschild bought billboard space in an effort to spark a public campaign for a clean-up.

All along Lake Erie, and in many areas of Huron, Michigan, and Ontario, lovely beaches are posted with warnings that waters are "unsafe for swimming." Rochester, New York, without beaches for seventeen years because of the condition of Lake Ontario, has spent $18 million for facilities to end waterfront pollution.

By 1965, the contamination of Lake Erie had become so serious that the state of Ohio requested the Public Health Service to call a conference. The five states bordering the lake—Ohio, New York, Michigan, Pennsylvania, and Indiana—agreed to an abatement program that could halt pollution within four years. It will take an investment of billions in new sewage and industrial waste treatment plants, but at stake is the environment for 10 million persons.

The agreement calls for "secondary" treatment of municipal sewage to reduce pollution from this source, "maximum reduction" of storm drains, and improved design of new treatment facilities to prevent untreated wastes from passing through.

A roadblock to pollution abatement—the insistence that local jurisdiction be protected—was highlighted by Ohio's objections to the conference findings. This state, which had called the conference, objected to provisions that called for clean-up of intrastate as well as interstate waters.

The Public Health Service is highly critical of petrochemical pollution on the Buffalo River. Its report on the condition of this stream was typical of findings on other rivers that empty into Lake Erie: "Under prevalent conditions of sluggish flow, the lower Buffalo River resembles a vast septic tank, with no dissolved oxygen and high biochemical oxygen demand during critical periods, and with oil, color, and exotic waste materials."

In a startling footnote, PHS added that even bloodworms and slugworms, which normally thrive on sewage and pollution, could not survive in the Buffalo River, where water takes up to 180 days to flow seven miles.

PHS cited the Mobil Oil Company as one of five chief industrial offenders. The company took indignant exception and asserted that it has cooperated willingly with PHS. "Where the weight of scientific evidence establishes the need," Mobil said, "we will take prompt, sound, and realistic corrective action."

Lake Michigan has also had to endure rising pollution. To counter it, the Public Health Service is demanding better industrial practices and more modern sewage treatment in the Calumet areas of Illinois and Indiana. Following a 1965 conference, PHS reported that the largest sources of industrial waste in the Grand Calumet River and the Indiana Harbor Canal are the U.S. Steel Corporation, Youngstown Sheet and Tube Company, and Inland Steel. "Three petroleum refineries [Cities Service, Sinclair, and Mobil] are less but still major sources of waste," PHS said. Even if these big sources cut pollution, the demands of Chicago are so great that Lake Michigan could still face annihilation.

Chicago's population of 3.5 million city dwellers and 1.5 million suburbanites, together with a gigantic industrial complex in contiguous northwestern Indiana equivalent to another 2 million, give the queen city of the Great Lakes a "sewage population" of 7 million. Chicago once flushed raw sewage down the Illinois River into the Mississippi. The city now treats its municipal wastes and pumps effluent that is 90 per cent purified into the Illinois. Other large cities provide far less adequate treatment, but return waste water to the Great Lakes. Because Chicago does not return wastes, it has been able to maintain municipal beaches and water fit for swimming and water sports. Lower Lake Michigan, near Chicago, is almost without current. Were the city to discharge even its highly treated effluent into the lake at this point, it would soon be faced with a sea of sewage.

Every day, Chicago sends a billion gallons of treated waste down the Illinois waterway and into the Mississippi to the Gulf of Mexico. To flush the effluent down the Illinois it takes a billion gallons of Lake Michigan water daily. The city has asked for additional billions of gallons to meet the needs of an exploding population.

Conditions on the Merrimack, the Nashua, and the Great Lakes are only samples of the water sickness that infects America. Almost every river of consequence suffers from excessive pollution.

Although the Hudson River has some distance to go before deteriorating to the state of the Merrimack, it has become increasingly polluted. The shad runs that existed during the 1930's are gone, and fish life has become relatively scarce. There are areas of the Hudson, one of the world's most beautiful rivers, in which the only existing form of life is a vicious scavenger eel.

The "horrors of the Hudson" were viewed by seven members of the House Subcommittee on National Parks and Recreation during the summer of the great drought in 1965. "Oil slicks, dead fish, detergent bubbles, beer cans, and other debris rode the majestic bosom of the river as seven members (of the subcommittee) boarded the power cruiser *Firefly* here this morning (July 25, 1965)," *The New York Times* correspondent Homer Bigart reported. Around noon, the *Firefly* "fetched up" beside one of the biggest sewers of the city of Newburgh, where "milky white" wastes were being poured into the river.

"Obviously," said Representative Ralph J. Rivers of Alaska, the subcommittee's chairman, following the cruise and a public hearing, "the water is badly polluted and many eyesores appear on the banks." Earlier, Secretary of the Interior Stewart Udall had said that the nation is passing the Hudson River on to the next generation as "an open sewer." A subsequent conference on the Hudson, called by the Department of Health, Education, and Welfare at the request of New York's Governor Nelson Rockefeller, confirmed these findings and charges.

Moving west, the story of contamination is repeated. The Cuyahoga carries red rust; the Ottawa, petrochemical wastes from a huge oil-company complex; the Grand River, mine salts and chlorides. All reaches of the Arkansas are contaminated by mining, metal processing, packing, and agricultural runoff wastes. The Columbia's pollution from paper mills poses more threat to the salmon than the river's dams; this waste does not create bacterial pollution but is a major robber of dissolved oxygen in the waters. Canning wastes pollute the San Joaquin and the Sacramento in California, especially around San Francisco Bay. Oil-refinery wastes taint the lower reaches of the Yellowstone. In Utah, the Jordan, which empties into Great Salt Lake, brings municipal sewage and copper-refinery residue into the concentrated salt brine.

According to the U.S. Public Health Service, ten times as much industrial waste per million persons went into our waters in 1960 as in 1900. Municipal waste per million persons trebled in that period. In 1900, total water pollution was three parts municipal, two parts industrial. By 1960, total water pollution had become one-third municipal, two-thirds industrial.

Pollutants entering U.S. water courses include the following classes:

1. Domestic sewage and other oxygen-demanding wastes. These are the organic substances that come from humans and from industries such as food processing; in pure waters, they are reduced by bacteria.

2. Infectious agents. These are organisms that cause typhoid fever, virus infections, and intestinal disorders. They are carried into streams, lakes, and ground water from cities, sanatariums, tanneries, and slaughter houses.

3. Plant nutrients, such as nitrates and phosphates. Algae and water weeds feed on minerals in solution. Although they occur naturally in streams, when introduced in large quantities, they stimulate excessive growth of the water plants and set up a complex water-destroying cycle.

4. Organic chemical exotics. These are new chemical substances—detergents, weed killers, pesticides.

5. Other minerals and chemicals. Of these, salts and acids are the most common; they include many metals, metal compounds, and manufactured chemicals.

6. Sediments. These are soil and mineral particles washed from the lands by storms and flood waters.

7. Radioactive substances.

8. Heat.

The organic chemical exotics have added a new dimension to river pollution. In her book *Silent Spring*, the late Rachel Carson described our streams as "rivers of death" because of the toxic impact on living organisms of the pesticides they carry. Pesticides are washed into the streams by rains, or are brought in by ground waters contaminated by the new chemicals.

Although some opponents of her point of view called Miss Carson guilty of gross exaggeration, industry has begun to take note of her warning. The action comes none too soon because chemicals washed into streams are largely unaffected by municipal water-plant treatment. Whether continued consumption of waters contaminated by pesticides, herbicides, and chemical fertilizers is harmful has at least been opened to debate.

Silent Spring vividly portrayed the politics of water use arising from the conflicts between the "sprayers" and the conservationists. In that battle, the sprayers were supported by the Department of Agriculture, many in the field of agriculture, and the chemical industry; the conservationists were supported by the Fish and Wildlife Service, the state fish and game agencies, and hundreds of citizens who wrote protesting the killing of song birds, small animals, and fish. In 1964, the *Wall Street Journal* reported that a "million-dollar monument to Rachel Carson" had been dedicated at Walnut Creek, California. The "monument" was a pesticide research laboratory built by private industry. Together with other industry action, research at Walnut Creek resulted from more stringent controls that followed publication of Miss Carson's book. New products being produced are safer for man, wildlife, and fish.

Decay of the Estuaries

A special problem of water pollution is the contamination of estuaries and stretches of coastal shoreline, which have great value as residential areas, recreation resources, and producers of numerous species of aquatic life. Estuaries are the areas where rivers meet the sea. Here, tides ebb and flow, and polluted river waters may linger for long periods, producing pernicious changes in the environment. Estuarine pollution is more complex—and therefore harder to study and control—than river pollution.

In a 1965 report, the Environmental Pollution Panel of the President's Science Advisory Committee cited three dramatic case histories of the effects of pollution on bay areas. One described the action of both human and industrial waste on Raritan Bay, New Jersey, previously famous for shellfish and water sports:

> Its once clean waters . . . were transformed by the pressures of industrialization and the resulting population expansion into a septic, despoiled

environment, murky with domestic and industrial wastes, and . . . peculiar, undesirable flora.

Another New Jersey bay, Barnegat, suffered a "red tide" in 1964, caused by a "massive proliferation" of two dinoflagellates (a class of marine plants) having "an absolute requirement for organic molecules as fuel." It was determined that this sudden growth, and its resulting fish kill, was cause by human waste seepage from the large number of cottages that line the northern rim of the bay.

The third case involved Great South Bay and Moriches Bay, Long Island, where serious pollution caused the failure of a once prosperous shellfish industry and cut recreational use. Hydrographic studies showed that the bays held pollutants from duck farms (and later, from an increasing number of homes) long enough to permit massive proliferations of minute algae that injure oysters. In 1964, rotting material produced gases that gave off foul smells and even discolored the paint of houses near the water.

In late 1966, the American Littoral Society reported that fish stocks in Atlantic coastal waters had suffered a loss of "critical proportions" from water pollution and decay of coastal marshes. Catches of eighteen species along the coast were said to have dropped nearly 50 per cent from 1960 to 1965.

Several of our coastal states have concerned themselves with estuarine pollution. Other nations are also concerned: Britain has completed a seven-year study of pollution in the Thames, a tidal river, and in South Africa, industrial firms must obtain licenses before waste products can be disposed of in the ocean.

Ground waters as well as surface waters can be infected with pollution. Since they are not often subject to the action of oxygen-consuming bacteria, ground waters can remain contaminated for long periods.

Disposal of animal wastes creates a special pollution problem that is on the increase in the United States, affecting both surface and ground waters. The animal population is expanding just as the human population is, but there is no increase in either land or water for disposal of bodily excretions. Pollution of ground water from poultry and farm animal wastes can cause undesirable changes in taste, odor, and color, and can raise nitrate levels in nearby wells. Substantial nitrate contamination of ground water has been reported in the Dakotas, Minnesota, Iowa, New York, Pennsylvania, New Jersey, Nebraska, and Texas.

Pollution has been defined by the courts as "any impairment in water quality that makes water unsuitable for beneficial use." Not all pollution is harmful to man—sedimentation, for example—but all injures water quality. The Colorado is polluted but swimmable. Its pollution comes in the form of mineral salts resulting from use and reuse of the water for irrigation. Water seeping back into the river produces an ever higher salt content. This has brought loud protest from Mexico, which expects its share of the river to be usable.

Although thermal pollution (heat) introduces no new physical element into a stream, it alters water quality. A case in point is the Patuxent River, near Washington, D.C., where the Potomac Electric Power Company has a huge, thermal generating plant that uses the stream for steam and cooling purposes. Thus far, the Patuxent has escaped the population explosion, and, consequently, most types of pollution. It remains one of the purest rivers in the East. But the question has been raised as to whether its quality is impaired by heat.

Maryland regulations require water to be less than 100° F. within 50 feet of a plant's waste outlet. Pepco has claimed that the Patuxent's maximum natural temperature is 87° F. and that its steam plant raises this by 11° or 2° below the legal ceiling. University of Maryland, Johns Hopkins University, and state and federal researchers have reported that the river's maximum natural temperature is 90° F., and that Pepco adds 20°. They have warned of exhaustion of dissolved oxygen, excessive algae growth, destruction of marine life, and the unbalancing of stream ecology.

(In late February, 1967, a team of Maryland scientists declared that Pepco's Chalk Point plant on the Patuxent River had brought about "profound and damaging" changes to marine life. According to Washington press reports, no violation of the 100° limit was alleged, but it was expected that lower effluent temperatures might be sought. Among plant and animal changes reported since the generating facility began full operation in 1965 were a significant increase in green-colored oysters, a reduced population of whitefish and estuarine flatfish, a reduction in egg-hatching capacity of microscopic animals, and the discovery in the previous August of 40,000 dead crabs. Several members of the state legislature—then in session—expressed concern, particularly because the company planned to build a larger plant on the Potomac River in Charles County, Maryland.)

There are simple answers for thermal pollution. Plants and municipalities that heat water during use must return it at near natural temperatures to water courses. This requires the use of cooling ponds, tanks, or towers. These devices may add slightly to costs, but the costs must be borne to avert the deterioration of our inland waters.

Federal Pollution

The U.S. Government has spent $640 million to fight pollution during the past decade but itself bears a share of guilt for the sad state of our streams. Wastes from federal installations add seriously to pollution. Recommendations for clean-up have been made annually by the Public Health Service, but have been ignored either because funds are not appropriated or are diverted to other uses, or because of sheer lethargy.

Testimony of Maurice E. Biladeau, base civil engineer at Grenier Air Force Base in Manchester, New Hamphire, during the Merrimack River conference of 1964, revealed what had been happening there. This witness testified that the field had been programed for a sewage treatment plant as far back as 1958, but that "no funds have been allocated for construction." The base was then dumping raw sewage into the river.

Murray Stein, Public Health Service antipollution enforcement officer and conference chairman, pointed to a statute "which provides that the federal installations are to show the lead in waste treatment practices and facilities." Yet, a House Government Operations Committee survey in 1965 found that 19 million gallons of sewage and 2.4 million gallons of industrial wastes were pouring into our streams at 64 military bases and 4 other federal installations. The committee asked for $5 million a year to start the clean-up job.

Basic national legislative policy has been an insistence that water pollution control is a state responsibility. In 1948, the federal Water Pollution Control Act was passed. It was experimental, originally limited to a trial period of five years but later extended to 1956. In 1956, the first comprehensive act was passed, providing grants to assist state and interstate agencies and to assist in the construction of municipal sewage treatment works. A permanent procedure permitting federal abatement action against interstate pollution was established.

By this act, Congress sought to stimulate—and assist financially— state and municipal programs. Although much of the discussion here revolves around Congressional action, it must not be deduced that any lessening of state and local action is called for. On the contrary, such action must be expanded. Many states, and many cities and counties, are spending large sums to meet their antipollution responsibilities. An example is the billion dollar clean-up bond issue that New York state approved in 1965 by a four-to-one vote. Generally, federal grants for municipal sewage-treatment plants have been limited to 30 per cent of the cost—the cities have had to pay 70 per cent from their tax monies.

Industry, too, is vitally concerned with pollution, and although it may not have moved as fast as necessary to meet its responsibilities, a great deal has been done. Significant progress in industrial cooperation was shown at the Lake Erie conference in 1965. As the conference began, a number of companies agreed to furnish the Public Health Service with data regarding the nature and quantity of pollutants added by their operations. (A roadblock to pollution control has been that many firms have insisted on withholding such data, arguing that it would reveal trade secrets to competitors. The PHS has offered to guard secrets, if they are involved, but some responsible federal officials have scoffed at industry's alleged fears, declaring that firms refusing to co-operate simply do not want to divulge the degree of pollution for which they are responsible. In the case of Lake Erie, the firms have had the protection of an Ohio law sanctioning concealment.)

Despite the corrective efforts of local and state governments and industry, Congress has decided—on the basis of studies extending over many years—that federal action must be expanded in the pollution field, both to institute higher water quality standards and to help raise more money.

The Eighty-ninth Congress, which met in 1965 and 1966, took major steps both years. One was the Water Quality Act of 1965, some aspects of which have already been discussed.

The scope of the nation's water-use conflict and the difficulty of changing established practices were displayed during the struggle to enact this bill. The Senate passed its bill in January; the House passed its version in late April. Then, for five months, it was tied up because of basic differences over water quality standards. The Senate had passed a version calling for immediate federal quality standards on interstate waters. The House version—vigorously supported by big industry— would have given the states two years to enact water quality legislation before considering federal legislation. It was not until the end of July that agreement could be reached even to hold a conference. It was the middle of September before the Senate-House conferees submitted their report, and October 2 before the act was approved.

The *Deseret News,* published in Salt Lake City, has generally opposed extension of federal authority, but supported the Senate position on water quality standards. Addressing itself to the House-Senate deadlock, the paper said in an editorial on July 26, 1965:

> . . . uniform national standards are necessary to prevent pollution effectively and keep it controlled. Because streams and rivers pass from one state to another, that state that falls down on the job of controlling pollution effectively unnecessarily complicates the task of those states which are conscientious about combatting dirty water.
>
> Supporters of the House version contend that States should be given an opportunity to act first because they are closest to the sources of pollution. The trouble is that States have had an adequate opportunity to act on their own, yet the pollution problem grows greater every year as the country gets more people and industry . . .

The compromise bill that finally cleared Congress gave the states about two years in which to legislate their own standards, but it did strengthen federal authority over water quality, even though procedures are complex and filled with opportunities for delay. In the absence of state action, the Secretary of Health, Education, and Welfare is authorized to publish standards for all or part of a stream. Prior to publication, however, a conference of interested parties must be called. The states, cities, and industry have the right to protest federal standards. If they consider those established by HEW too stringent, a second conference must take place to work out an agreement, and the decision reached then is binding upon all concerned, including the federal government.

The Water Quality Act of 1965 increased the authorization for grants to municipalities for pollution abatement facilities from $100 million to $150 million a year. It doubled the grant ceiling on single projects to $1.2 million and that on joint projects to $4.8 million. It authorized funds for research on sewer design and established a pollution control administration under an assistant secretary in HEW.

A little-noted clause in the Housing Act of 1965 marked an important advance in federal participation by authorizing up to $700 million in 50 per cent matching grants to help communities modernize treatment plants. The Economic Development Act, also passed in 1965, authorized 80 per cent federal grants for economically distressed areas.

In a 1966 report titled "Steps Toward Clean Water," the Senate Subcommittee on Air and Water Pollution named "three basic elements in the Federal Government's water pollution control effort: treatment, enforcement, and research." The subcommittee further said it advocated a "systems approach" to pollution abatement.

With this study as a foundation, the Clean Water Restoration Act was passed late in 1966. It was not an administration measure but, to a degree, incorporates theories advanced by President Johnson in his message to Congress on the quality of the environment. It envisions the establishment of river-basin commissions to plan pollution abatement on a basin-wide scale.

A vast increase in federal funds was authorized, both for pollution research and for construction of municipal waste treatment works. For the latter, more than $3 billion may be spent over four years.

A "bonus" system for federal grants was established. Previously, the federal share of the cost of a municipal sewage treatment plant could not exceed 30 per cent. Under the new act, the federal share may be 40 per cent if the state government puts up 30 per cent, and the federal share goes to 50 per cent if the state puts up 25 per cent and adopts state-wide water quality standards. To advance coordination in the planning of water development projects, the Water Pollution Control Administration was transferred by the President from HEW to the Department of the Interior.

Total appropriations to the Federal Water Pollution Control Administration for the 1966 and 1967 fiscal years were $187,076,000 and $233,063,000, respectively. Of the 1967 total, $153 million was for waste treatment works and would help finance construction of 1,170 sewage treatment plants. The 1967 budget also contemplated a nearly 30 per cent increase in FWPCA personnel.

Adequate water quality standards are the key to solution of America's massive pollution problem. Downstream communities will be forced to contend with pollution originating upstream so long as such standards are lacking. The water quality laws of 1965 and 1966 represent progress —although significantly less than many, including the author, believe necessary. These laws will result in state standards that may be adequate in some cases, but in others will tend to be minimal because of costs to industry and municipalities.

Federal aid is increasing but it must become significantly greater to win the battle against inland water pollution. Part of the national income of past decades has been derived from living off the capital of our precious waterways. Now, a share of that capital must be invested to restore purity to our waters.

CHAPTER VI

The Well Runs Dry

THE SECOND VERY SERIOUS water problem is shortage. A lack of water can be temporary, as in a drought, or it can be permanent in arid regions. It can also result from resource destruction.

In both arid and humid regions, weather alternates in long-term, wet-dry cycles. The reasons for the alternation are ill understood. Some weather observers link the cycle to sunspot intensity. Others attribute it to oscillations between different parts of the earth's atmosphere. Research has permitted few conclusions, although it is known that horizontal circulation of air in the upper atmosphere affects rainfall.

Drought: From the Atlantic States to the Great Lakes

Whatever the reasons, from 1962 to 1966 the eastern United States was caught up in a drought. Apparently a shift in wind patterns caused rain to fall over the ocean that previously had fallen upon the coastal land surface. The effects were particularly severe because the weather adversity centered on the nation's most densely populated region. It was already suffering from massive water pollution, which was made worse as waters declined but waste loads did not.

In the eastern drought area, three pollution problems were intensified: salt-water intrusion into estuaries for prolonged distances, low dissolved oxygen content in estuaries and streams, and increased fertiliza-
tion in lakes and streams.

During the dry spell, public attention was focused on two areas—
New York City and the Great Lakes. But the drought spread throughout most of the East.

In Florida, a man-made dry spell coincided with nature's. To prevent
recurrence of costly floods from Lake Okeechobee that had come in the
wake of hurricanes, the U.S. Army Corps of Engineers completed a
project that cut overflow into the Everglades. Damming of the lake
water, combined with drought, brought near disaster to the 'Glades'
unique population of fish, birds, and animals.*

In 1966, the Potomac River at Washington, D.C., fell to its lowest
flow since surveys were started in 1930. *The Washington Post* reported
that the flow had averaged 18.4 billion gallons a day in 1965, but that
the average in March, 1966, was only 8.3 billion gallons a day and on
March 31 dropped to 2.7 billion gallons—only two-thirds the flow measured at the end of March, 1930. In September, Washington had just
announced fines for washing cars and watering lawns when the area
was hit by a storm that dropped as much as 7 inches of rain in 24
hours.

The pattern of the drought varied considerably from area to area.
Because it takes at least a year for a reduction in precipitation to be reflected in reservoir levels, 1963 was the first year of noticeable water
shortage. For New York City, 1965 was the worst year; by 1966, use
of some Hudson River water, and conservation practices, had eased the
situation. For Washington, D.C., Baltimore, Maryland, and York, Pennsylvania, 1966 was the worst year. Advance planning paid off for Baltimore when, with 100 days' supply left in its reservoirs, water from the
Susquehanna River became available. The autumn rains of 1966 appeared to indicate that precipitation was returning to normal along the
Atlantic seaboard.

The New York Times crusaded for water metering as a conservation
measure during the summer of 1965. The crusade ran counter to a philosophy long held by the city fathers, who regarded water as a necessity

---

* See Chapter X for a more complete discussion of the Everglades problem.

that should be provided without charge to the individual. With the arrival of cool weather, the metering crusade muted. However argued, there is no denying that metering saves water, but it also presents New York political leaders with serious economic and philosophical problems.

Meters must be paid for, maintained, and read—adding to consumer costs. Meters do not differentiate between pauper and millionaire, both of whom pay the same price for each gallon used. One possible solution is the provision of a minimum gallonage without charge or at a nominal cost.

Although New York meters water for commercial use, it is among the minority of cities that do not meter water for domestic use. Experience elsewhere shows that metering leads to more efficient use of supplies. Figures also show that where water is provided without cost, it is needlessly wasted. Unlike air, water is limited in amount and is no more free than any other commodity that must be sought out, treated, and transported to the consumer. The real question is whether the social good is better served through meter charges or by payment from general taxation or, as in New York, through the real estate tax structure. London's 7 million people use about 420 million gallons of water daily. New York's 8 million *waste* an estimated 300 million gallons daily. According to press reports, water mains in New York leak badly. Meter advocates claim that pipes would be kept in good repair if wastes were reflected in consumers' water bills. Metering would not eliminate water shortages, but undoubtedly would reduce waste.

In a report to the President entitled "Drought in Northeastern United States," the Water Resources Council declared that the water shortages for major cities in that region were due to reliance on "narrow margins of reserve." The council pointed out that cities such as New York have tended to use the flow of small streams of high quality rather than that of larger streams with better sustained flow and concluded that "the drought propensity of a stream increases greatly as the demand approaches its average yield."

Four specific cases were cited to illustrate the necessity of adequate storage. Eastern cities ranged from "safe" to "very critical" as follows:

> *Boston* Metropolitan Water District is an example of a city that is essentially "drought proof." Its yield is 50 per cent greater than current use, and its reservoir system has a 6-year capacity. *Philadelphia* depends on

THE DELAWARE RIVER BASIN

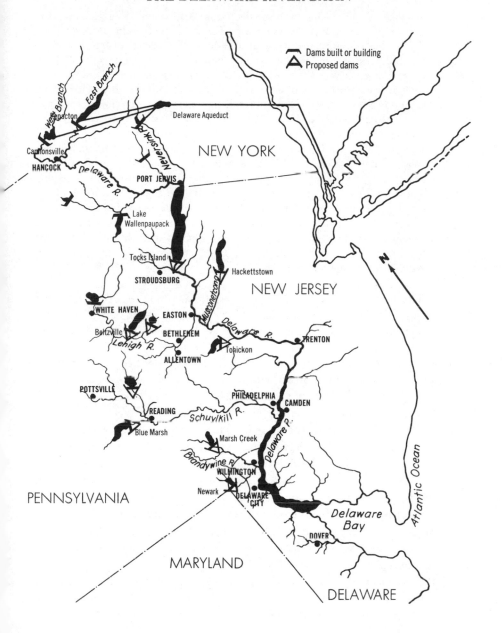

Dams built or building
Proposed dams

East Branch
West Branch
Pepacton
Cannonsville
HANCOCK
Delaware Aqueduct
NEW YORK
Delaware R.
Neversink R.
PORT JERVIS
Lake Wallenpaupack
Tocks Island
STROUDSBURG
Hackettstown
NEW JERSEY
WHITE HAVEN
Beltzville
EASTON
BETHLEHEM
Lehigh R.
ALLENTOWN
Musconetcong
Delaware R.
TRENTON
Tohickon
POTTSVILLE
READING
Blue Marsh
Schuylkill R.
PHILADELPHIA
CAMDEN
Marsh Creek
Brandywine R.
WILMINGTON
Newark
DELAWARE CITY
Delaware R.
N
Atlantic Ocean
Delaware Bay
DOVER
PENNSYLVANIA
MARYLAND
DELAWARE

the flow of the Delaware and the Schuylkill rivers. The demand for water is 40 per cent of the safe yield. The current difficulty in *New York City* is due to the relatively small 10 per cent margin between safe yield and the average use. While the city has reservoir capacity of 400 days of *normal use for itself*, and present curtailment in use should assure enough water to last until next spring, the city cannot be considered in isolation. The problem is not merely the risk entailed considering the size of the city and the consequences of a real shortage that would entail loss of pressure and other dangerous consequences should the drought continue. The risk is compounded by its potential impact on interrelated areas of need, such as Philadelphia and Camden, by a fifth year of drought. *North Jersey* cities were in danger even before the drought. There is virtually no excess of reserve supply, the average use being about equal to the safe yield. Although reservoir capacity totals about 250 days of normal use, this is insufficient in view of the fact the the streams are developed nearly to the average annual supply. Reservoir storage now on hand totals only about 90 days' use. The North Jersey water supplies are indeed in a dangerous condition.

The water level of the nation's most tremendous reserve—the Great Lakes—has declined substantially since 1952, although there are indications of a reversal of the trend as this is written. The level of lakes Michigan and Huron in 1964 was 2.3 feet below the 10-year June average, Lake Ontario was down 1.2 feet, and Lake Erie was down 1.3 feet. At Cedar Point, near Sandusky, Ohio, swimmers must walk a quarter of a mile from the shoreline to reach the water of Lake Erie. In the early 1950's, the same point was covered with 5 feet of water.

A drop of 1 foot in the 95,000 square miles of Great Lakes waters means the loss of 2.7 trillion cubic feet of water. The substantial drop since 1952 has dealt local economies hammer blows. Total losses run into the hundreds of millions of dollars. Pleasure boats rooted in mud are tied up at docks that not long ago reached out into blue water. Grain ships bound for Buffalo and Cleveland no longer carry maximum cargo because they cannot clear harbor entrances with full loads.

The Collingswood Shipbuilding Company of Collingswood, Ontario, laid off 1,000 workers in 1964. Although there was no slack in demand, the company was unable to launch its ships because Lake Huron's waters had retreated so far from the construction docks. Company officials have said that a drop of another foot in Huron's level will force them to close down completely. The Chicago and Northwestern Railway was forced to spend $1.3 million at Escanaba, Michigan, to provide new loading facilities for ore ships because they could no longer tie up at its docks. The low lake water in 1964 forced shippers to carry maximum loads 950 tons below capacity from the docks of the Huron Portland Cement Company at Alpena, Michigan. Ore-ship operators estimate that they lose $13 million annually because of present low lake levels. Every inch drop in level cuts the potential revenue of an ore freighter $8,000 annually.

The outlets of sewage treatment plants once hidden in the lake waters are now exposed along the banks of the St. Clair River at Detroit. Their ugly discharges are made uglier by the putrid odors belched forth. And the falling lake levels have brought charges that Chicago is "stealing" water and protests from the Canadian Government. In an official 1959 protest, the Canadian Foreign Ministry said: "The government of Canada is opposed to any action which will have the effect of reducing the volume of water in the Great Lakes basin. Canada considers that many agreements and understandings between the United States and Canada would be broken if unilateral action were taken to divert additional water from the Great Lakes watershed at Chicago."

The stern note caused President Eisenhower to veto two measures passed by Congress to permit Chicago to withdraw more Lake Michigan water. The decline in lake levels has brought the United States and Canada into continuing negotiations regarding withdrawals, obligations, and rights. Water levels on the lakes are of utmost significance to eight U.S. states and two Canadian provinces. Long ago, agreement on the need to find a solution brought about the formation of an International Joint Commission to settle problems of border waters.

Electric power producers are vociferous in their demands that something be done. New York State's Power Authority has become a major adversary of Chicago over water diversion. The Power Authority claims that Chicago robs it of more than $1 million annually for every 1,000 cubic feet of water per second diverted from Lake Michigan to the Mississippi. In the view of the Power Authority, the output of its Massena, New York, generating plant would be significantly greater were Chicago's treated effluent returned to the lakes.

Chicago bears too much blame for lower lake levels. The city's with-

drawals are smaller than the amount diverted from Long Lake in Ontario to Lake Superior. The Niagara power plants lose 7,000 cubic feet
of water per second because of diversion around Niagara Falls through
the Welland Canal. And an additional 1,000 cubic feet per second are
diverted to maintain navigable water levels on the New York State
Barge Canal.

Many measures can be taken to save water during a drought and to
alleviate the effects of prolonged water shortages. The most publicized
during the drought in the East was New York City's rule against serving water in restaurants unless it was asked for. Other measures include
credit extension to local government and business, provision of interest-
free planning advances, establishment of emergency fire-prevention and
antipollution measures, utilization of flood and of power generation
storage in reservoirs, and grazing of soil-bank lands. Most of these
measures are expensive in terms of depleted lands, delayed development,
increased costs of transportation, higher food prices, and cutbacks in
farm production. But the return of wet weather will overcome most of
the immediate problems.

In the case of the Great Lakes, emergency measures had little effect.
As the Canadian Minister of Transportation said in proceedings before
his nation's House of Commons, "The Minister of Public Works and I
and our officials have been considering this matter and we are doing
everything we can to alleviate the situation by dredging. But the water
just is not there. This is something I am afraid can be cured only by
more water."

There are differences of opinion as to the permanence of the Great
Lakes shortage. Some believe that the low levels are due entirely to
cyclical shortages and that, with the inevitable return of wetter weather,
the lakes will rise again. Others believe that the dry cycle is compounded by increased use of Great Lakes water and inadequate regulation. In discussing the nature of the Great Lakes crisis before the Senate
Merchant Marine and Fisheries Subcommittee, Senator Philip Hart of
Michigan said, "We are told there are various causes of these low water
levels, among them lack of precipitation, the dredging of channels for
improvement of navigation and the diversion of water out of the basin
. . . from my preliminary study, it seems evident that no matter what
might be done in controlling the waters in the basin, the long-range
solution lies in diverting additional waters into the basin."

If "narrow margins of reserve" truly describes the condition of the Northeast, long-term solutions are what must be developed. Even the heavy economic losses of the 1960's are minor compared to the possibility of trouble inherent in a water crisis of major proportions, possibly coinciding with a national emergency, which might come in a time when the region is even more populous and more heavily industrialized than it is now.

The Water Resources Council offered several recommendations for long-term improvement. They included planning and construction of authorized federal projects, a comprehensive water- and related land-resource study of the North Atlantic region, and a study by the Department of the Interior of the applicability of desalting to the area's long-term water requirements.

Energetic efforts are being made to expand water supply. For example, more than 200 separate water projects are planned or are under construction for the great Delaware River watershed. Several New York communities are eying the Hudson River, and, in 1966, the Hudson River Valley Commission reported that as the state's pollution abatement program is carried out, it is possible that the river could become "a major source" of supply.

Whatever measures are necessary, the alleviation of the threat of crippling water shortage to the industrial heart of the nation is a matter of high priority and quite beyond the issue of personal losses to business or individuals, unfortunate as these may be.

The Dry Lands of the West

Permanent shortage of water is the condition of some 40 per cent of the land area of the contiguous forty-eight states—that region lying between the 100th meridian (Dodge City, Kansas) and the Sierra Nevada mountains. It has an average annual rainfall of about 12 inches, less than a third of that enjoyed by the state of Virginia.

This vast region includes Montana, Wyoming, Utah, Colorado, Nevada, Arizona, and New Mexico. It includes eastern Oregon and eastern Washington; Idaho, except for the oasis created by the Great Snake River; and the western portions of the Dakotas, Nebraska, Kansas, Oklahoma, and Texas. Skirting the Sierra Nevada, it also includes the San Joaquin Valley and southern California.

The economic and political history of the West is intimately tied to water; not only its ownership and use, but also the realities imposed by the average annual precipitation figures. In *The Great American Desert*, W. Eugene Hollon has vividly told of how such men as Major John Wesley Powell warned that land use was limited by water availability, of the success of business promoters and overanxious public officials in convincing prospective farmers that "water followed the plow," and of how—three times—dry years followed wet to parch the land and bring varying degrees of disaster.

In the early 1880's, Easterners flocked to the plains, hungry for land and eager to stake out new towns, which were to become important centers of agriculture and commerce. After 1885, a series of crop failures bankrupted the area, drove these people back East, and spawned the Populist Party.

The rains returned by 1897—and so did the farmers. This time, science played some part in their operations. There were the "rainmakers," who argued that concussion could induce rainfall, but there was also dry farming* and the introduction of some drought-resistant plants. Then, in 1933, the effects of the "Great Depression" were compounded by another drought. For four or five years, Hollon tells us, "the desert smouldered like a giant fire." The topsoil was blown away, and with it went the farmers again, this time to California. That drought led to the birth of the Soil Conservation Service.

For a third time, crop lands were extended too far, this time to meet food shortages during World War II. Four years later, the dry cycle returned. However, understanding of the land and preparation in the form of greatly increased water storage held the losses far below those of the previous droughts.

The driest portion of this region is that comprising the southwest quadrant of the nation, which is also our fastest-growing area. Here, a significant characteristic is that precipitation seldom falls except in the mountains. For the most part, the clouds move over the flat, desert land, releasing no moisture and evaporating a great deal from rivers, lakes, canals, and irrigated lands. Then, when the mountains are reached, the precious water is discharged. Often, the winter's stock of

---

* The term "dry farming" is used for cultivation of nonirrigated crops timed to take advantage of seasonal rainfall.

snow moisture is the only water supply. In the truest sense, the mountains are oases in the desert.

Huge areas of the arid West grow no crops. Agriculture is dependent on irrigation fed by reservoirs or on pumping of ground water. Throughout much of the region, cattle and sheep raising is the largest-volume agricultural activity, and great acreages of irrigated land are used to grow hay for winter forage.

In 1902, the Bureau of Reclamation was created in the Department of the Interior to develop the water resources of seventeen states to "reclaim" land for agriculture. The bureau has been a major factor in the economic life of the region. Between 1904 and 1912, fifteen storage dams were constructed in nine states.

There were many reasons why the early reclamation program mired in financial difficulties. For one thing, land speculation made it hard to pay back water costs. For another, not enough was known either to build satisfactory dams or to locate them properly. In 1924 a fact-finder committee made a series of recommendations that led to comprehensive economic feasibility studies of every project and the addition of hydroelectric power as an income-producing factor, making the projects sound financially while reducing costs for irrigation water.

By 1965, there were some 39 million acres of irrigated land in the 17 western "reclamation" states, of which 8 million were served by federal projects. The modern bureau employs more than 10,000 persons, 1,400 of them in the office of the Chief Engineer in Denver. Several regional headquarters are maintained, at Denver, Boise, Sacramento, Boulder City, Salt Lake City, Amarillo, and Billings.

The Colorado River drains a 250,000-square-mile area of the southwest quardrant and is the lifeline to one-twelfth of the land area of the United States. It is an area that, to those who saw it early, promised little. Lieutenant G. C. Ives, the Army officer in command of the first navigation up the Colorado, wrote: "The region . . . is, of course, altogether valueless. It can be approached only from the south and, after entering it, there is nothing to do but leave. Ours was the first, and will doubtless be the last party of whites to visit this profitless locality. It seems intended by nature that the Colorado River, along the greatest portion of its lonely way, shall forever be unvisited and undisturbed."

Scarcely more than a century later, that waterway is the most completely harnessed and regulated major river in the nation.

The Colorado River rises high in the Rockies in north-central Colorado. Fed first by mountain snows and then by tributaries in seven states, the river flows southwest into Utah, on through northern Arizona westward to Nevada, turns south abruptly to create the Arizona-California border, and finally cuts through northern Mexico into the Gulf of California.

The Colorado River dates back to the Archean era, oldest of known geologic time. Over eons since, the 1,370-mile river has cut fantastic gorges into the sandstone rock crust that lies immediately beneath the earth cover of its drainage area. The river once raced seaward through a land green with vegetation. But some 11,000 years ago, rain ceased to fall and an ages-long arid cycle began. The cycle reached its peak about 4,000 years before the coming of Christ, and the story of the Colorado has remained relatively unchanged since that time.

The Spaniards discovered the lower Colorado not long after Columbus reached the new world. The conquistadors looked out on a river heavy with silt and named it Colorado—Spanish for red. It was later nicknamed the "Big Red" by early American settlers, who feared the murderous floods that came each year, but could not survive without the river's precious waters.

Not until 1922 were the initial steps taken to harness the river. Meeting that year in Santa Fe, representatives of the basin's seven states drew up the Colorado River Compact, which divided the river into an Upper Basin (Colorado, Wyoming, New Mexico, and Utah) and a Lower Basin (Arizona, California, and Nevada.) The dividing line between the basins is at Lee Ferry, south of the Arizona-Utah border.

The compact allotted each basin a share for all time to come. The Lower Basin states were given an entitlement of 75 million acre-feet every 10 years, plus an additional million acre-feet a year when available; the Upper Basin states could retain and use 7.5 million acre-feet per year or the part thereof available after the Lower Basin allotment and the Mexican allotment had been supplied. Mexico was to get an unstated share to be established by a U.S.–Mexican treaty. Should no surplus exist for Mexico, each basin was to allot from its own supply half of Mexico's entitlement. By treaty, Mexico now is entitled to 1.5

THE COLORADO RIVER BASIN

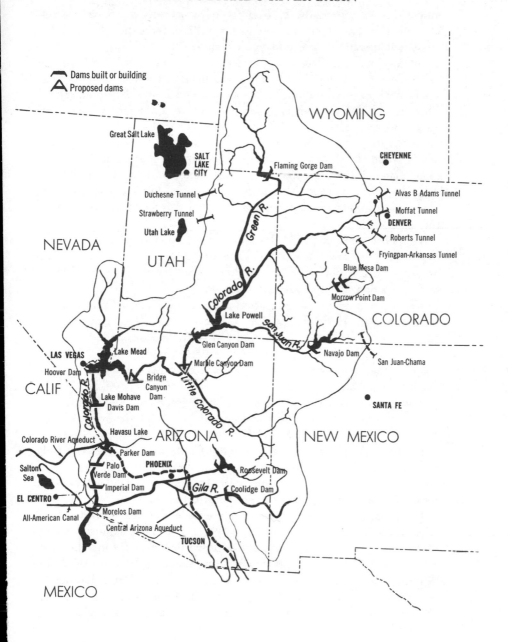

Dams built or building
Proposed dams

Great Salt Lake

WYOMING

CHEYENNE

SALT LAKE CITY

Flaming Gorge Dam

Duchesne Tunnel

Alvas B Adams Tunnel

Strawberry Tunnel

Moffat Tunnel

DENVER

Utah Lake

Roberts Tunnel

NEVADA

Fryingpan-Arkansas Tunnel

UTAH

Blue Mesa Dam

Green R.

Colorado R.

Morrow Point Dam

Lake Powell

San Juan R.

COLORADO

Glen Canyon Dam

LAS VEGAS

Lake Mead

Navajo Dam

San Juan-Chama

Hoover Dam

Marble Canyon Dam

CALIF

Bridge Canyon Dam

Little Colorado R.

Lake Mohave

Davis Dam

SANTA FE

Colorado R.

Havasu Lake

ARIZONA

NEW MEXICO

Colorado River Aqueduct

Parker Dam

Salton Sea

Palo Verde Dam

PHOENIX

Roosevelt Dam

Imperial Dam

Gila R.

Coolidge Dam

EL CENTRO

Morelos Dam

All-American Canal

Central Arizona Aqueduct

TUCSON

MEXICO

million acre-feet annually. If the Lower Basin received 7.5 plus 1 million acre-feet, and Mexico received 1.5 million, then the Upper Basin might retain water in addition to its basic entitlement.

Signatories to the 1922 compact proceeded under the belief that the Colorado flow averaged 18.5 million acre-feet each year, more than sufficient to meet allocations to the Upper and Lower Basin states and Mexico, and with enough left over to cover net evaporation losses estimated between 750,000 and 1 million acre-feet. The signatories were too optimistic; flow at Lee Ferry averaged only 13 million acre-feet annually from 1930 through 1964. The Upper Basin states divided their share in 1948. Acrimony and ultimate resort to the courts has dogged the Lower Basin. Mexico has complained bitterly both of inadequate water to meet obligations due it and of deterioration of quality in the water delivered.

The 1922 compact paved the way for construction of massive dams that have harnessed the Colorado and stored its water. In 1928, Congress passed the Boulder Canyon Project Act authorizing the Bureau of Reclamation to build Hoover Dam.

The key to downstream regulation and control, Hoover Dam began to store water in 1935. Rising 726 feet above the river bed, Hoover stretches 1,244 feet across Black Canyon between Arizona and Nevada. The dam impounds water to form Lake Mead, which has a maximum storage capacity of 29.8 million acre-feet of water—about 2 years of average river flow.

The Boulder Canyon Act also authorized construction of the All-American Canal System and the Imperial Dam and Desilting Works. Imperial Dam, 300 miles below Hoover, diverts water from the Colorado to the All-American Canal on the California side and the Gila Gravity Main Canal on the Arizona. The desilting operation prevents river sediment from entering either of these major irrigation diversion projects. Water entered the All-American Canal in 1940.

Davis Dam, completed in 1963 in accordance with terms of the U.S.–Mexican treaty, regulates flow into Mexico. There is a storage capacity of 1.8 million acre-feet within Lake Mohave Reservoir behind the dam. Parker Dam, 88 miles farther downstream, was completed in 1938 as a desilting project and forebay for the Metropolitan Water District of Southern California. At Parker, Colorado River water is diverted through a 242-mile aqueduct to Los Angeles and San Diego. Lake

Havasu, a 45-mile-long reservoir behind Parker Dam, has a storage capacity of 716,600 acre-feet. Lands bordering it are preserved as a national wildlife refuge.

There are some who, in the name of preservation, would prevent dam building on our major rivers. The benefits from Hoover Dam should answer these well-intentioned but mistaken individuals. Since 1935, there has not been a major flood or drought on lands served by the Lower Colorado. Hoover Dam stores water for irrigation, industrial use, municipal use, and recreation. Fish and wildlife have prospered. More than 3 million visitors a year come to see, swim, boat, water ski, and fish on 115-mile long Lake Mead. Thanks to Hoover Dam, the Colorado now provides about 80 per cent of the water used by southern California. Water stored in Lake Mead irrigates three-quarters of a million acres of land in the United States and another half-million in Mexico. Economically priced water is made possible by the nearly 1.4 million kilowatts of power generated at the dam and used by consumers in southern California, Nevada, and Arizona. Water delivered by the All-American Canal has produced crops worth some $2.5 billion in 25 years. Crop wealth is 37 times the federal investment. Water users are repaying 92 per cent of the $65.5 million federal outlay for irrigation.

Years of planning to control and conserve the waters of the Upper Basin of the river culminated in 1956, when Congress authorized the Colorado River Storage Project (CRSP). Four major storage units were approved: Flaming Gorge, on the Green River in Utah just downstream from the Wyoming border; Glen Canyon, on the Colorado River in Arizona just downstream from the Utah border; Navajo, on the San Juan River in New Mexico; and Curecanti, on the Gunnison River in Colorado. The first three are completed. Construction is proceeding on Blue Mesa, one of the three dams of the Curecanti Storage Unit.

The 4-state project will have a total reservoir capacity of 34 million acre-feet and an electric power capacity of 1.3 million kilowatts. Glen Canyon is by far the largest of the storage units. Its dam—710 feet high —backs up Lake Powell, which, when full, will be 186 miles long and have a shoreline of 1,860 miles. The reservoir will store 27 million acre-feet of water and provide 900,000 kilowatts of power.

The question has been asked: Why was Glen Canyon Dam built, since not a drop of irrigation water will be taken from it? The answer is that, under the terms of the Colorado River Compact, the Lower Basin must receive its share of water even in years of low flow. Under the law that governs water use in the West, the Upper Basin cannot draw irrigation water from the tributaries of the Colorado—and thus put to use its legal share—unless its commitment to the Lower Basin can be met. Thus, by keeping water on hand, the storage dams guarantee that the commitment will be met in dry years. Further, the dams are the "cash registers" for the project. Sale of hydroelectricity produces most of the revenue to pay back the U.S. Treasury for its advance construction funds. (Hoover Dam will be paid off in 1987, after which $11 million worth of electric power revenue will be available each year to help pay for other Lower Basin projects, or to be returned to the Treasury.)

Water users will pay about 5 per cent of CRSP costs; sale of power will yield the other 95 per cent. Power generated will be fed into a massive grid connecting both private utility and public power resources. Income from sales of power and water will go into a "basin fund" for the Upper Basin states, which will be used to repay project costs and interest to the U.S. Treasury and to make project assistance payments.

The Upper Basin can now put to use the Colorado's tributaries through "participating projects." An example is the Central Utah Project, which will take water from smaller rivers that flow into the Green River to use in some of Utah's populous areas. Eventually, the Green itself will be tapped for use in the Colorado Basin. Potentially, there is room for more than forty participating units within the CRSP. Four have been completed, and some twenty-four are in various stages of construction and planning.

Reclamation is made possible because surplus flow in wetter years can be stored for use in dry years. There are losses from evaporation, but they are small compared with the waste that takes place where river waters flow unused to the sea. There are losses from seepage into porous sandstone walls of canyons, but this is water that will return during dry periods when the reservoir level sinks below that of the stored waters.

As it ran downstream before Glen Canyon was built, the Colorado was red with sediment. Lake Powell's waters, nestling within the time-carved orange-red sandstone canyons, are a deep blue.

Critics have complained that Lake Powell has covered irreplaceable natural beauty that should have been left untouched for the generations to come. But without the reservoir, water and power for tomorrow would not be available. The untouched beauty of yesterday was available only to a hardy handful who entered the area by pack horse or river raft. Today's beauty is for all to enjoy. Preservation has an important place in water use planning, but not at the expense of essential conservation to ensure that a major region shall not die of thirst or for want of economic electric power.

Inability of Lower Basin states to reach agreement on division of allotted water caused Congress when it passed the Boulder Canyon Act to lodge ultimate responsibility in the Secretary of the Interior. The act provides that in years when the flow totals 7.5 million acre feet, plus 1.5 million for Mexico, California will receive 4.4 million, Arizona 2.8 million, and Nevada 300,000 acre-feet. Any Lower Basin surplus over 7.5 million and over 1.5 million for Mexico will be divided equally between Arizona and California.

Disagreement over Lower Basin allotments was finally resolved by the Supreme Court's ruling on *Arizona v. California,* June 3, 1963. The battle began in 1950 when the Senate enacted the Bridge Canyon Dam and Water Diversion Act to create a new reservoir and the Central Arizona Diversion Project. The measure, opposed by California and Nevada, died in the House of Representatives. After the House Interior Committee stated in 1951 that it would not consider the measure until legal questions were settled, the issue was taken to the courts.

Arguing before the court, California called for inclusion of all tributary waters in the Lower Basin, including the Gila in Arizona. Arizona argued that the division applied only to mainstem water. The court held with Arizona.

A second issue involved apportioning cutbacks in any year when less than 7.5 million acre-feet of flow are available. California, then using 5.2 million acre-feet, argued for cutbacks according to the rule of prior appropriation. This meant that the most recently built projects, located chiefly in Arizona, would be cut first and that California, with older projects, would suffer less. The court ruled that the Secretary of the Interior is free to use any method he wishes in apportioning cutbacks during years of low flow.

Arizona's hopes of soon putting to use its share of the Colorado's waters went glimmering when, in October, 1966, the House of Representatives adjourned without taking action on the Lower Colorado bill the House Interior Committee had reported. After some two years of work, the committee and numerous water officials of the states of the Colorado Basin framed a comprehensive measure for development of the Lower Colorado. It would provide for construction of two dams, Marble Canyon and Bridge Canyon (later called Hulapai); the authorization of five participating reclamation projects for both Upper and Lower Basin states; and a study of future water needs of the Southwest.

Bitter opposition to the construction of the dams was generated. Arguments of the Sierra Club, a leader of the opposition, were given nation-wide publicity by *Life, Reader's Digest,* and other national publications. California—which has long used more than its legal share of the Colorado water—and some other states felt that they had little to lose if the bill was not passed, but considered the whole package a net gain.

Representative John Saylor of Pennsylvania, ranking minority member of the House Interior Committee, and a long-time foe of western water projects, announced that he would offer an amendment on the House floor to delete everything but the construction of Marble Canyon Dam. With this threat added to the existing opposition, it appeared futile to bring the bill to a vote. No doubt, another try will be made. As this is written, the Department of the Interior is considering proposals to be presented to Congress. But the outlook for the construction of the two dams is bleak.

If the Colorado is the nation's most developed river, the other great river of the Southwest—the Rio Grande—is a leading candidate for the title of most abused. Although it evokes a mental picture of a stately river flowing placidly beneath a semitropic moon, the reality is often a near-dry river bed and sometimes a raging or near flood-stage torrent. Literally dozens of development projects have been undertaken, but almost all have been dismal failures. The Rio Grande, flowing through arid country for most of its length, simply lacks adequate water for the demands placed on it.

The *Water Atlas of the United States,* published by the Water Information Center, Port Washington, New York, includes a schematic representation of the flow of U.S. rivers. The Mississippi, greatest of the nation's rivers, discharges some 620,000 cubic feet of water into the Gulf of Mexico each second of each day. Average flow of the Colorado is 20,000 cubic feet per second. The Rio Grande has an average flow of

RIO GRANDE RIVER BASIN

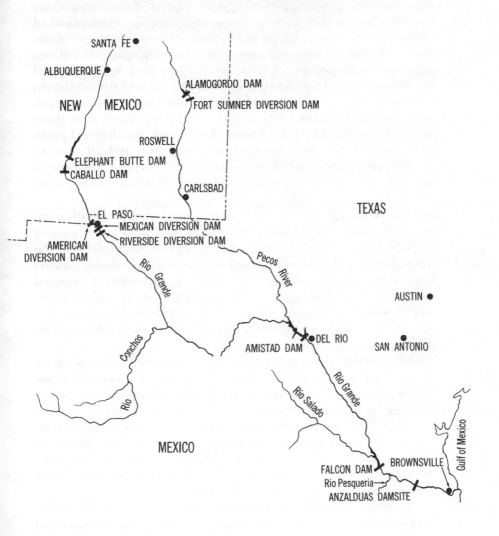

U.S. Bureau of Reclamation

7,200. The *Atlas* does not include the Rio Grande on its schematic map because it is "too small in discharge" to be shown. Flows have often been so low that the river at one time served as a crossing point rather than a barrier for illegal *bracero* labor.

The Rio Grande begins its 1,885-mile flow in the mountains of San Juan County in south-central Colorado. Among North American rivers, the Rio Grande is exceeded in length only by the Mississippi and the Missouri. It slices through central New Mexico serving numerous communities, including Albuquerque, San Antonio, and Las Cruces. Starting at El Paso, the Rio Grande becomes the international U.S.–Mexico boundary for 1,250 miles. Downstream from El Paso, the waters of the river are governed by the International Boundary Waters Commission under terms of the 1944 U.S.–Mexican Water Treaty.

The Rio Grande was the route of Coronado and other conquistadors who sought the fabulous "city of gold." In 1540, they found along the river's banks some non-nomadic Indians using rudimentary irrigation systems to water their crops. The early Spanish settlers, who called the river Rio Bravo del Nort, established trading posts and explored the upper river to the site of Santa Fe. The Spaniards called the trip upstream the "journey to death," because of arid lands between El Paso and Socorro, New Mexico.

Later, the Rio Grande basin became the land of the cowboy and the big herds that were driven north to Fort Dodge, Abilene, and other railway terminals after being grass-fed on the seemingly endless plains. Irrigation for crops followed. Ranchers diverted water from the upper river for growing livestock herds, and farmers upstream took water for irrigation heedless of downstream needs.

Following a 1906 compact among farmers and ranchers, state officials, and the Bureau of Reclamation, Congress authorized Elephant Butte Dam near the present town of Truth or Consequences in New Mexico. Elephant Butte, dedicated in 1914, alleviated water shortage downstream but caused unexpected problems upstream, where overgrazing accelerated erosion and caused rapid siltation.

Demands for ever scarcer water multiplied as grazing, farming, and population grew. Finally, in 1941, a conference of opposing interests authorized a study, which resulted in a three-state pact allocating the waters of the river. The pact solved little because it failed to take into account pumping of ground waters and population growth.

New Mexico claimed a population of some half a million in 1940. In 1950, Albuquerque was a city of fewer than 100,000. Today, New Mexico has a population of nearly a million and a half, with growth concentrated along the upper Rio Grande. Defense industry, climate, and nearness to the great outdoors have transformed Albuquerque from a sleepy small town to a metropolis of nearly 300,000. Located on the troubled Rio Grande, the city has laid claim to an ever greater share of the diminishing water supply.

Beginning in 1943, dry years followed each other like a plague of locusts. Ranchers, farmers, and municipalities turned to ground waters. Water tables fell, and even with the return of more normal rainfall, the river ran low as the earth sought to recover its losses. Downstream, severe salinity caused abandonment of many farms. By 1956, water tables had fallen so low that 75 per cent of the river flow was lost as seepage.

Hudspeth County in Texas was an immediate beneficiary of storage at Elephant Butte, but has since paid a fearful price. Water not used by the upstream irrigators was plentiful and free to Hudspeth farmers, who saw little reason to become partners in the Elephant Butte project. Drought years brought more stringent upstream water management, and Hudspeth turned to underground sources, which became increasingly salty until, by 1956, according to a study of the American Association for the Advancement of Science, the well water "averaged 5.5 tons of salt per acre-foot." Two-thirds of the irrigated area, which included many elaborate homes, was abandoned.

Downstream, the story of the Rio Grande is quite different although still not encouraging. Fortunately, the downstream channel is fed by tributaries that add water.

Legally, downstream begins near Fort Quitman, Texas, about 80 miles below El Paso. For 600 miles downstream—from Fort Quitman to Amistad—the river flows through mountainous, arid, and largely unsettled country, with irrigated cotton and feed crops on both banks. Above Fort Quitman, the waters consist almost entirely of flow released from reservoirs. At Quitman, the Rio Grande is chiefly waste water from irrigation seepage and drainage canals. Below Quitman, flow is built up from some 152,000 miles of drainage area, mostly on the Mexican side. The Pecos, the Devil, and smaller tributaries on the U.S. side and the Rio Conchos and other Mexican rivers add significant quantities of water.

From Amistad to the site of Falcon Dam, a distance of 300 miles, the Rio Grande flows through a floodplain about half a mile wide. Within this area are the border cities of Del Rio, Ciudad Acuma, Eagle Pass, Piedras Negras, Laredo, and Neuvo Laredo. Inhabitants on the U.S. side number 120,000 and on the Mexican side about 100,000. Some 66,000 irrigated acres exist on each side of the river.

The Mexican Water Treaty of 1944 covered both the Colorado and the Rio Grande rivers. On the Rio Grande, each nation is allotted, generally, the inflows of its tributaries. However, a third of the inflows of the principal Mexican tributaries above Falcon Dam are allotted to the United States. All flows not otherwise allocated are divided equally. In exchange for the third of Rio Grande inflows allotted to the United States from Mexican streams, Mexico receives 1.5 million acre-feet of Colorado River water.

The treaty authorized construction of three international dams to control the downstream Rio Grande—Falcon Dam, one at Amistad, and one at Anzalduas, southeast of McAllen, Texas. Falcon, some 160 miles above the mouth of the Rio Grande and 75 miles below Laredo, began to produce power in 1953.

Much of the inflow at Falcon Dam comes from the Rio Salado in Mexico. Downstream from Falcon, there are no live tributaries from the United States, but the Rio San Juan and the Rio Alamo feed the mainstem from the Mexican side. Most of the flood waters below Falcon rush unused to the Gulf of Mexico.

The year Falcon was completed, there was only a trickle of water in the Rio Grande. A year later there came great floods, originating on the Pecos and the Devil. The waters were checked at Falcon, whose storage area was almost empty. Damage above Falcon was estimated at $18 million. In 1958, another major flood took place on the Rio Grande. This time, the Falcon reservoir was almost full. Water from upstream ran over the spillway and caused $5.5 million damage below that site and the loss of a year's supply of good water, which poured into the Gulf of Mexico.

Falcon storage contributes to the irrigation of a million acres, which serve as the economic base for a population of more than 800,000 on both sides of the Rio Grande.

A bill to build a dam at Amistad was introduced in the Senate in 1960 by Lyndon B. Johnson, then Senator from Texas. He described the project as a "tremendous bargain" for both the United States and Mexico, and stated that flood losses on the lower Rio Grande were running to $1.8 million a year. Amistad Dam has been completed. Its reservoir capacity is 5.6 million acre-feet. Total costs were some $79 million. Cost to the United States is about $56 million on the basis of a 50-year life. The United States will receive 56.2 per cent of the water, Mexico 43.8 per cent.

Primary per-year benefits at Amistad are estimated at $1.8 million in flood control, $1.8 million in conservation, and $340,000 in hydro-electric power—a total for the United States of over $4 million. Secondary benefits in recreation, commercial fishing, sports fishing, and wildlife preservation are estimated at $5 million annually. Benefits to Mexico are less in money, but of more relevant value to that nation.

Costs of the final dam provided by the treaty will be shared by the two nations on the basis of water delivered. With the building of this third dam—still a project for tomorrow—the full potential of the lower Rio Grande for storage, navigation, flood control, and power will have been realized. But, as on the Colorado, that potential will be woefully inadequate for the region's human and economic potential.

There is no final solution for the Rio Grande area except transfer of water from surplus areas, although along the Gulf of Mexico, some municipal problems might be solved by desalination. For the upper Rio Grande, the day of reckoning has almost arrived.

No major river waters the High Plains of Texas, which are located in the western part of that huge state. Ground water is the chief source of supply for the region's irrigation needs and for hundreds of its communities. Texas accounted for more than one-fifth of the nation's ground water use in 1960, largely because of the demand in the High Plains area. In 1958 alone, more than 1,000 new wells were added to the thousands already operating.

The Ogallala Formation underlies the southern High Plains area. This great aquifer once stored about 250 million acre-feet of water. By the end of 1961, nearly 50 million acre-feet had been pumped out. Water mining today is removing the ground reserve at a rate 50 times faster than it is being recharged.

There is little danger that the Ogallala Formation will be pumped dry, but falling water tables increase the cost of water. Inevitably, the time will be reached when further pumping becomes uneconomic. Efforts have been made to recharge underground aquifers by the use of artificial wells through which rain water that accumulates in earth depressions is fed. Minimum well spacing is required to reduce drawdown. But this is a region of little rain. A return to dry farming and grazing would alleviate the problem, but would also require a significant emigration of population. The High Plains' economy is firmly based on ground-water mining. Other conservation measures may help to stave off a day of reckoning, but, with present use of the ground-water reserve, that day will surely come.

In 1966, New Mexico was putting to use some 2.9 million acre-feet of water, of which 1.45 million came from underground sources. A state conservation program has been established to stabilize ground-water reserves. Water basins have been designated as extending 20 to 30 miles on both sides of rivers. Within the basins, wells for industrial, agricultural, or municipal use may be dug only with permits issued by the state engineer. Individual householders, however, may dig wells for their own use without a permit. Because the program is based on average precipitation and use figures, there is a downdraw in dry years.

More than 70 per cent of Arizona's water comes from beneath the ground. Between 1960 and 1965, Arizona increased demand on its ground-water reserve from 3.2 to 4.9 billion gallons daily. Population and industrial growth accounted for part of the increase, but use for these purposes is small compared with agricultural demand. Arizona is mining its ground-water reserve by 2.25 million acre-feet more than is considered safe to withdraw. Climate encourages both population growth and irrigated agriculture. It has been said that more people and less agriculture will cure Arizona's ills. But more people almost inevitably result in more agriculture, as the history of California and Florida shows.

About 4.7 billion gallons daily of Arizona's ground-water reserve is used for irrigation. With irrigation, the desert lands produce bounteous crops. A highly mechanized and profitable agriculture has developed, adding $500 million annually to the state's income. Although irrigation is the basis of today's flourishing Arizona, it threatens to undermine the state's economy. Arizona's ground-water supplies are being mined at an annual rate of 3.5 million acre-feet, and ground water is being overpumped from residual reservoirs by 2.25 million acre-feet per year. According to Geological Survey experts, a safe yield of ground water in Arizona would be 1.25 million acre-feet annually.

Nearly 95 per cent of Arizona's scanty annual precipitation of from 5 to 10 inches is lost to evaporation and transpiration from natural desert vegetation. Only about 1 per cent is available for ground-water reserves. Irrigation water supplies to crops are largely exhausted in the same way, with only a small portion finding its way back to the water table.

Tucson had a population of 260,000 in 1962, and was growing by 15,000 annually. At the end of 1965, Tucson counted 350,000; by 1970, it will probably have a metropolitan population of half a million. The city has major water problems. It is the largest city in the United States that depends solely on ground water for municipal supplies.

Although it is not likely that Tucson will go waterless in the near future, since there is a large reserve deep below the ground, the water table—as in the case of the Texas High Plains—continues to fall and the cost of pumping to rise. Sooner or later, Tucson will have reached the limit of usable supplies. Agriculture or municipal growth, or both, will suffer.

Phoenix has grown rapidly, too; in 1965, nearly a million persons lived in its metropolitan area. But Phoenix is watered by an early reclamation development, the Salt River Project. Six storage dams have been built: Theodore Roosevelt, Horse Mesa, Mormon Flat, and Stewart Mountain on the Salt River, and Horseshoe and Bartlett on the Verde River. Theodore Roosevelt, the largest, was built between 1903 and 1911 and is listed by the Bureau of Reclamation as its eleventh completed storage dam. Its capacity is 1,382,000 acre-feet. The last, Horseshoe, was completed in 1945. Two diversion dams have also been constructed. Two main canals, the Arizona and the South, carry water to the north and south sides of the project. Electric power is produced, and the reservoirs are used for swimming, boating, and fishing. As Phoenix has expanded, farm water has been taken over for municipal needs, in the same pattern that has been followed in many areas of the West.

Major Powell's dictum—that land use is limited by water availability—applies to the modern West as much as to the one he explored. Irrigation may give way proportionately to industry for use of water, but population growth alone requires large additional supplies. For recreation, for agriculture, for industry, or just for personal use, water remains the key to a West of full value to the nation.

For both East and West, the water management of the future must put people (so far as possible) beyond nature's caprice. In neither region can the national interest permit a narrow margin of reserve in water supplies.

CHAPTER VII

Floodstage

A THIRD WATER PROBLEM is "variability"—the name given to fluctuation in streamflow. For the country as a whole, variations in water supply range from 50 per cent to 140 per cent of the average. For particular rivers in particular seasons, the variations can range from a dry bed to a raging torrent far overflowing its banks.

For example, climate, rainfall variation, and topography have combined to make the Rio Grande a river of extremes. Average annual rainfall in the watershed near Brownsville, Texas, where the river empties into the Gulf, varies from a meager 7.8 inches to a moderate 26.8, intermittently causing drought and flood. The upper Rio Grande, above El Paso, is dependent almost entirely on snow thaw in the San Juan Mountains for its water. Average annual rainfall in the New Mexico area drained by the river is less than 8 inches. Temperatures vary even more drastically than rainfall. Fort Sumner, on the Pecos in New Mexico, has reported tempertures ranging from 127° F. to –27°. El Paso has sweltered in 106° heat and shivered in deep freeze temperatures of 10° below.

On the Colorado River, early settlers often experienced flood as snow

HYDROGRAPH OF A RIVER
Shows the Uncertainty of Water Availability

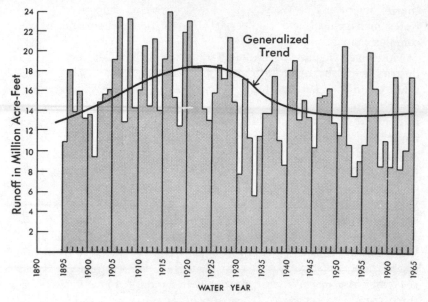

Colorado River at Lee Ferry, Arizona

U.S. Bureau of Reclamation

melt added huge quantities of water to the parched stream. In late summer and fall, the river dried to a relative trickle. It is probable that ancient Indian civilizations disappeared in part because of inability to cope with the erratic river. Even after the settlement of the West by the white man, attempts to divert water from the Colorado generally failed because the river ran too high or too low. During dry seasons, crops perished although water lay near at hand; during flood stage, the water swept away livestock, crops, and property and snuffed out lives. In 1905 and 1907, disastrous floods poured down the Colorado, sweeping into California's Imperial Valley and permanently flooding the area now occupied by the Salton Sea.

In arid regions, flood flows are a valuable resource, which must be captured and conserved for future use. Even in humid regions, flood waters must frequently be retained for use when needed. Thus, flood control by means of reservoir storage becomes an important tool of water management and cannot be divorced from other parts of the complex management task.

Most rivers require regulation if they are to provide cities and industries with the quantity and quality of water they require at the times when they need it. The low phase of variability is most acute, of course, in arid regions, which suffer from shortage of supply in relation to demand. Dams are absolutely necessary on the streams of western mountains. Otherwise, water from the melting snows runs off in the spring and early summer, leaving nothing for fall and winter. The larger the stream, the more dependable its flow; therefore, careful management is particularly essential on smaller streams if they are to provide substantial amounts of water for use in seasons when natural flows are insufficient.

At the extreme end of the scale is the most destructive phase of variability—flood. Flooding is part of the normal life of a river, and occurs in a statistically predictable sequence. For example, a typical river may rise to bank level twice a year, produce minor floods every three years, and overflow its banks to inundate all or part of its flood plain on an average of every ten years. Each river is unique, of course, and some never flood.

Floods frequently result from sudden storms—the West calls them "flash floods." Runoff rushes down steep, bare slopes, carrying masses of earth and debris in the path of the waters. A flash flood can roar down a dry canyon without warning, and hikers and travelers must be alert to the danger. Every summer in the West and Southwest, newspapers carry stories about near tragedy—sometimes real tragedy—when people on Boy Scout hikes, or Fourth of July picnics, or family trips are washed out by flash floods.

Floods in the humid areas range from the brief event that inundates a city street or a farmer's pasture and may occur in the same place as often as once or twice a year, to the sustained floods on major rivers such as the Ohio or Mississippi, where waters rise as much as seventy feet above low waters over a huge area. Fortunately, these disastrous major floods occur rarely. However, they are so destructive when they do occur that control of humid-area floods is primarily to prevent loss of life and damage to property.

FLOODS ARE NORMAL
IN THE LIFE OF MOST RIVERS

Half the time, only 10 per cent of the channel is used.

At average flow, the channel is about half full.

The stream fills or overflows the bank about twice a year.

Moderate flooding occurs about every ten years.

Peak flooding occurs about once in fifty years.

U.S. Geological Survey

Because of the disruption of the nation's economy as a result of floods, a substantial federal program of flood control has been mounted over the past half century. During those years, as earlier, the history of flood control in the United States has been inextricably linked with that of the U.S. Army Corps of Engineers.

The Corps dates its origin from June 16, 1775, when the Continental Congress passed a resolution providing for "one Chief Engineer of the Grand Army. $60 per month." From this modest beginning there evolved a Corps of Topographic Engineers that participated in many of the explorations of the western wilderness and investigations of proposals for development of roads and streams as arteries of commerce among the states.

When the nation was very young, the federal government took the position that it was not constitutionally empowered to expend funds for "internal improvements." This attitude prevailed in Congress until Chief Justice John Marshall held in 1824 that: "The power of Congress comprehends navigation within the limits of every state in the Union." Congress then appropriated $75,000 to remove sandbars and "sawyers, planters, and snags" from the Mississippi and Ohio to aid navigation, and selected the Corps of Engineers to perform this work. In the same year the Board of Engineers for Internal Improvements was established as a part of the Army Corps of Engineers to carry out works for improvement of rivers and harbors. Navigation improvements predominated in the civil works program until 1879, when the Mississippi River Commission was created with power to inaugurate comprehensive programs of river development, including flood control.

The federal government did not intervene directly in flood control until 1917, and Congress acted in that year only after disaster had already struck. Mississippi floods had caused great damage in 1912, 1913, and 1916. In California, the Sacramento had followed suit with sickening results. Finally, Congress appropriated federal funds to assist the flood victims and authorized studies of flood control, along with the river and harbor programs.

In 1927, the Corps was directed to make surveys of U.S. rivers with regard to navigation, flood control, irrigation, and power generation. These surveys resulted in the "308 Reports," which presented basic data and plans for developments on 191 rivers. (The Grand Coulee Dam and the Tennessee Valley Authority, among other developments, grew out of these reports.)

Not until 1936 did Congress approve a general flood control policy. Then it enacted the first Federal Flood Control Act, which authorized the expenditure of $310 million to begin work on 250 flood control projects.

By 1966, the Corps employed more than 31,000 civilians to carry out its civil functions. Of these, 400 were in the office of the Chief of Engineers in Washington, and 695 at the Waterways Experiment Station in Vicksburg, Mississippi. (Almost 400 workers were stationed outside the continental United States.) The Corps maintains 44 districts, divided into 10 divisions with offices in Boston, New York, Atlanta, Chicago, Cincinnati, Omaha, Vicksburg, Dallas, Portland (Oregon), and San Francisco.

An "educated estimate" of all Corps projects built or authorized up to 1967 would be 3,600, for a total dollar value of 23 billion. Under construction at the end of 1966 were 64 flood control dams, 116 other flood control works, and 31 multipurpose reservoirs. More than 270 additional projects were authorized.

In 1943, flood waters from the Missouri and other tributaries roared down the Mississippi River's 2,466 miles with unchecked fury and swept away $1.6 billion worth of property. Catastrophic loss of life and property has preceded almost every major flood control project in the land, and those on the Missouri have been no exception. Since settlers homesteaded along its banks, the mad river has continued to battle to retain its fertile flood plains. Hundreds have been killed by swollen waters inundating farm, hamlet, and city. Today, the nation's biggest flood control effort has all but tamed the river, even though it still rises up on occasion in new challenge to those who would harness its waters.

Following the 1943 Missouri-Mississippi catastrophe, General Lewis A. Pick, then head of the Missouri River division of the Corps of Engineers, rushed to completion a report recommending authorization of a huge project to control the floods and improve navigation on the lower Missouri. At the same time, W. G. Sloan, a regional engineer for the Bureau of Reclamation, was developing a comprehensive plan for irrigation and hydroelectric power production on the upper reaches of the Missouri River and its tributaries. The two plans, completed at the same time, proposed many of the same dams. As a result of the direct intercession of President Franklin D. Roosevelt, the two plans were coordinated and brought together into a multibillion dollar scheme to control the river. It was a "shotgun wedding" brought about by the pressure of public opinion and the remembrance of the tremendous flood damage. The Pick-Sloan plan involved a waterway stretching through ever-changing channels from headwaters in western Montana to the Missouri's confluence with the Mississippi just above St. Louis. The area involved is equal to that in ten Tennessee River Valley basins.

Congress authorized the Pick-Sloan plan in the Flood Control Act of December 22, 1944. General Pick had called for dams and other flood control measures along the river's mainstem. Sloan had urged dams and reservoirs on the upper reaches of the river and its tributaries for flood control, irrigation, and power generation. Congress combined both proposals into an over-all program of flood control with subsidiary benefits. The Pick-Sloan plan called for seven massive dams to hold the Missouri floodwaters in check. All are now in place. Yellowtail Dam, rising 525 feet from the bed of the Big Horn River in Montana, is the only one of the major dams not located on the mainstem. With Yellowtail, man has all but housebroken the "Mighty Mo."

Fort Peck, first of the Missouri dams, was built in the 1930's. It was the only possible protection against massive flooding when the river went wild in 1943. By 1952, when flooding recurred, several upstream dams had been started, but were not able to store water. Fort Peck dam alone, however, held back sufficient water to save Omaha and Council Bluffs from inundation; these cities were largely spared because the dam held back a single foot of flood crest.

The close call in 1952 brought a speed-up on Pick-Sloan dam construction, and all mainstem dams were in place when floods struck once more in 1960. That year, more than $200 million in flood damage was averted. Again in 1963 and 1964, the dams proved their value, preventing possible loss of life and massive property damage.

Engineers have urged further dam construction on Missouri tributaries, particularly below Gavins Point Dam. They argue that the lower Missouri area is still vulnerable to flash floods, which can be averted by more tributary dams. Yellowtail, the big tributary dam, is expected to assist in flood control in the upper basin, reduce the present heavy silt load on the mainstem, and result in 250,000 kilowatts of power. When the generating station at Yellowtail is complete, the Mighty Mo will have a capacity of more than 2 million kilowatts of power. Revenues resulting from power generated in 1965 amounted to $37.4 million, and each installation will add to the total.

The taming of the Missouri through Pick-Sloan multipurpose dams is bringing additional dividends in the form of navigable waters. Once considered unnavigable, the Missouri last year carried 2.6 million tons of freight. This is but a token of the potential. Tonnage is almost certain to skyrocket as new irrigation projects under construction or on the planning boards are completed.

Congress last year authorized the Garrison Diversion, which will feed irrigation waters from the Garrison Reservoir to 250,000 parched acres in eastern North Dakota. This project alone has a potential for irrigation of a million acres. Also under consideration is the diversion of water from Oahe Reservoir to 195,000 acres in South Dakota. These and other irrigation projects of similar magnitude will greatly increase

MISSOURI RIVER BASIN

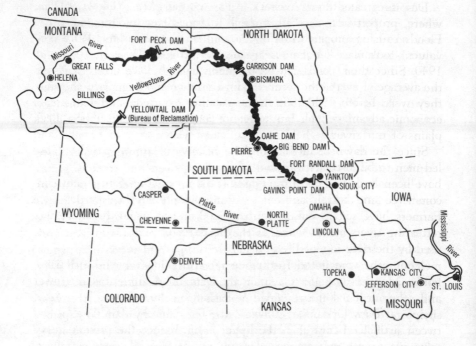

U.S. Army Corps of Engineers

the yield of these dry lands and bring new growth to the sparsely settled Dakotas. Grain and other produce will be shipped cheaply by
barge down the mainstem to big cities on the lower basin and along
the Mississippi.

By 1970, the Missouri should produce an estimated 11 billion kilo-
watt hours of power each year. Power will be purchased by an amalgam
of private and cooperative utilities which, by 1980, are expected to
spend $2 billion to integrate their facilities into a huge pooled grid to
serve midcontinental United States.

Behind each huge dam now in place along the waterway is a man-
made lake. Stability along the lower waterway and reduction of siltation are opening up a new recreation potential. The Missouri is becoming an important playground and tourist magnet for much of the nation.
Boat sales already are booming, with more per thousand of population reported for South Dakota than for any other state.

Despite greater flood control on the Missouri-Mississippi and elsewhere, property damages attributable to floods have mounted steadily. Floods causing property loss of $50 million or more (at 1959 dollar values) took place on the average of every 6 years between 1900 and 1940. Since then, floods causing as much damage have taken place on the average of every other year. Floods are no greater in magnitude than they were before 1940, but the population explosion and immediate economic advantage have brought more people and industry to the flood plains of our rivers.

Since the dawn of civilization, the benefits of running water have led men to build their cities and towns along rivers and streams. Cities have been built on flood plains because rivers have offered a means of commerce and travel, as well as water supply and waste disposal. Farmers have settled on flood plains because the muck deposited by retreating rivers greatly enriches the land. Flood plains—the land area used by the river to move flood waters resulting from excess rains, snow melt, or other precipitation—often extend for miles beyond the river banks. Men have sought to contain the waters with dikes, levees, dams, and other artificial means. (Airline passengers flying above the Mississippi at New Orleans may look down on a muddy river flowing between artificial banks far above the city.) Because serious flooding takes place with relative infrequency, people tend to settle on flood plains to reap the associated economic development as if the last flood were exactly that—the very last. This tendency adds seriously to flood danger and loss.

Since 1940, improved warning systems have made loss of life a secondary consideration in floods. Between 1900 and 1940, floods snuffing out the lives of a hundred or more victims were recorded on an average of once every three years. Since 1940, only two floods have claimed the lives of a hundred or more persons. Today, floods caused by hurricanes are the chief threats to life. Until recently, hurricanes struck with little warning. Although the use of weather satellites and radar have made early warning possible, the tremendous force of hurricane winds drives river waters from their banks, inundating whole cities, and hurricanes sometimes travel such an erratic course that the warning is ineffective. Hurricane Betsy was tracked and appeared to be turning away from the Louisiana coast when it struck in the fall of 1965. Betsy rammed into the coast at 5 A.M., only a few hours after citizens were assured that it would not present a severe problem in the area. Many died because of Betsy's flooding force, and thousands of others were made homeless.

Fremont, Ohio, was struck twice in three weeks by a rare kind of flood—an ice flood—in 1959. Huge chunks of ice fused at the mouth of the Sandusky River on Lake Erie. The frigid waters underneath were unable to reach the lake and were forced out over the river's flood plains. Wild currents ripped under the mile-long icepack and threatened to crush the city's business area under tons of ice. Attempts to bomb out the jam at the mouth of the river failed. Nature intervened opportunely before great damage was done and freed the water by melting a hole through the ice dam.

Some local and state flood control projects have been of great value, although most have been sporadic and insufficient, limited by inadequate funds, municipal and county boundaries, and state borders. One exception stands out as an example of what local initiative can accomplish in limited and exceptional circumstances. That exception still protects thousands who live and work in the Miami River Conservancy District in Ohio.

Torrential rains fell in Ohio on Easter Sunday in 1913, causing floods throughout the state. Dayton, where three streams join the Great Miami River, was hardest hit; bridges were washed away and communications and transportation were disrupted. Gas lines broke, resulting in fire and explosion. Homes with helpless families perched on the roofs were washed downstream. Rain fell for five days, and the state's death toll mounted to 363 persons. There was nearly a billion dollars in property damage—a sum far more tremendous in real value then than today.

Citizens of Dayton determined to prevent another such tragedy. Henry M. Waite, a Cincinnati engineer, was hired to manage city affairs. Waite was backed with $2 million, subscribed in 2 months, for flood prevention. Arthur E. Morgan, an engineer who later headed TVA, was called on to draw up a flood control plan. The Ohio legislature cooperated by enacting a law creating the Miami Conservancy District.

Construction of 5 dams was begun in 1918 and 5 years later, after an expenditure of $32 million, reservoirs to impound the flood waters were completed. In 1937, winter rains fell with unceasing fury until the

Ohio crested at heights unknown before on the river. At Cincinnati, the Ohio rose to a record level of 79.9 feet; almost 25 feet above flood stage. Even the city's water works was flooded out.

On "Black Sunday," January 24, flood waters backed into Cincinnati's sewers, toppling oil tanks en route. A spark from a trolley ignited the oil film on the water. Firemen fought a fire 3 miles long and up to 300 feet high with muddy waters pumped from the raging flood. Only two Ohio River areas escaped significant damage and loss of life.

During this flood, the Miami Conservancy District System saved Dayton from damage. And in the nearby Muskingum River valley, where a similar local flood control project begun three years earlier was near completion, damage was held to a minimum. But floods such as these on the Ohio are generally beyond local resources to control. And, unfortunately, only after massive property losses and needless loss of life did Congress begin to consider floods on interstate waters a matter of national concern.

No flood control project can guarantee that there will be no future flood of greater magnitude than those that have gone before. Sometimes, flood control protection adds to potential danger, since it offers reassurance to people and industry who build in flood plains. If a flood beyond planned limits of protection finally comes, the damage is greater than ever.

Increasingly, hydrologists advocate flood-plain zoning to prevent building on areas over which future flood waters may some day sweep. Zoning involves three major types of restriction: prohibitions on the use of land lower than the elevation of spillway dams; definitions of the kinds of construction permissible in flood-hazard areas lacking protection; and conversion of some flood-plain areas to uses that would not suffer great damage from flooding. Recreation is an example of the last. Flood-plain zoning is a complex matter requiring intensive study of potential hazard, flood frequency, and potential flood cresting. Los Angeles has an ordinance prohibiting plot development in "dangerous areas . . . which are subject to inundation, overflow by storm water or any other dangerous condition. . . ." However, this restriction, together with a less severe county restriction, has had little effect on land development for housing.

The Miami Conservancy District included zoning as a part of its flood control plan to minimize flood damage. In the five retaining-basin areas, which are kept empty except during and after the occurrence of floods, the authority permits only structures built of materials that will not float, and even these cannot be built on ground more than twelve feet below spillway dam levels. Home building is restricted to sites not lower than 5 feet above the spillway. Milwaukee County, Wisconsin, has enforced an ordinance requiring all buildings to be constructed with main floors at least 3 feet higher than high-water levels shown on county maps. Zoning to use flood plains as parkland has been successful in Washington, D.C., and in Milwaukee County.

Flood insurance has been much talked about, but very little has been done about it—even though flood losses equal one-fourth of fire losses. The difficulty is that the risk is harder to spread. When floods hit, losses are concentrated in one area, and they are so great that they could bankrupt an insurance company.

Flood control programs most often involve dams and direct barriers to the waters such as levees and flood walls. Other flood control methods include reforestation and such conservation practices as contour plowing to hold waters from rushing down bare slopes. Grass planted on hillsides holds water that otherwise would plummet, silt-laden, into streams. Although such measures can help prevent flooding in watersheds, it is generally conceded that they have little effect on downstream flooding on rivers that are focal points for collection of waters in major drainage basins.

Levees and flood walls are practical, but they create problems by blocking more than the passage of water. Where levees are built, bridges, power lines, and railroads must be lifted higher at considerable expense. Underground sewers must have entrance to rivers beneath the levees. Constriction of rivers by flood walls concentrates flow, which may undermine the foundations of the flood walls and cause them to fail. Seepage through levees may also be serious when rivers rise above normal flow. Flooding waters cause water tables to rise near levees and underground waters to attack the bottoms of structures. Even with these disadvantages, levees and flood walls generally offer the best protection per dollar expended. A great network of levees along the lower Mississippi from Cap Girardeau, Missouri, to Head of Passes, Louisiana, protect persons, farms, and industry along 3,000 miles of flood plain. They also complement a network of reservoirs that capture flood waters.

Engineers and hydrologists have had a running feud over the efficiency of small dams upstream or large dams farther down. Luna B. Leopold and T. Maddock in their book *The Flood Control Controversy* take the position that:

> Hydrologic principles alone . . . demonstrate conclusively that for control of floods downstream on the main stem of moderate or large-size river basins a series of upstream reservoirs of small size will not provide the degree of protection ordinarily considered adequate. A system of upstream reservoirs cannot replace protection works downstream, nor is the reverse true.

Reservoirs upstream offer protection to their immediate areas, but the protection grows less with distance downstream from the dam. Like lakes, reservoirs eventually die because of vegetable growth and sedimentation. In most cases, dredging sludge out of the bottom is too expensive. Usually, a more economic solution lies in adding to the height of the dam or in building another dam in a new location. Reservoirs have the added problem of evaporation, which, as indicated elsewhere, is yet to be solved. Nonetheless, reservoirs are effective flood prevention works, as shown in the case of the Missouri. The Senate Select Committee on National Water Resources reported that there will be 17,300 reservoirs by 1980 and more than double that number by the century's turn.

Large-scale dams and reservoirs are also favored because of the hydroelectric potential involved. Power pays for dams; in most cases, multipurpose dams for flood control, water storage, power, recreation, and other uses make good economic sense.

An interesting example of additional regulation to reduce water losses is offered by the operation of Senator Wash Dam, a new Bureau of Reclamation offstream dam and reservoir in the lower Colorado River basin.

Senator Wash has eliminated a special kind of "variability." Water orders for the lower Colorado are consolidated by bureau dispatchers, who then schedule releases from Hoover, Davis, and Parker dams. Because of changes in the weather—a sudden rainstorm, for instance—the needs of farmers frequently change significantly between the time water is released from the reservoirs and the time of its arrival. Flows reaching Imperial Dam, from which most of the releases are made, are usually more or less than the needed volume. Storage is limited at Imperial Dam, with the result that excesses have been lost to Mexico, and it has not been possible to supplement shortages. Now, extra water is pumped into Senator Wash, which is maintained at about half its capacity. Shortages are augmented by releasing water through a dual purpose pumping-generating plant, thereby saving water while ensuring adequate supply.

CHAPTER VIII

Stripping the Earth

VARIABILITY AND DEPLETION are often closely linked. Variability has to do with the natural fluctuation in streamflow. Depletion may intensify the destructiveness of alternating drought and flood.

But depletion is caused by man. It results from destruction of water resources—or water resource capabilities—by timber cutting, fire, farming, grazing, mining, or construction. As land and water are indivisible, mistreatment of the land injures the water resource. Thus, the care given a watershed shows up in the quality of the stream it feeds.

Overuse is a depletion problem. When too heavy a burden is put on either the water resource or the land surrounding it, the resulting ills are a consequenc of depletion, not of variability or shortage as such.

Most Americans are familiar with the basic ecology of the watershed. They know that it took nature thousands of years to produce the soil; that soil is a complex world, which must be preserved if it is to nurture plants; that it is held in place by the root systems of vegetation; and that nature only rarely strikes with rain or wind strong enough to disturb soil covered with growing plants. However, once the vegetation is torn away, the topsoil can be blown off or washed into streams. On slopes, where 60 per cent or more of the cover can be kept in grasses, brush, and trees, more than 90 per cent of the rainfall is retained by the earth. When cover drops below 60 per cent, progressively more water runs off, carrying the soil with it.

Erosion by Overgrazing

The history of the Rio Puerco, a major upstream tributary of the Rio Grande, vividly illustrates destructive erosion of farmland. Since measurements began in 1885, between 600,000 and 800,000 acre-feet of soil have been washed by the Rio Puerco into the Rio Grande. Water from the Rio Puerco accounts for only about 3 per cent of the runoff of the Rio Grande Basin.

The tributary was once a fairly permanent river, but today it has waterflow the year round only in the upper few miles of its channel. Its major feeder streams, the Rio San José and the Arroyo Chico, carry water only after rains. The annual runoff is a scant 60,000 acre-feet. Always subject to drought, the Rio Puerco basin has been overgrazed until much that is left is ugly gully and arid badland. The area is one of violent summer rainstorms, which have cut deep arroyos into the land.

As the danger of Indian wars came to an end about 1870, small farms and villages were established along the Rio Puerco and some of its tributaries. The flow of the river was next to nothing, but still there were brief, occasional floods. Where water did flow, it could be readily channeled for irrigation by simple diversion devices. And when floods watered the flood plains, the valley floor produced excellent crops of beans, corn, and wheat. Farming prospered in a limited area that became known as the "breadbasket" of New Mexico. But erosion and the ungovernable river caused gradual abandonment of the villages and farms. Irrigated areas had to be cut back repeatedly as ditches carried off the soils.

An American Association for the Advancement of Science study has reported:

And now, what was once deep, fertile, irrigated alluvium has largely been replaced by deep fingering arroyos. This network of gullies, aided by soil piping, has extended upstream into formerly good productive rangeland. These adverse conditions are further aggravated over most of the rougher uplands, breaks and mesas, where the deteriorated vegetation cover is absent or too sparse to provide effective protection against torrential rains or even minor storms. As a result, runoff water produced from rainstorms rushes down the existing arroyos, cutting them deeper and wider and extending them headward. The washed silt is added to the vast quantities of sediment already deposited at one point or another in the Rio Grande Valley.

Overgrazing has depleted many western watersheds. Year after year, cattle and sheep have been allowed to eat too much of the cover grass of mountain hillsides. In the higher areas, these animals compete with deer for forage. Many are the valley communities that have had to pay—perhaps years later—for poor husbandry. One example is the town of Mt. Pleasant, which lies in a green valley in a county of central Utah noted for stock raising. Surrounding the community are rugged mountains that have been largely stripped of earth mantle and forest. Some years ago, the town was bedecked for a great parade for which hundreds of people had come from the surrounding communities. A sudden angry summer storm struck the mountains and the valley. Within minutes, the merry-makers were startled by rumblings louder than thunder. A massive flow of mud and rock crashed into the town, smashing some houses beyond repair. Acres of land were buried too deeply under debris to be reclaimed. The people of Mt. Pleasant spent months clearing homes, stores, and streets of slime and boulders.

Erosion by Deforestation

Early in 1965, the beautiful Eel River in Northern California suddenly became a raging torrent, washing piles of yellow mud into hundreds of homes that had just been dug out from a similar catastrophe the winter before. Every evening for a week, television screens across America showed old people and children being carried out of flooded homes, livestock being pulled—more dead than alive—from collapsed barns, and bitter residents talking, one after another, about leaving their homes for good unless "they" would do something to curb the floods.

The Eel is a magnificent river, winding through majestic groves of coastal redwoods. But soil-protecting forests have been ripped from its watershed, and a four-lane highway has been cut directly through the groves. The gutted earth can no longer hold back the heavy winter rains.

Several decades ago, an unusual atmospheric disturbance seemed to suck water rapidly from Utah Lake, which lies at the foot of the Wasatch Mountains. The clouds rushed along the mountain tops and dropped their moisture in a burst some forty-five miles north, deluging two small communities, Farmington and Willard, and leaving them under mud many feet thick. Since these disasters, reforestation has greatly reduced the danger.

Another Utah case shows some of the costs of depletion. In 1962, Congress passed a bill to authorize purchase of 23,800 acres of land to be added to the Wasatch National Forest for rehabilitation. This was private land that had been depleted by overgrazing and poor timber-cutting practices. But it was a watershed serving an extensive federal reclamation development, the Weber Basin Project. Flooding from the area would endanger utilities, railroads, an interstate highway, and numerous homes and commercial enterprises. So Congress agreed to spend $400,000 to buy the land and another $150,000 to restore it.

A Wyoming state forester who testified before the Senate Select Committee on National Water Resources told of "accelerated erosion due to fires in Wyoming forest areas, old abandoned roads, and the overuse of range due to livestock and big game." He said that a U.S. Forest Service survey showed the need for rehabilitation of 1,600 miles of streams in his state's national forests.

Erosion along the road beds was traced back to practices of the pioneers, who dragged heavy trees behind their wagons to act as brakes on steep slopes. These skid trails have turned into deep gullies, and the earth continues to wash away. "Hundreds of miles of abandoned roads are eroding heavily," the forester said.

As an example of the need for reforestation work following fire, he cited the Crandall Creek area in the Shoshone National Forest in northwestern Wyoming. "Here," he said "about 40,000 acres of timber were burned in 1935. Not a single tree has been planted, with the result that quantities of soil and debris wash off the slope after every rainfall and every spring during the snow melt."

Gold or Water?

Resource depletion in the United States has taken many forms. In his book *The Quiet Crisis,* Stewart L. Udall has described the destruction of California watersheds by hydraulic mining. To get at the gold in the ground, miners developed huge hoses to wash hillside soil into placer pits where the metal could be extracted. For every ounce of gold collected, we are told, tons of topsoil were washed into the streams that drain the country above Sacramento. Concerning the economic circumstances that made the practice possible, Udall says:

> The townsmen and farmers who suffered damage protested, but they got nowhere. Gold was California's first industry, and by the standards of the times, the hydraulic miners had as much right to slice off the hills as the farmers had to cultivate the valleys below. Minerals are not a renewable resource, and the land legacy of any mining operation is, necessarily, a pit, a shaft, or a hole. However, in their reckless effort to extract gold, the hydraulic miners asserted the right to damage other resources irreparably—and the homes of other citizens as well. In the 1870's, the right of each individual to do as he pleased was sacrosanct. The miners had enough friends in Sacramento to enable them to continue their onslaught on the mountainsides until the devastation forced the California legislature, in 1884, to outlaw hydraulic mining altogether.

The Cost of Strip-Mining

Watershed depletion has usually been most serious in the West, where aridity makes it harder for seeds to germinate and get plant cover growing again on barren areas. However, strip-mining of coal is a relatively new method of tearing earth cover, and it is one that has affected the East more than the West.

Harrison County, in southeastern Ohio on the Kentucky border, is part of Appalachia—although its topography is hardly that of mountain country. Cadiz, a typical small-town county seat of 3,300, is area headquarters of the Hanna Coal Company, a division of the huge Consolidation Coal Company.

The damage done Harrison County by strip-mining is summed up in cold statistics by the Ohio Division of Natural Resources, which reports that 38,800 acres—over 15 per cent of the county's land surface—has been stripped. Stripping has despoiled millions of acres of U.S. land surface. The resulting deterioration of land resources and soils has been tragic.

Earth-stripping is dominated by the performance of the "big shovels." One shovel, the "Mountaineer," has been described in company booklets as costing $2.6 million, weighing 2,700 tons, and having a scoop capable of carrying 98 tons of earth away at a single bite. The Mountaineer, however, is a baby compared with the huge $8 million "Silver Spade." The Spade weighs 7,000 tons, has a 200-foot boom, and is capable of scooping up 150 tons at a lift. Electricity needed to power the monster is sufficient to meet the needs of a city of 15,000 persons.

Strip-mining of itself is not evil. On the contrary, results can be beneficial if the lands are properly restored after operations. The problem is to fix responsibility for land restoration and to enforce that responsibility.

The mining industry has instituted land restoration practices, but a controversy rages as to their adequacy. One point of view was presented in an article by Grace Goulder in the July 25, 1965, "Sunday Magazine" of Cleveland's *The Plain Dealer*. Seen through the eyes of this seasoned reporter, the picture that emerged was one of eerie devastation:

> We prevailed upon our long-time friend, Milton Ronsheim, editor of the *Cadiz Republican*, to guide us. And it was a mighty good thing we did. Without him we might have become lost. We invaded a desert, upheaved and de-peopled, without landmarks of any sort. There was no house, no barn, no filling station, no place where one might seek directions. The countryside was criss-crossed by dirt roads, some of them the company's, others country roads, a few of which still carried signs. Villages, though their names might be carried on maps, no longer exist. Whole townships have disappeared.
>
> The naked, tortured land was silent—except when a distant dynamite blast erupted. Rocks were belched up like pebbles, billows of smoke rose heavenward and the earth trembled.

The *Cadiz Republican*, alarmed by the exodus of between 1,000 and 2,000 people annually from Harrison County, has been crusading for laws to require restoration of the lands. "No one," editor Ronsheim has said, "wants to interfere with the removal of coal. . . . All we want is that the land be restored so it will be habitable after the coal runs out."

The other point of view is shown in handsome brochures prepared by Hanna Coal Company, summing up its strip-mining reclamation program as a "model for the industry." A ride along main roads tends to confirm this claim, since here the company has planted lines of trees that hide a small part of strip-mining damage. And where trees aren't feasible, lavender-pink vetch, a quick-growing ground cover, hides the worst of the earth's scars.

However, additional efforts are needed. Calling for more effective legislation to deal with the problem in his state, Kentucky's Governor Edward T. Breathitt, Jr. stated: "When I speak of good conservation practices, I am not referring to the present half-hearted attempt to get fruit trees or elderberry bushes or pine seedlings to grow in thin acid soils left at the mining sites. I am talking about practices that will leave the land in a productive and an attractive state for ourselves and our children."

Fearing that higher costs will put them out of business, the coal industry has generally opposed conservation legislation. For example, coal companies have fought every reforestation bill offered in the Ohio legislature. The industry argues that strip-mining affects comparatively little land and cites a Tennessee Valley Authority report that says that the United States has utilized fifty times as much land for highways as for stripping. It is true that much of the highway land has top value for uses such as farming, while little of the strip-mined land has similar worth.

A code of restoration ethics has been adopted under the title of "Voluntary Industry Program for Mined Land Conservation." In the state of Colorado, strip-mine reclamation is governed by a "Memorandum of Understanding" signed by the state's Department of Natural Resources and the strip-mine operators. A brochure published by an affiliate of the National Coal Association stated that more than half of Colorado strip-mine land was reclaimed during 1965 under this voluntary conservation plan. It said that the coal companies are seeding the reclaimed land with a variety of grasses. These will establish soil cover, control erosion, furnish forage for large game animals, and give food and cover to upland game birds.

The brochure also stated that 1966 will go down as the year Lynnville, Indiana, solved its water shortage—thanks to the Peabody Coal Company's "Operation Green Earth" in which strip-mine planning resulted in the creation of a lake over 4 miles long and 50 feet deep, holding 400 million gallons of potable water.

The Hanna Coal Company claims that its restoration activities, plus nature, will restore the lands to habitable condition in 20 or 25 years. But even if this estimate is correct—and the history of Appalachia seems to contradict it—stripping may well have poisoned water resources beyond repair.

Discharges of acid waste from active or abandoned mines—whether strip or tunnel—contain large amounts of pyrite, a compound of sulfur and iron. Pyrites are particularly prevalent in coal seams. As mine wastes are dumped into the open, pyrite is exposed to air and water and breaks down. Sulfuric acid and acid-producing iron compounds are formed. These flow or are pumped into streams or enter ground waters in the mine area.

Streams are usually unable to neutralize these acid wastes, and fish and marine life die. Many streams become unfit for human use without extensive and expensive treatment. Such acid waters cause significant damage to concrete and metal bridge piers, canal and river locks, dams, turbines, and wharves.

The Monongahela River is a ghastly warning of the consequences of stripping and other uncontrolled coal mining. Rising just above Fairmont, West Virginia, the stream flows through coal country for a mere 129 miles to Pittsburgh, where it joins the Allegheny to form the Ohio. With almost every yard of its short flow, the Monongahela picks up acid wastes. The stream empties an average of 200,000 tons of sulfuric acid into the Ohio every year. This is twice the amount of acid used annually in the manufacture of industrial explosives in the United States. The Ohio is contaminated by these wastes for 170 miles downstream.

Threat to the Wetlands

A nation's wetlands are an important, though often ill-understood resource. A swamp is a reservoir. Wetlands storage helps maintain water tables. The remarkable fertility of coastal marsh lands has already been noted—acre for acre they are our most productive area. The damage that conflicting uses of wetlands has done to some animal environment is discussed in Chapter X.

When the white man arrived on this continent, there were 127 million acres of marshes, swamps, and overflow lands. By 1959, this estate had shrunk 40 per cent, to 76 million acres. Since that time, thousands of other acres have fallen prey to the dragline and the bulldozer.

The greatest threat to the wetlands is the filling in of marshes to make real estate. We are told that on Long Island, New York, over 13 per cent of the wetlands were destroyed by land-fill projects between 1954 and 1959. Draining wetlands and swamps for subdivisions, industrial parks, and agriculture—often the reverse of progress—is going on in every state endowed with coastal marshes.

In the Tucson area of Arizona, water mining has caused the land surface to sink about 10 inches, with resulting land fissures and damage to buildings. Greater depletion of ground-water reserves is expected to bring further land settling and building damage. Lowering the water table has raised the cost of water and threatens future economic expansion.

Tucson was built on the Santa Cruz River, and the area to the northwest once was swampy. Tall grasslands extended into the hills from a streamside forest. Water for the small community came from El Ojito Spring, within the town limits, and a public bath was built at the site. In 1857, a dam was constructed across the Santa Cruz to form Silver Lake. Silver Lake's water turned water wheels for flour milling. In 1882, the Tucson Water Company began to pump water from underground sources, putting El Ojito Spring out of business. Steam-driven flour mills were introduced. The trees of the streamside forest served as fuel for the mills, the railroad, and the water works. Soon, the forest was stripped of timber. The grasslands gave way to irrigated farms and grazing. Vegetation retreated, and floods demolished Silver Lake Dam in 1880. The flood dangers were only temporary, since pumping soon caused the Santa Cruz to disappear as a surface stream. The city turned to ground water exclusively.

Use of water for the municipality and for three copper mines averaged about 50,000 acre-feet annually in the 1956–60 period. Recharge was at about the same volume. The water balance would have been maintained had it not been for agriculture, which used another 46,000 acre-feet. Thus, with all uses, Tucson was drawing on its underground reserve at a rate twice as fast as recharge.

The Suburban Toll

Another facet of depletion, which particularly threatens heavily populated areas, is explained clearly in *The Big Water Fight,* the League of Women Voters' book referred to earlier. The book uses the words "rurban watershed" (rural and urban) to describe the area that may have its natural cover torn up as a city expands its suburbs.

An example cited is the Rock Creek watershed in Maryland, the drainage basin of a stream that empties into the Potomac River. The lowest portion of the watershed lies in Washington, D.C., and, except for Rock Creek Park, has long been entirely developed. Before World War II, the watershed's middle third was rich farming area. By 1965, mammoth housing developments had replaced pastures and woods there, and urban sprawl was pushing into the upper third.

Floods came oftener, carrying ever-increasing loads of silt. The Rock Creek Watershed Association was organized. A master land-use plan was agreed on. But developers also had plans, and the master plan had scarcely been adopted before zoning variances began to be voted in contradiction to it.

The League's book states:

Control of flooding, conservation of resources through better soil-treatment procedures, new recreational areas, protection to roads and parks in the lower Rock Creek areas, and decreased silt deposits in the Potomac River will eventually result *if the project is carried out as planned* and pressures for intense development are resisted [italics added].

Citizen groups were alarmed by the rezonings. To study the question, the Montgomery County Council set up a task force composed of local and federal officials and representatives of two large home-building organizations. In 1965, the task force presented recommendations—a major one being the adoption of procedures to govern subdivision approval. Despite these actions, however, the book declares that "present prospects for limiting development are not bright." Since those words were written, the prospects have dimmed further. After defeat of most members of the Montgomery County Council in the 1966 election, the outgoing council called hearings. In an action without precedent, it then proceeded, within a period of 5 hours, to approve 46 zoning applications covering more intensive development of 1,912 acres. As this

ROCK CREEK WATERSHED

1913   1966

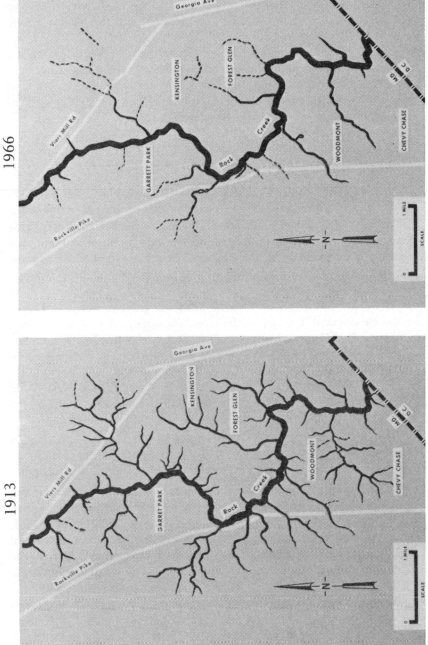

Expanding suburbs of Washington, D.C. caused the Rock Creek drainage area to decrease 55 per cent in fifty-three years.

is written, it appears that the action may not be final. Many citizens' groups have protested, and the new council has the matter under review.

Housing, services, and shopping facilities must be provided for the nation's expanding population. The problem of accommodating such expansion while protecting the "rurban watershed" is complex and difficult in the extreme. Failure to protect it, however, must open to serious injury not only newly developed areas but the cores of the cities as well.

The Appalachia Story

At some point, of course, depletion of water and related soil resources must be stopped. Otherwise, the region so abused must be abandoned. Essentially, this is what happened to the ancient civilizations that perished for lack of water or inability to manage it. Too often, the pressure of competition in the United States has extended to resource destruction to cut costs. Many years of this process can place a region beyond recovery.

In 1960, when John F. Kennedy was campaigning for the Democratic Presidential nomination, he cited the depressed coal fields of the Appalachian Mountains to make this point. He pointed to Appalachia as the pre-eminent example of an area whose devastated economy could not be brought back without outside help.

Appalachia stretches from northern Georgia to southern New York, along the Appalachian Mountain chain. The region covers all or part of 11 states. Its land area, 167,432 square miles, has a population of 16 million. About 50 per cent of these persons live in communities of 2,500 or more (compared with 86 per cent in California, which has a similar area and population.) Nearly a third of Appalachia's families have incomes under $3,000. There are some large oases of prosperity —such as Pittsburgh—within the region.

Appalachia's majestic mountain lands and water resources have been sadly maltreated by an ungrateful nation, much of whose prosperity has been powered by the region's massive coal resources. Whole mountains were denuded of cover to meet yesterday's demands for mine timber. Even so, a great potential for harvesting timber still exists.

The heart of Appalachia is the Cumberland Mountains of West Virginia and eastern Kentucky. This area was explored originally by restless frontiersmen seeking new space in which to hunt, fish, and farm. Some of them stayed. In the early nineteenth century, their descendants were joined by farmers who settled on the bottom lands along the plentiful, clear-flowing creeks.

Timber brought the first real contact with the world outside, and it was the sale of logs as a cash crop that started the uncontrolled stripping of the mountainsides. The logs were first cut by the mountain men on their own lands and floated to market down streams and rivers during the spring thaw. As the timber market grew after the Civil War, speculators organized corporations and sent in agents who bought up lands and timber rights from the unsophisticated mountaineers for a song. Around the turn of the century, railroads finally pushed into the West Virginia and Kentucky mountains. Hunger for timber seemed insatiable as World War I, and the housing boom it engendered, called for greater and greater supplies. Trees were cut without rules or care, and the destruction of Appalachia had begun in earnest.

Many of the same speculators who purchased timber rights before the coming of the rails also bought up mineral rights. Often, residents were left with only surface rights, which turned out to be valueless. Soon a major share of the Cumberlands was owned by "outsiders." They controlled three-fourths of timber rights and 85 per cent of mineral rights on land still nominally owned by descendants of the original settlers.

With the railroads came the coal patch and the company town. The mines expanded timber demands, and the remaining mature trees were cut with abandon. With ground cover gone, rainwater cascaded down the slopes—bringing with it the eroded earth. In the towns, sanitation was rudimentary or nonexistent. The creeks and streams, already polluted by human and mine wastes, became running sewers choked with debris and dirt.

Near every tipple rose a culm pile, which began to burn and smolder. Many continue to besmog the mountain air. Even now, acid wastes formed as water runs off eaves on rainy days, further pollute the dirty streams.

Following World War II, the mining industry in Appalachia collapsed as low-cost pipeline transportation for oil and natural gas usurped the heating domain of "King Coal." Automation and stripping became the answer for the big operator. Small wildcat producers sought to compete by opening "dog hole" mines. Today's mining techniques have advanced from the huge shovel to ingenious massive auger devices that extract broken coal and throw unwanted earth aside.

The first big bill of the Kennedy Administration was the Appalachia legislation aimed at reshaping the region depleted by decades of neglect. Congress passed it promptly, and authorized the spending of more than a billion dollars over five years. The promise of that measure—and of other measures the nation has undertaken to restore depleted lands and watersheds—are the subject of a later chapter.

CHAPTER IX

No Place for a Kid to Swim

THE DAY WAS HOT and humid. Washington, D.C., was having the kind of summer weather for which it is famous. In front of Union Station, near the Capitol, the fountain surmounted by the statue of Columbus spouted cooling streams. Kids in bathing suits splashed in its waters. They had little choice of other ways to keep cool. There really was no place for a kid to swim.

The historic Potomac River, flowing sluggishly nearby, was once the local "swimming hole." But today it is like most of the nation's major rivers: Pollution has made swimming in it both unpleasant and hazardous.

On summer weekends, Washingtonians jam into the little upstream town of Seneca, Maryland, hauling small boats behind their cars. Those lucky enough to find parking space wait their turn at boat launching sites and then get into another traffic jam on the river. On many Saturdays and Sundays, cars queue up to cross the two-lane, single-span Chesapeake Bay Bridge that gives access to Maryland's Eastern Shore and the Atlantic Ocean resorts of Delaware and Virginia.

Washington, D.C., is not alone in its overwhelming need for recreation waters. Each summer weekend, tens of thousands of New Yorkers crawl to jam-packed nearby beaches in their sun-beaten automobiles. Available local waters are too dirty to be used as swimming holes. Although the city has 575 miles of waterfront, fewer than 35 miles are considered safe for swimming.

The need is evident. More Americans with more time and money for play find it harder and harder to get to a stretch of water they can use to swim, sail, or just cool off. Recreation usually comes out last in the water tug-of-war. Pollution, shortages, and lack of planning have taken a heavy toll. Some people are fortunate enough to be able to afford backyard pools or have access to club or community pools. But even the best of these artificial swimming holes are a poor substitute for the freedom of the uncrowded beaches, lake fronts, and clean rivers of yesterday's America.

On the subject of outdoor recreation, the nation is fortunate to have in hand a study that is factual, comprehensive, and authoritative. In 1958, Congress created the Outdoor Recreation Resources Review Commission (ORRRC). It was headed by Laurance Rockefeller, and its membership was drawn from inside and outside Congress. Using interviews with thousands of Americans, it inventoried the nation's outdoor resources and projected recreation demand to the year 2000.

In 1962, the commission released a report, "Outdoor Recreation for America," containing its findings and fifty recommendations for action. Almost everything said about outdoor recreation in America since has drawn on that report.

The one-fourth of Americans who live in the Northeast and the mid-Atlantic states have a scant 4 per cent of the nation's public recreation lands. The 15 per cent who live in the West occupy only 39 per cent of the country's total land area, but this region includes 72 per cent of all federally owned land suitable for recreation. Because of its open spaces, where one still may find room to enjoy swimming, boating, fishing, hiking, and picnicking, the West has become a vacation Mecca.

While U.S. population was growing 20 per cent during the 1950's, visits to state parks rose 123 per cent; to national parks, 87 per cent; to other federal recreation sites, 238 per cent. Recreation use of the reservoirs of the Tennessee Valley Authority has risen almost 15 per cent each year since the end of World War II. Even in the West, favorite locations are becoming too crowded. During most of its season, the capacity of Yellowstone Park is taxed, and lovely Yellowstone Lake carries an overload of pleasure boating.

Population is expected to double by the year 2000, but demand for space for outdoor play is expected to triple, because twice as many people will probably be able to afford vacations away from home. (This trend has its good side—if space can be made available, supplying equipment and servicing leisure needs can be the basis of more new jobs than any other single source, with the possible exception of education.)

Water, said the ORRRC report, is a "focal point" in recreation, adding that "As the population grows and interest in water-based recreation increases, the already heavy recreation pressures on water resources will reach critical proportions. The problems stemming from this pressure are among the most difficult in the entire outdoor recreation field."

The reclamation projects of the 17 western states already draw more than 20 million vacationers and tourists annually—a number about equal to the populations of Massachusetts, New Jersey, and New York. The U.S. Army Corps of Engineers maintains recreation reservoirs on many rivers, prominent among them being the Columbia, the Missouri, the Sacramento, the Ohio, and the Arkansas. The Corps reported 43 of its reservoir projects drawing in excess of a million visitors in 1964. Heading the list was Lake Sidney Lanier on the Chatahoochee River in Georgia; it drew 8,314,000 visits. The next three most popular locations were also in the South—where the weather permits year-round use—Lake Texoma, on the Red River in Oklahoma and Texas; Lake O' the Pines, at Ferrells Bridge, Texas; and Whitney Reservoir, on the Brazos in Texas.

The Corps improves and maintains more than 20,000 miles of inland waterways and 250 small-boat harbors along the coastal shores of the United States, in the Great Lakes region, and along inland waterways. Recreational craft use all of these facilities. In addition, the Corps has developed, and maintains, an intracoastal waterway—a route almost entirely protected from the open sea—running from Boston to the Mexican border, a distance of 2,900 miles. Thousands of small boat owners cruise these waterways.

The number of pleasure boats owned and operated by individuals and their families nearly tripled during the 1950's. Residential swimming pools increased in number from 3,600 to 175,000 over the decade.

Beach and pool attendance rises to new highs each year. In many places today, bumper-to-bumper drives to beaches are followed by elbow-to-elbow swimming or shoulder-to-shoulder fishing. Typical is the almost unbroken stand of fishermen that lines the drainage canal west from Miami along the Tamiami Trail in the Everglades on a winter afternoon.

In its recommendations aimed at expanding our outdoor recreation resources, the commission outlined jobs for private business, local governments, the states, and the federal government.

The role of private owners is varied. The timbering corporations must open up lands and make the streams on them accessible. The recreation industry must police itself, so that resorts will not degenerate into lakeside or seaside slums. Farmers must be assisted to make unused land and water available for public use (thereby providing a large new source of farm income as well as filling a recreation need).

The function of the states is a key one—acquiring more land and making it suitable for recreation. Local government has the task of facilitating this process in its areas of jurisdiction, with emphasis on expanded recreation space for those living in crowded cities. The federal government is providing leadership, establishing more national parks and shores, and helping states, cities, and counties finance their programs.

As part of the federal task, the ORRRC called for creation of a national Bureau of Outdoor Recreation. The bureau was established by the President in 1962 and, a year later, Congress enacted legislation to place the agency in the Department of the Interior and make it responsible for leading a national outdoor recreation program. The bureau is organized on the basis of six regions with regional directors at Philadelphia, Atlanta, Ann Arbor, Denver, Seattle, and San Francisco.

The Bureau of Outdoor Recreation does not manage land or water areas. Its function is to provide technical information, planning, and recommendations. The physical tasks—such as building roads and trails, constructing and managing picnic grounds, and contracting with concessionaires—are carried out by the traditional land management agencies.

To raise the money to buy land and build improvements, Congress passed the Land and Water Conservation Fund Act. Into the fund go proceeds from a modest user fee (the $7 sticker) at federal recreation centers, receipts from sale of surplus federal lands, present federal taxes on motorboat fuels, and repayable advances appropriated by Congress. The fund is expected to reach $60 million a year during its first decade, and to increase thereafter. From this, 40 per cent will go to finance land and water resource purchases by the National Park Service, the U.S. Forest Service, and the U.S. Fish and Wildlife Service, and to help pay for recreation facilities at federal water projects. About 60 per cent of the fund will be distributed to the states on a formula basis. To qualify for a share, a state must prepare a plan for the development of its outdoor recreation resources. When this plan is approved by the Secretary of the Interior, half the cost may be paid from the Land and Water Conservation Fund. The state, in turn, may transfer federal grant funds to local governments for their projects that are part of the state plan.

Congress has also authorized a federal cost-sharing program for recreation development on the reservoirs that the Soil Conservation Service builds as part of its watershed protection work. Another step forward came when the Federal Power Commission made it mandatory for power companies applying for water power licenses to include recreation in their project plans.

Nongovernmental leadership in the field of recreation should be expanded. America needs more organizations like the National Wildlife Federation, the Izaak Walton League, and the Sports Fishing Institute to speak up for recreation as well as conservation. In this field, a people's lobby is overdue. Millions of Americans want to save and extend fishing, hunting, and other aspects of recreation. Citizens' organizations can keep the public abreast of need and can require candidates for public office to make clear their views on recreation issues.

In its analysis, the ORRRC declared that the nation's water resources —unlike land for recreation—are well distributed according to population. It also declared that there are three serious water problems, which will cost time and money to solve.

According to the commission, the first problem concerns quality, which is as important as location, acres of surface, or miles of bank. Polluted water is of little use for recreation. The silt load, the bottom condition, temperature, and aquatic plants also affect usefulness for recreation. The commission said the trend to increased swimming and

other water sports will be greatly accelerated "if pollution control programs are successful in cleaning up streams, lakes, and seashore areas
that are presently off limits for recreation, or are now so unattractive
as to preclude many activities."

The second problem (the point that keeps coming up in almost all
discussions) is demand for water for other uses. Only the most careful
planning will ensure a supply for recreation. Many existing reservoirs
used for recreation were not planned with that activity in mind. The
commission urged that these structures be "re-examined to determine
their suitability for recreation development," and that outdoor recreation henceforth be guaranteed "full consideration in the planning, design, construction and operation" of all projects. (It is possible that
review of the status of public waters would show that multiple use of
many bodies of water could be permitted. Defense installations, it was
suggested, should be periodically reviewed to determine whether more
of the land they use—often including lakes and streams—could be made
available for recreation.) The commission proposed flood-plain zoning
as a means of expanding outdoor recreation space, pointing out that
many attractive areas adjacent to streams and rivers are lost to outdoor
recreation—or, being subject to intermittent flooding, when used for
residential or industrial purposes, must be protected by dams and levees.
It was suggested that, in many cases, it would be more economical and
efficient from a public point of view to "restrict the use of flood plain
areas to purposes, like outdoor recreation, which require only limited
development and which are not frustrated by periodic floods."

Access is the third recreation water problem. Most bodies of water
are publicly owned, but the adjacent land usually is not. According
to the commission, "Reservoir planning should provide for acquisition
of adequate shoreline lands for public access and use." It was stated
further:

A most pressing problem of supply is ocean and Great Lakes shoreline.
This resource is one of the most in demand, and it is one of the most
scarce in public ownership. The situation is particularly acute near large
cities.

The 48 contiguous States have almost 60,000 miles of shoreline. About
one-third of this can be considered as possible recreation supply. This includes beach, marsh, and bluff areas.

Less than two per cent of the total shoreline is in public ownership for recreation—only 336 miles on the Atlantic Coast and 296 miles on the Pacific Coast. Yet both Coasts are centers of population, and they will be more so in the future. The present supply of publicly owned shoreline for recreation is not adequate, and acquisition will be needed.

Prior to 1961, only 70 miles of our ocean shoreline was in federal ownership for recreation—this at Cape Hatteras, North Carolina, acquired in 1937. The Cape Cod National Seashore was authorized by Congress in 1961, adding 40 miles of shoreline. In the next five years, another 316 miles of shoreline were added, with these national seashore authorizations: Point Reyes, off San Francisco, California; Padre Island, in the Gulf of Mexico between Brownsville and Corpus Christi, Texas; Fire Island, New York; Assateague Island, in Maryland and Virginia; Cape Lookout, North Carolina; and Indiana Dunes, Indiana. Also authorized was the Ozark National Scenic Riverways, incorporating 101 miles of the Current River and 39 miles of the Jacks Fork River in Missouri.

To protect the right of its citizens to use ocean shoreline, the state of Oregon has enacted an interesting law, which may have significance for other states. It provides that the Pacific Ocean shore "between ordinary high tide and extreme low tide" from the Columbia River south to the Oregon-California border (except portions disposed of before July, 1947) is vested in the state and "declared to be a public highway."

President Johnson's call for action to make the Potomac River a model for the nation has probably changed the course of development on that waterway. The President inserted the word "swim" in his 1965 message, and planning was finally started to make the Potomac fit for bathing. It may be decades before this goal is achieved, but our children and children's children may spend pleasant days on a safe Potomac beach. If successful, this program could provide information to benefit other river basins in clean-up and expansion of recreation use.*

The blueprint for the Potomac called for multimillion dollar outlays to transform the river basin into the "Central Park of a huge metro-

---

* Programs of the Tennessee Valley Authority also benefit other river basins through demonstration of methods. In the Land-Between-the-Lakes, a 170,000-acre isthmus between Kentucky Lake and Lake Barkley in western Tennessee and Kentucky, TVA is showing how an area can be converted into a recreation asset. As experience is gained, TVA will offer planning assistance to state and local agencies.

politan area stretching eastward from Harpers Ferry," the historic land-
mark from which John Brown launched his raid upon the old Con-
federacy.

Although it remains a dirty and polluted river, the Potomac was
much improved over the decade 1955–65. Thanks to White House support, an interstate commission on the Potomac, although working with
a much too limited budget, was able to accomplish a good deal. Every
major community above Washington built or improved sewage treatment facilities except the distressed community of Cumberland, Maryland, which continued to pour raw sewage into the stream. Large
industry cooperated and installed modern treatment facilities, but the
commission still had work to do with smaller communities and seasonal
canning industries whose wastes added pollution to the Potomac.

The Potomac River task force includes representatives of the federal
government and the states within the basin. Proposals presented to it
have included: pumping of highly treated human wastes from Washington into the Chesapeake Bay or the ocean—about 125 miles away—
instead of into the river; utilization of the newest sewage treatment
methods; building of dams to catch sediment and force settling before
it can reach the Washington area; and adding coagulants to the water
to make microscopic dirt particles coalesce and settle.

Legislation to set aside the Potomac banks from Washington to
Cumberland, Maryland, as a National Recreational Reserve has been
suggested, as has utilization of the hundreds of acres of military lands
on the Potomac banks for recreation.

Preservation or Development?

The proposed setting aside of more Potomac lands for recreation
raises again the question of competition for use of land and water resources. One facet of this problem important to a discussion of recreation policy has not been examined in detail: preservation versus development.

What are we to strive for—opening up more areas for heavier recreation use or keeping them undeveloped and therefore unspoiled? The
answer is to strike a balance.

An indispensable part of recreation is the spiritual enrichment that
comes from contact with unspoiled nature. Oliver Wendell Holmes'

observation that "a river is a treasure" refers to much more than its utility as a source of drinking and cleaning water. It is essential that stretches of scenic and undeveloped rivers be kept in their natural state, and that dams, marinas, and other structures be kept out permanently. A bill passed by the Senate in 1966 (which did not become law) illustrated how this might be done. It provided for creation of a National Wild Rivers System to be composed of 865 miles of segments of five rivers: the Salmon and Clearwater in Idaho, the Rogue in Oregon, the Rio Grande in New Mexico, and the Eleven Point in Missouri. Segments of other rivers would be studied for possible future addition to the system.

From the economic point of view, the wonders of nature can be among the greatest assets of a region if they are wisely protected and attractively presented. Writing in *The Washington Post*, Verne Williams described Florida's Everglades as "this natural Disneyland." Discussing the effect of drought and water diversion on the glades, he said, "At stake is a vast outdoor show of strange birds and animals that attracts 800,000 visitors a year and shelters subtropic species found nowhere else in the United States."

The preservation versus development issue also has been raised in connection with the proposal to build two more dams on the Colorado River—a controversy already discussed in another context. The failure of the Colorado River Basin Project bill to be acted on by the House in 1966 has made the future of these dams highly uncertain. The situation described in the following paragraphs may be changed radically in any new proposal. It is relevant here, however, because the issue will remain important—and will come up in many places in the nation in the years ahead.

Preservationists have argued that water backed up from the proposed Bridge Canyon Dam would mar the natural beauty of Grand Canyon National Park. Were there danger that magnificent Grand Canyon National Park would be flooded, the author would be among the first to fight the building of a dam, as my record on national parks legislation demonstrates. I sponsored the new Canyonlands National Park at the junction of the Green and Colorado rivers in southeast Utah. To win Canyonlands, agreement was reached to keep it essentially untouched for all time.

It is true that a dam in Bridge Canyon would back water up the

Colorado River for 94 miles, raising the water level within Grand Canyon National Monument south of the park. But the Grand Canyon is a full mile deep. Water levels would be raised not more than 90 feet within the area. It is nonsense to claim that the park would be flooded out and its values lost even in the area affected. A clearwater lake would be a valued addition. A dam in Marble Gorge would cause no flooding within the Grand Canyon National Park or Monument, but would stabilize water flow in the scenic area of Grand Canyon, which, itself, would be untouched.

The crux of opposition to full development on the Colorado River lies in the plea to save the stretch of white water that now delights intrepid outdoorsmen able to afford the exhilarating voyage downriver by open boat. But only 1,300 people have made this trip in the past decade. Under the proposed development, more than 100 miles of free-flowing river would remain traversing Grand Canyon National Park from east to west, except for a short stretch along the northwest border of the park, and millions would obtain enjoyment from the reservoirs created by the new reclamation dams.

When Glen Canyon Dam was built, Congress was almost inundated by mail from the *status quo* conservationists. The question then was whether the values created by the Colorado River Storage Project or those of nature undisturbed were to prevail. Based on personal observation as well as Congressional investigation, I sincerely believe that the correct choice was made.

I had the opportunity to go by boat down the Glen Canyon of the Colorado past the dam site before construction began, and I have always been grateful for the experience. But this was not a trip to be recommended for most, since costs were high and it was not a journey for the very young or the old.

The view of the canyon from the muddy surface of the river was indeed awe-inspiring, but that view remains almost unaltered today. Lake Powell, backed up behind Glen Canyon Dam in northern Arizona, has added the crown jewel to the view, and the area has been opened up to the many who come to see, swim, boat, and enjoy the outdoors. Those who visit the lake will return home enriched by their look at a magnificent setting created jointly by man and nature. The towering cliffs still change color as daylight shifts to evening—and are made more beautiful by their contrast with the blue waters added by modern engineering.

Lake Powell is an outstanding example of the kinds of balancing required by today's realities. The lake stretches north and east into Utah. The blue waters provide 1,860 miles of shoreline in one of the nation's most scenic water recreation wonderlands. The ten recreation areas being completed will provide accommodations for all budgets—those of low-income campers as well as those who can afford luxury. Rainbow Bridge, a beautiful national monument in the State of Utah, was once accessible only to the hardy few who packed into the rugged country. Vacationers at Lake Powell may now take a boat to floating docks at the entrance to Rainbow Bridge Canyon, then walk the trail along the canyon's side. Undamaged by the water, Rainbow Bridge soars high in arched and graceful sandstone beauty carved by time, wind, and rain.

Every mountain stream cannot be turned into a lake for mass recreation. But every undeveloped and unpolluted stream cannot be set aside for the use of a few or left unused simply because that is how it has been for years. New high-density water recreation areas must be created. New recreation areas for less intensive use must be created. And those few remaining truly wilderness streams must be protected and cherished.

This is being done. Conservation is not being forgotten. At the same time that areas are made more accessible for public use, maximum protection is being given to vast acreages. There are now two national parks on the Colorado gorge—Grand Canyon and Canyonlands. Through the Wilderness Act, millions of acres will be preserved. These will include portions of national parks, national monuments, game ranges, and wildlife refuges as well as primitive and wilderness areas of the national forests.

With pressures on our resources and potential park sites increasing, there should be agreement for limited additional land uses within future national parks. Such use must not interfere with the main purpose of the parks. At Canyonlands, it was necessary to agree to certain phaseout grazing rights. Padre Island National Seashore was saved because agreement could be reached on oil extraction. In neither case will there be harm to the great natural beauty preserved within our national park system.

The Colorado River controversy dramatizes the need for long-range planning that will permit consideration of coming problems while there is time to choose between alternate solutions. Preservation versus development will be debated in many regions in the 1960's; future decades will see the conflict intensify if our development thinking and plans are incomplete.

CHAPTER X

Fish and Wildlife

LATE SUMMER RAINS eased the 1965 northeastern drought slightly, but brought little joy to the thousands who fish the middle reaches of the Susquehanna in Pennsylvania. Threatened, they knew, was a major fish kill.

"Recent heavy rains in the acid-producing section of the West Branch Watershed . . . are certain to result in flushing of acid mine wastes into the stream," the state Fish Commission told the press.

Tales of pollution fish kills are repeated monotonously across the country. Contaminated streams carrying low flow often carry thousands of dead fish on their surfaces. The Public Health Service reported that 18 million fish perished in polluted waters in 1964. The agency said that 485 kills were reported, "by far the largest number of reports ever received, and the number of fish killed was also the largest." For 1965, the Water Pollution Control Authority reported that pollution killed 11 million fish.

Sewage from our cities, waste from our processing plants, weed killers and insect killers from our farms—all are at fault.

In 1964, industrial pollution caused 193 kills and the death of 12.7

million fish. Municipal pollution killed 4 million, and toxic agricultural wastes 1.5 million more. Some authorities say that, nationally, about two-fifths of our fish kills are due to agricultural chemicals—which are also lethal to song birds, waterfowl, and quail. Chemicals distributed wholesale over forests, large agricultural acreages, or wetlands pose great danger. Of the 485 kills reported for 1964, 15 were major disasters, each of which destroyed more than 100,000 fish. The greatest single kill took place on the Great Miami River, near New Miami, Ohio, where industrial pollution destroyed 7.9 million fish.

Huge kills of this kind are the most dramatic indicator of how misuse of our waters destroys fish and wildlife. But the significance of individual kills is far less than at first appears. One reason is that we are unlikely to hear about most of them. State reporting systems differ, and it is virtually impossible to monitor thousands of miles of fishing streams and even more thousands of miles of lake and ocean shores.

A more important reason was stated by the Public Health Service, in warning against "relating fish kills to the well-being of a fishery." The PHS said:

A kill occurs because of some sudden and deadly change in the aquatic environment; if given sufficient time, the stream may be expected to recover and the fish to return. Water pollution exerts its greatest toll on a fishery not by causing individual fish kills but by destroying habitat. Serious fish kills seldom occur in badly polluted waters because there are usually few or no fish in the stream to die.

From the point of view of the fish, it is destruction of its environment that is the villain. The great dead area of Lake Erie—scum-covered and without oxygen—returns to mind. The reason the fish has come off so badly in the competition for water is that almost every other use degrades its environment. This is true of wetlands drainage and development. It is true of dam construction to produce power. It is true of waste-dumping in lakes and streams. In a 1966 report to the Outdoor Recreation Resources Review Commission, the Bureau of Sport Fisheries and Wildlife stated: "It is estimated that more fishery habitat is lost annually through the extension of pollution than is reclaimed through restoration programs of state and federal conservation agencies." Even the use of water for cooling often raises the temperature above the

level that maintains the oxygen fish must have. Many uses of water
require its being diverted from natural channels. Fish habitat can be
severely injured by such diversion, both because of the quantity taken
out of the waterway and the quality of the water that may be returned.

Of all the uses of water, that for fish and wildlife habitat is the most
dependent on wise management. Man can adapt himself to available
supplies of water within a wide range. Aquatic creatures can adapt
themselves only within a very narrow range. Conversely, wildlife populations that have been virtually eliminated through habitat deterioration come back very fast once the environment is restored.

The Disappearing Salmon

The story of the effect of the Columbia River dams on the great runs
of Chinook salmon has been told many times, but new chapters con-
tinually open up. For a number of years, about one-fifth of the salmon
that passed Bonneville Dam near Portland failed to show up past The
Dalles and, therefore, did not reach the Columbia's great tributary,
Idaho's Snake River. In 1965, a frightening development occurred:
80 per cent of the salmon and steelhead that passed Bonneville did not
pass Ice Harbor Dam on the Snake. Of even more concern, the specialists of the state fish and game agencies and the Bureau of Sport
Fisheries and Wildlife did not know where the fish had gone. And
the mystery remains.

Anadromous fish—including the salmon, steelhead, striped bass, and
shad—are born in fresh, inland streams and lakes. When mature, they
migrate downstream to live for several years in the ocean. They then
fight their way back upstream, each fish returning instinctively to the
lake or stream of its birth, there to spawn and die. Interruption of this
life cycle destroys the species. To enable the fish to pass the Columbia
dams, fish ladders have been constructed. These are a series of steps of
the height fish can leap as they do natural waterfalls in their remarkable
ascent upstream. Many of the Columbia salmon must reach the Snake
River and one of the three forks of its tributary, the Salmon River.

The tremendous drop in the running salmon in 1965 caused Idaho
to close salmon fishing for the first time in history. The Pacific Salmon
Inter-Agency Council recommended a crash program to evaluate both
fish losses and causative factors. Senator Frank Church of Idaho, joined

by many western Senators, urged the Bureau of Sport Fisheries and Wildlife and other agencies to take up such a program at once. The Department of the Interior allocated $49,000. The Army Engineers set aside $12,700 to go to Oregon's fish and game agency for continuation of a testing program as part of the larger survey. For the fiscal year that began July 1, 1966, Congress appropriated $249,000. A special technical subcommittee of the Pacific Salmon Inter-Agency Council concluded that several possible factors caused the disappearance of the fish. Among these were unreported catches by Indians, nitrogen supersaturation, turnoffs into interdam tributaries, and difficulty passing navigation locks. Proposed was an extensive fish-tagging program employing both sonic and nonsonic equipment to furnish information on the location and rate of fish loss. Large-scale field studies were planned for the Bonneville-Dalles area in 1967 and in the McNary—Priest Rapids—Ice Harbor area in 1968. Extending over 4 fiscal years, the cost was estimated at more than $500,000.

The most important part of the survey was the tagging of several thousand salmon with sonic tags, consisting of battery-operated sound transmitters, both external and internal. The external transmitter is about one and a half inches long, three-eighths inch in diameter, and is clamped to the fish's back. The internal device is similar, though smaller. It is inserted into the esophagus of the fish. Hydrophones located on stream banks or on boats can pick up the signals emitted from the transmitters carried by the fish. Modified signals are used to differentiate between fish species. More than $200,000 was expected to be spent on this phase of the survey.

The program included several other parts. One was a continuation of the Bureau of Commercial Fisheries study of nitrogen supersaturation at various points in the Columbia River for 1966, 1967, and 1968. The amount of unreported fish catches by Indians above Bonneville Dam would be checked by additional field personnel.

On the plus side of the salmon story is the development of new strains. A species of land-locked salmon now thrives in Lake Roosevelt, behind Grand Coulee Dam. In 1966, the Bureau of Reclamation and the Bureau of Sport Fisheries and Wildlife began a program that is expected to result in a new strain of salmon on the Tehama-Colusa Canal north of Sacramento. An artificial nursery has been built on the canal. Some of the adult salmon headed up the Sacramento River are being trapped and planted in the new beds. After the eggs hatch, the fingerlings start down the Tehama-Colusa on their journey to the Pacific Ocean. A series of fish screens guide them out of the main canal into the canals that flow into Coyote Creek. After three or four years, these fish will instinctively return up the Sacramento and into the Tehama-Calusa Canal to their birthplace to lay their eggs. The beds will accommodate about 40,000 salmon a year. In addition to creating new artificial spawning beds, the bureau's construction of the Tehama-Colusa Canal will better natural spawning conditions in both Tomes and Stony creeks, tributaries of the Sacramento.

The salmon will find almost ideal conditions for spawning in the new man-made beds. The gravel will be selected to conform with that found in the best natural beds, and excellent 50–55° water will come from nearby Shasta and Trinity reservoirs. To prevent the fine silt that collects on the gravel bottoms of spawning areas from suffocating eggs and fingerlings, the Bureau of Reclamation has developed a new device to cleanse a three-mile-long "delivery room." It is a rig that lowers a steel baffle to extend across the waterway's spawning ground. The baffle goes down vertically 6 to 12 inches into the water and is moved upstream at a speed of about 2 feet per minute. Its normal flow restricted, the water rushes across the gravel floor at a velocity that flushes out the silt.

Development of the canal spawning grounds and improvement of the nearby natural beds are expected to enhance the value of the Sacramento River salmon fishery by $1 million a year.

Pointing up the importance of the anadromous fish to both sport and commercial fisheries, the National Anadromous Fishery Program Act was passed in 1965 to set up cooperative federal-state projects to preserve and enhance fisheries for salmon, shad, and striped bass living in the sea or in the Great Lakes. The act permits up to $25 million to be spent through June 30, 1970, for research on anadromous fish problems—access to spawning areas, improved breeding conditions, and free migration of fish. New fish hatcheries will also be opened. Such measures are necessary to restore habitat for anadromous fish.

Over the nation, destruction of the water environment has inflicted tremendous losses on a fishery resource worth uncounted millions in food and recreational values.

Commercial fishing provides direct and indirect employment for half a million workers. There are more than 12,000 vessels of 5 tons or more in the U.S. fishing fleet. Fresh-water resources are vital to the industry. Of the $446-million, five-billion-pound catch in 1966, 60 per cent was accounted for by species that depend on fresh-water environment during all or part of their lives.

Population pressures on food supply call for the addition of another 5 billion pounds of fish annually by the turn of the century. Of this harvest, some 3 billion pounds should be taken from fresh waters. But unless deterioration is stopped and development of fishable waters stepped up, we may have to be satisfied with an increase in supply of only 2 billion pounds.

Proposed sources of increase include fish farming on inland ponds, but so far their contribution to commercial fishing is limited. Attempts to increase fish crops are offset by destruction of breeding grounds through draining of wetlands and potholes.

The oceans were once considered an inexhaustible source of fish, with the result that fish have been hunted rather than harvested. U.S. fish-hunting is now in competition with fleets of other fish-hungry peoples. The United States has been losing ground rapidly as a fishing nation. In the decade 1956–66, we dropped from second to fifth place. This decline is more a diplomatic, economic, and industrial problem than it is a water resources problem. It is, however, also very definitely a conservation problem. Heavy Soviet and Japanese fishing close to our coasts has been depleting some stocks. The once bountiful yield of such familiar grounds as the Newfoundland Banks grows smaller with the years. Most commercially valuable fish are not caught in deep waters. More than 90 per cent of the sea-food harvest from waters off the United States is taken on the continental shelf. Congress has extended U.S. jurisdiction over fisheries to twelve miles, making possible some sustained yield management of the offshore fishery.

Sport fishing has been a delight to Americans since the first settlers reached our shores. The colonists emigrated from European countries that, in the main, reserved streams and fields for landed gentry. Most of the charters of the original thirteen colonies granted the settlers the right to fish and hunt freely on lands not in private ownership. These rights were highly prized, and our zest for these pursuits has never waned.

A 1955 survey showed that a fisherman or hunter lived in one of every three U.S. households, that one-fourth of all males fished, and one-fifth of them hunted. Fishing and hunting now account for as much consumer expenditure as household electricity.

The United States had a population of 146 million in 1946, when 14 million fishing licenses were issued. Ten years later, the population had grown to 174 million, but the number of fishing permits had increased to 20 million—an increase of 43 per cent in fishing licenses against a population growth of 19 per cent. By 1980, there will be 47 million fishermen looking for fishing waters, and by the century's end there will be some 63 million. Sports fishing alone will account for 930 million man-days of recreation and $4.5 billion of expenditure annually.

Such demands for fish can never be met unless we protect our aquatic resources. The 95,500 square miles of U.S. inland fresh waters are—or were—nearly all suitable for fish. By types of waters, the total is divided as follows: public streams, 4,985,000 acres; private streams, 917,000 acres; public natural lakes, 9,130,000 acres; private natural lakes, 200,00 acres; public reservoirs, 8,095,000 acres; private reservoirs, 2,068,000 acres (principally farm ponds averaging slightly more than one acre each in area). In addition, Alaska has 12,400,000 acres of fresh water. Virtually all of it is in public ownership. In Hawaii, 4,647 acres—more than three-fourths of the state's total—is in private ownership.

Fishing waters are classified as cold and warm. There are variations in definition, but cold water usually means that below about 65° F. Trout, salmon, and whitefish live in cold waters; bass, muskellunge, northern pike, and yellow perch prefer warm. Slightly more than half of our 707,000 miles of public streams are cold water. All the Great Lakes contain both cold and warm water habitats. Two-thirds of our natural lakes and almost seven-eighths of man-made reservoirs are managed for warm-water fish. Alaska's waters are all cold; Hawaii's nearly all warm.

Productive waters for fishing are those that maintain nature's biological balance. To support fish, three physical factors must be present in a body of water—a tolerable range of temperatures, sufficient light penetration for production of energy by photosynthesis, and currents to transport nutrients and carry off waste. In addition, there must be the chemicals to nourish plants and organisms to feed the fish.

We have seen that there is an intimate relationship between the quality of stream and the care of its watershed. In the same way, the fertility of a stream reflects that of the watershed. Excessive land clearing, farming, and grazing cause siltation that deteriorates water quality and injures fish-breeding grounds. Flooding washes away foods upon which fish depend. Nonselective timber cutting, fire, and overgrazing reduce fish production as well as the yield of land crops.

Building dams and diverting water through canals can injure the capability of streams to support fish life, although (as will be shown) the building of a reservoir often increases fishing opportunities. Reduced streamflows and silt from returned irrigation flows cut the quantity of pure water, which fish need.

In any consideration of fish habitat, the brackish water of the coastal estuaries deserve special mention. These are the tidewater and salt-marsh regions of the river mouths, a zone of interplay between the margins of the sea and the land.

We have noted the ease with which these acres can become infested with pollution, and the dire consequences of such contamination both to fish habitat and to other beneficial uses of the bays and sounds. The estuaries are of great value because of their fertility and the unique character of the life they support. The example of the Sapelo marshes of Georgia, which produce nearly seven times as much organic matter per unit area as the water of the continental shelf, has been cited. Many of our most prized sea foods—oysters, soft clams, crabs, and diamondback terrapins—come from there. The zone is a nursing ground for prawns, menhaden, bluefish, croaker, mullet, and channel bass. Numerous forms of sea life feed on the plentiful plankton in the shallow waters, and, in turn, provide food for the larger fish.

Migratory fish, such as the salmon, enter the estuaries during their journey upstream to fresh-water spawning grounds. Of the great fish harvest of our continental shelf, nearly two-thirds is composed of species that live in the estuaries at least part of their lives or must pass through on their way to spawning grounds.

These wetlands also provide winter feeding grounds for our most valued waterfowl species—ducks, geese, swans. They support marsh birds such as herons, ibises, and cranes, and shore birds and fish-eaters such as pelicans, loons, cormorants, and sandpipers.

In other words, there is no substitute for the unique aquatic environment of the salt-water estuary. Destruction of this environment by pollution and depletion has had most undesirable consequences for many species and for the industries dependent on them. Planning for the future must include effective measures to preserve large areas of this resource.

Since early times, Americans have shown concern for the protection of fish and the waters they inhabit. Before 1750, local laws had been enacted: Middlesex County, Virginia, prohibited the use of "jack lights" for night fishing; New York City permitted the taking of fish from fresh-water ponds with "angle rod, hook and line only." Today all fifty states maintain fish conservation programs, at least for their inland waters.

In 1871, Congress appointed the Commissioner of Fish and Fisheries; in 1903, the Bureau of Fisheries was designated. In 1956, the Fish and Wildlife Act was passed, Congress declaring that fish, shellfish, and wildlife resources are a "living, renewable form of wealth" that can be maintained and increased with good management, but destroyed if neglected or unwisely exploited.

The act created the Fish and Wildlife Service within the Department of the Interior. The service has two bureaus: Commercial Fisheries and Sport Fisheries and Wildlife, which together employ about 5,000 persons. Aided by the state fish and game agencies, they exhort and educate in a valiant effort to maintain the nation's outdoor resources. But the accomplishments of the conservationist are limited by the means placed at his disposal. In 1962, the Bureau of Sport Fisheries and Wildlife stated: "The fishery biologist is largely dependent upon the sanitary engineer, the construction engineer, the industrialist, and the politician, to provide the quality and quantity of waters he believes essential to maintain fish life."

Of all these, the most important is probably the politician. Only if the conflicts for use of water are resolved—if laws are enacted to keep streams clean, forests and watersheds planted and estuaries protected—can the scientists and technicians do their part.

Despite the act, conservation has failed to keep up with the destructive forces of our industrial society. Water pollution, unwise exploitation of land and forest resources, draining of wetlands and other commercial encroachment have continued to deplete our stock of fish and wildlife.

A decade ago, fishermen lined the banks of the lovely Connecticut

River during shad runs. River pollution has ended sports fishing in the stream, which was termed the world's best landscaped sewer by conservationists who surveyed it in 1965. Pollution and dams have all but destroyed anadromous fish in the East. The Atlantic salmon is almost extinct in U.S. rivers; the shad runs have all but ceased; the alewives are almost gone. As we have seen, dams on the Columbia, Snake, and other western streams have been equipped with fishladders, but these have produced less than spectacular results.

One cause for optimism, however, is that most of our cold-water streams are still clean, even though all major river systems suffer from pollution.

Just as good watershed management can restore the land for other purposes, it can improve fishing and bring back wildlife habitat. A prominent example is the Spring Creek watershed of Missouri, which was logged out, burnt over, and badly eroded at the time 5,000 acres were purchased for addition to the Missouri National Forest in the mid-1930's. Good management has made Spring Creek, which flowed only sporadically, a year-round stream. Trees, grasses, and shrubs have been planted, and insects have returned to feed hungry fish. In 1954, after three years of drought, the creek still contained enough water to support sports fishing.

On the Roanoke River, cooperation has minimized the impact of serious pollution and saved both commercial and sports fishing. The Roanoke is a major source of municipal water supply. Its lower reaches are spawning ground, nursery, and migration area for striped bass, alewives, menhaden, white perch, and shad. Low oxygen content and toxic wastes have caused serious fish kills. In 1959, a steering committee made recommendations for cooperation among the Corps of Engineers, private utilities, state agencies, and the Fish and Wildlife Service. Regulated discharges of water from behind Kerr federal dam and two private utility dams have maintained minimum streamflow; submerged weirs have increased the water's oxygen content.

Resources for the Future, a private, nonprofit research organization, has proposed an experiment on the Potomac that could have important implications for sports fishing. It calls for mass aeration of the river by 100 anchored barges, each equipped with a propeller to churn up the water. New oxygen would burn up pollution and permit the fish population to flourish.

Paradoxically, it is possible to increase the amount of available sports fishing even while habitats are being destroyed. For one thing, reservoirs create vast new fishing opportunities. The TVA is a sports-fishing playground second only to the Great Lakes. A great new fishery was established in Utah and Arizona when the Glen Canyon Dam was built and backed up water for 180 miles to form Lake Powell. Lake Mead, farther down the Colorado River, behind Hoover Dam, has long been famous for its stock of bass and trout.

Usually, the creation of a reservoir does not reduce fishing in adjacent streams. The same number of stream fishermen use the reduced stream acreage, while a new, more numerous group of fishermen come to use the reservoir. Private reservoirs, especially farm ponds, are of increasing significance to sports fishing. Their greatest growth has been in southern and midwestern states.

As is true with all aspects of recreation, accessibility can make larger areas of desirable water available to fishermen. Many remote streams and wetlands are still reached by only a few. Pressure on inland waters, combined with the availability of larger and better boats, is rapidly expanding ocean fishing. Zoning of waters may help solve the problem of fast motor boats, water skiers, and spearfishermen competing for water use with sportsmen using angle rod, hook, and line.

Fish hatcheries, both state and federal, are already an important element in maintaining supply. Undesirable fish species can be replaced by species attractive to fishermen, and the population of fisheries can be expanded, particularly as our knowledge grows.

And Bird and Beast

Like fish, birds and animals depend on readily accessible clean waters. Often, the existence of all wildlife resources are intertwined. This is particularly true of waterfowl, as well as birds that feed on fish. Water must also be available to large animals such as deer, elk, and bear, and to the muskrat, beaver, and other creatures that can survive only in water or wetlands.

Nowhere has the havoc wrecked by the "twin plagues of drought and drainage" been more evident than in the Everglades. Only a handful of years before this was written, southern Florida was a bird paradise. The graceful snowy egret, the white stork, the eagle, and the kite were common, and even the flamingo could be seen wild on occasion. Few such birds fly overhead any longer. The Everglades kite, according to one recent report, has been reduced in number to ten in the entire United States.

The Everglades was once viewed as one of the nation's great natural wonders. Its tall grasses waved uninterrupted for miles. In the 'Glades and adjacent Great Cypress Swamp, fish were abundant in hidden pools. The alligator, the bear, many waterfowl, and beautiful subtropical birds fed on the fish. Except for the Seminole who made his home there, man was almost unknown in these unique wetlands.

Within the 'Glades, water accumulated in pools above the porous rock formed by the death of billions of shellfish over the eons. To this swamp water was added the normal overflow of huge Lake Okeechobee, which spilled over its south bank at floodstage and created a wide shallow river that brought extra water supply to the vast wetlands. No drought was bad enough to alter the ecology of the area. In dry periods as in wet, the fish, birds, alligators, bear, and other wildlife flourished.

Drainage of the 'Glades began nearly half a century ago. Then, following a 1948 hurricane that struck Okeechobee, massive canals were built to prevent future floods and reclaim rich muckland for agriculture. To further reinforce flood control, Okeechobee was diked along its south bank to a height that made the lake surface invisible from the road that passes by it.

Nobody foresaw the results for Miami and other cities built on the ocean ridge. Withdrawals of water from the wetlands soon brought salt-water encroachment along the coast. Water tables at Miami were lowered five feet as ground waters ran into the new canals. The inland migration of salt water caused Dade County to embark upon an expensive control system.

In 1947, Congress created the 1.4–million–acre Everglades National Park at the southern tip of Florida. When drought struck Florida in 1962—and persisted—Everglades National Park, no longer fed by the shallow Shark River overflow from Okeechobee, began to dry up. Drainage canals on the northern border of the park sucked up fresh waters from the pools remaining. Birds ceased to return because their feeding grounds had evaporated. The situation became so bad in 1964 that Park Service naturalists hunted out alligators and turtles struggling over hot, dry land in search of water. Many were transported to the last remaining water holes. Nature had taken revenge for man's poor planning.

The 'Glades and its estuaries were nursery grounds for such Florida game fish as the tarpon and snook and breeding areas for the commercially important Tortugas pink shrimp. Fish and shrimp have shrunk rapidly in number. Southern Florida has salt-water intrusion to reckon with; unless it can be checked, lands drained for sugar and other cash crops may suffer ultimate destruction.

The National Park Service sought to obtain new water for Everglades Park, but its pleas to the state Flood Control District fell upon deaf ears. Finally, with the 1965 crisis, the House and Senate Appropriations Committees permitted Secretary of the Interior Udall to divert $287,000 of available funds to pump water from Okeechobee through the old Shark River slough into the park.

Enough water was deposited by heavy rains and Hurricane "Betsy," which struck southern Florida in September, 1965, to provide planners time in which to find new sources of water for what remains of the irreplaceable Everglades. Although corporate agricultural interests have complained that more water for the park means less for agriculture, experts have declared that there is sufficient water in Okeechobee to harmonize both interests—if waste caused by poorly planned flood control can be ended.

As of 1966, planning and improved precipitation for southern Florida appeared to mean that the Everglades, in part, are on their way back. The governor of Florida announced a $3.5 million emergency canal-digging project to bring water to the park from Lake Okeechobee, which often has a surplus. The five-man State Control Board consented to a temporary tenfold increase in water from the storage area—from 20 cubic feet per second to 200 cubic feet per second. But Park Superintendent Roger Allen noted that 200 second-feet is "a drop in the bucket" compared to the requirements of the park. Even if an ultimate solution is found, he said, it is questionable whether the plant and animal life so severely damaged by several years of drought will completely recover. The apparent end of the drought, however, improved the outlook for the Everglades. Further, the Army Engineers were making a $400,000 study to be reported in 1967—and some believed they would advocate a much larger canal system for moving water to the park from Lake Okeechobee than had been proposed before.

The coastal marshes along the Gulf of Mexico and along the Atlantic coast of our southern states once were black each winter with wild duck and other migrating water fowl. Returning north, flights of duck and geese temporarily shut out the sun over the pothole region of Minnesota and the Dakotas. Nature made the pothole ideal for waterfowl nesting. At peak, these areas produced perhaps 15 million ducks a year.

As elsewhere, conflicting demands for land and water have taken their toll, resulting in drainage of potholes and wetlands, river pollution, chemical spraying, and replacement of breeding areas with reservoirs and dams.

Potholes originally accounted for 115,000 square miles of the Dakotas and Minnesota. They were breeding grounds for small game and offered drink to the buffalo, as well as nesting area to waterfowl. By 1955, all but 56,000 square miles of potholes had been drained for croplands. Between 1943 and 1960, the federal government provided $25 million in financial and technical aid for this purpose. During the same period, it also took reverse steps to conserve the nation's wildlife resources.

Combined with a drought lasting nearly eight years, this depletion decimated the duck population, dropping it by 40 per cent from the mid-1960 level. The decrease in some important species, such as mallards, was even greater. American and Canadian hunters shot more mallards in 1958 than there were in the fall flight in 1962. Between 1958 and 1965, the mallard breeding population was halved. Drastic action was necessary to save the brood stock. In the face of calls for the complete closing of duck hunting in 1965, the Secretary of the Interior limited the take in the Central Flyway and along the Mississippi to one mallard and one pintail.*

In 1966, there were perhaps 3.5 million acres of wetlands within the federal wildlife refuge system and half that acreage within state systems. Despite accomplishments within these systems, wildlife experts believe that a minimum of 8 million more acres outside Alaska should be added and that 3 million of these must be in regions of high water-

---

* By 1966, there was some indication that the drought had been broken and that the duck population was increasing. At the time of writing, setting of the 1966 bag limits awaited results from the survey made twice yearly to evaluate the hatch.

THE FOUR ROUTES DUCKS AND GEESE USE
Between Northern Nesting Grounds
and Southern Wintering Areas

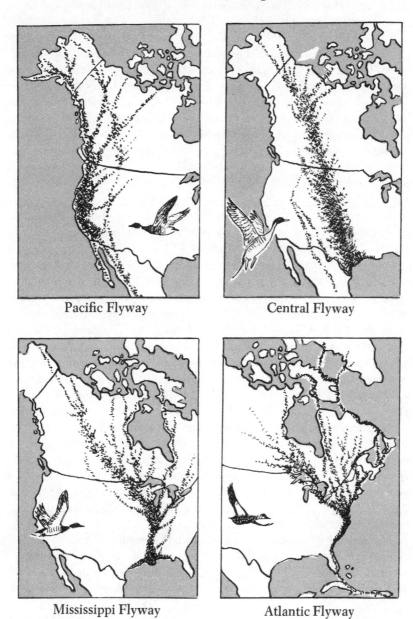

Pacific Flyway

Central Flyway

Mississippi Flyway

Atlantic Flyway

fowl production. The Land and Water Conservation Act will help; some of the funds for which it makes provision will be used for acquisition of lands beneficial to wildlife.

Senator Lee Metcalf of Montana has introduced legislation designed to "preserve a great natural resource, migratory waterfowl," by extending to fifteen years a program of land acquisition for waterfowl refuges. Metcalf is a member of the U.S. Migratory Bird Conservation Commission—a group composed of members of Congress and members of the Cabinet, headed by the Secretary of the Interior—which has as its responsibility passing on recommendations of the secretary for additions to the national waterfowl refuge system. The original program authorized the advance of up to $105 million for the acquisition of 2.5 million acres for refuges. The advances are to be repaid with receipts from the sale of duck stamps. (More than 1,500,000 hunters bought $3 duck stamps in 1965. Depletion of the birds cut the number of hunters to that figure from a peak of 2 million. Duck-stamp funds are used to buy land and develop waterfowl refuges.)

For general fish and wildlife restoration activities, the federal government allots to the states receipts from federal excise taxes paid by manufacturers and importers of firearms, fishing rods, and other types of hunting and fishing equipment. In 1966, these funds amounted to more than $18 million. Under such federal aid programs, the states spend their own funds on projects and are then reimbused for up to 75 per cent of the cost. Distribution of the funds is based on the number of paid license holders in a state.

Efforts have been made to induce farmers to cease drainage of privately owned potholes. Such efforts are likely to succeed only if alternative uses of wetlands are developed to add to farm income. Some potholes hold water for short enough periods to enable crops to be grown in them without drainage. In potholes where moisture lingers, additional crops can be raised without economic loss. Potholes can be used economically as water supply sources. They may also be used to produce fur crops and minnows, and for controlled duck hunting that could provide added income to farmers.

The federal government has long made payments to farmers for soil conservation purposes. Similar payments may be in order to preserve wetlands and potholes. Wildlife resources are as perishable as the soils, and both require conservation. Federal and state purchase of wetlands offer the best method of saving essential habitat. In addition, of course, water and related land policies must include fish and wildlife protection.

In urging Congress to enact the land and water conservation legislation, Secretary of the Interior Stewart Udall wrote:

> One of the unfortunate results of economic growth in the United States has been the extermination of some wildlife. Since the settlement of the 50 states, some 24 birds and 12 mammals native to the United States and Puerto Rico have become extinct. Examples are the passenger pigeon, heath hen, Carolina parakeet, spotted Hawaiian rail, eastern elk, Texas and California grizzly bears and the badlands bighorn sheep. These animals are gone forever from the face of the earth. They will be joined before very long by some 35 kinds of mammals and 30 to 40 birds unless special conservation efforts to acquire and maintain sufficient habitats for them are initiated.

A young bald eagle and a redhead duck were among the first arrivals at Pautuxent Wildlife Research Center near Washington in the fall of 1965. The bald eagle, celebrated as the nation's symbol, has been threatened with extinction. The redhead duck, once common throughout the land, is becoming increasingly rare. The Wildlife Research Center hopes to develop better wildlife management methods.

More land for sanctuaries, preservation of the wetlands, improved watershed management, restoration of clean waters, and research are crucial to the salvation of our fish and wildlife resources. Ultimately, however, the deciding factor will be the values the nation chooses and cherishes.

PART TWO

_____

The Way Out

CHAPTER XI

Make No Little Plans

SOUTHERN CALIFORNIANS watered lawns, washed cars, and filled swimming pools in 1965 while New Yorkers forfeited baths and drinking water in restaurants.

California's secret was planning. Even under drought conditions, twice as much rain fell on New York as on Los Angeles. Average rainfall in the New York area is normally triple that of southern California.

The preceding chapters have dealt with the condition of the nation's waters and with the political and economic pressures that have permitted their deterioration. Now the emphasis changes from problems to solutions. Science and technology will play an indispensable role in finding those solutions.

But of the highest priority is planning.

The size of the water problem for which southern California must plan can be gleaned from the fact that 10 million people live on a near desert within the Metropolitan Water District of Southern California. Most of their water is brought 242 miles across desert and through mountain ranges to a terminal reservoir, and is then distributed through

450 miles of lines. No less than 119 cities and many large unincorporated areas buy water from the district. Its manager, Robert A. Skinner, wrote in 1966 that, "thanks to those very far-sighted men who tapped the Owens River in 1913 and who brought the first Colorado River water to southern California in 1941, no water shortages exist now in the service area and we do not expect any."

Ironically, southern California had water partly because it had patterned its water supply system on an early New York City program.

The essence of southern California's water program is reaching out for water and bringing it from far sources to centers of population. In 1832, New York began to reach for new sources to replace the supply of unsanitary and inadequate wells. California was then a sparsely settled territory claimed by Mexico, Spain, and Russia. Four years later, American colonists proclaimed independence for California and, in 1845, made good their claim by driving out the Mexican governor. California's colonial way of life came to an abrupt end when James W. Marshall discovered gold on Sutter's Creek. San Francisco soon became the metropolis of the Pacific Coast. Then, as now, water was no problem in northern California, except when prospectors used guns to determine who owned claims along gold-bearing creeks. Heavy rains fed the still untouched redwood forests and watered the California laurel.

By 1890, New York had to go forty miles north to the Croton watershed for water. This supply soon proved insufficient. Shortly after the turn of the century, the city extended its reach to the Ashoken watershed in the Catskills. With an adequate supply seemingly assured, New York ceased to pay attention to water problems until it became necessary to share Delaware River supplies with Philadelphia and communities of New Jersey.

By 1904, Los Angeles had grown into a bustling metropolis of 100,-000 persons looking to an unlimited future. But in relation to its population and water supply, California is upside down. While people have flocked into the Southwest, water has poured unused into the Pacific from the more rugged and sparsely settled Northwest. South of the Golden Gate Bridge in San Francisco, no major stream empties into the ocean. Southern California experienced a brutal drought in 1903 and 1904. Wells were then the primary water source; most went dry and crop losses were extensive. The bitter lesson was not lost.

A self-educated Irish immigrant lawyer from San Francisco fathered the program that has assured sprawling Los Angeles enough water for growth as well as immediate needs. The lawyer, George H. Maxwell, took up the cudgels for water transfer in the 1890's when hard-pressed southern California farmers decided they needed a champion to fight their cause in the state legislature. The farmers had been taxed by the legislature for phantom irrigation projects that produced no water. They took their case to the state supreme court. The court followed the election returns and rejected their appeal. Maxwell had a reputation of being able to deliver, and it was to him the farmers went with their story.

"You have brought me a corpse," he said, "but there is a way to save you. You must educate the people of California. I figure it will take five years."

Maxwell was hired, and he took up his task with zest. Seeking to convince Californians that justice, right, and the future development of the state rested in water planning, he rode circuit by buckboard across the barren Southwest and into the central valley. He made speeches wherever he could find an audience and wrote a stream of letters to the local newspapers. His theme was unvarying: California could survive and prosper only if irrigation waters were brought southward hundreds of miles from their source. He called for water planning at least a generation ahead of need, a tenet of southern California water philosophy that remains firmly implanted to this day.

Shortly after 1900, Maxwell created the National Irrigation Association and set up offices in Washington. As part of a carefully thought-out strategy, he used the association as a platform from which to urge federal support for flood control on the Mississippi and the Ohio. He preached water conservation as a way of life, calling for contour plowing, upstream check dams, cover crops to halt erosion, and reservoirs to catch and store valuable waters.

Inspired by Maxwell's vision, others joined the battle and formed the National Reclamation Association. Maxwell continued his work throughout the years, calling for a civilian conservation corps long before New Deal days. He lived to see Franklin D. Roosevelt sign that concept into law. Maxwell died at the age of eighty-six, penniless and almost forgotten, in Phoenix.

Another Irishman, William Mulholland, became manager of the Los Angeles Water Department in 1905. He held with the theory that those who owned the land also owned the water rights—a belief blessed in the arid West with bullets as well as common law. Using this theory as his justification, Mulholland initiated a program that soon dwarfed New York's water reach.

He sent city officials into the Owens Valley posing as real estate buyers. They bought up 300,000 acres of land sought by the city for a right-of-way over which water could be run from the Owens River. The basin farmers were furious when they learned of the plot. Angry protests were registered against a project proposed by the Bureau of Reclamation to divert Owens River water for irrigation projects for the South. Mulholland's next move was the hiring of a key U.S. reclamation official. Los Angeles officials then conferred with President Theodore Roosevelt and his famed conservationist Cabinet member, Gifford Pinchot. The President and Pinchot were persuaded that Owens Valley lands purchased by the city should be classified as a "U.S. Forest Preserve," although there was hardly a tree in the area. Dams and reservoirs were built. The dams were dynamited by angry farmers only to be rebuilt by a determined city. Los Angeles won and has continued to win. Today, the city uses two-thirds of the water flowing in the Owens River.

Growth soon demanded more water. In 1928, Los Angeles joined other southern California cities to finance the tapping of the Colorado River. More than a billion dollars has since been spent to build aqueducts to bring in Colorado water from Parker Dam, 250 miles away. Most of the money has been raised by the City of Los Angeles, which receives the lion's share of the supply. Believing that a squeeze on Colorado River water could not be far away, California water planners began to look elsewhere for fresh sources.

A mainstay of the economy of the entire state of California is a massive agriculture, which long ago passed that of any other state in annual value. In 1963, California produced farm products valued at $3.4 billion. Most of these crops are raised on irrigated acreage. Nearly 9 million acres of the state's farmland is dependent on man-made waterlines. Although the greatest pressure for water comes from southern California, demand also grows rapidly in the central valley.

The water and population pattern has not changed since 1900. The northern third of California contains more than 70 per cent of the state's waters, vast forest lands, and a relatively small population, but some 77 per cent of the water demand lies in the southern two-thirds. In the northern third, 29 million acre-feet of water plunges unused from the Cascades into the Pacific every year. This amount is more than the state's present net water demand for all purposes.

As postwar population growth shifted southward, it became apparent to many that water resources should follow suit. In 1947, the California legislature ordered a survey of potential need and available supply. Twelve years later, the "California Water Plan" was formally adopted by the legislature amid mutterings of secession by northern regions, which refused to give up unused waters without protest. In 1959, the legislature enacted the California Water Resources Development Bond Act, more frequently known as the Burns-Porter Act. It called for a statewide referendum on a $1.75 billion bond issue to finance construction of the State Water Resources Development System—the California Water Plan. On November 8, 1960, Californians approved the largest money issue yet adopted by public vote. They did so in the full knowledge that it would not satisfy water demand beyond 1990 and that facilities provided would add only 4 million acre-feet annually when completed.

Although it will be confined within the borders of one state, the California Water Plan involves the biggest transfer of water yet attempted on this continent. Most of it will be financed by the state, but a great federal project will be incorporated.

Five projects on the Upper Feather River will be the plan's keystone. These, together with other supporting projects, will supply 1.3 billion gallons daily. Of this supply, half will go to the Metropolitan Water District of Southern California. The remainder will supply central California, including the growing San Francisco area.

Oroville Dam will hold 3,484,000 acre-feet behind its 747-foot-high concrete barrier. Located 4 miles north of the town of Oroville, the dam will create a lake covering 15,500 acres contained within a 167-mile shoreline. An underground power plant in the left abutment of the dam will house generators with a 644,000-kilowatt capacity. Aqueducts are being drilled through barriers once considered impregnable. These will carry water hundreds of miles to areas of need; the California Aqueduct, a major artery, will transport water 444 miles from the Sacramento–San Joaquin Delta to Perris Reservoir in southern California. Pumping stations will lift waters uphill over natural obstacles.

Miles of concrete-lined tunnels will carry the waters through mountains too high to be crossed by pumped water. Power for pumping will be generated by the project.

A highly flexible program, the plan provides that all water projects constructed by private companies, as well as state, local, and federal agencies, will fall within its jurisdiction. It seeks to satisfy northern interests by providing flood control, water storage, and local hydroelectric power to spur economic growth.

The federal program that was the California Central Valley Project was fitted into the California Water Plan. The Bureau of Reclamation had spent $855 million on it by 1963, and an additional $585 million had been authorized to complete this great facility. The Corps of Engineers supplemented the plan with outlays for flood control and multi-purpose projects amounting to $230 million by the end of 1964.

To determine water allocation and costs of delivery, and to gain right of condemnation from participating agencies, the plan created a unique network of supply contractors as public agencies. Located in all major project service areas, they contracted for their maximum annual water entitlement and organized themselves into the thirty-member California State Water Services Council. The council has participated in planning and in exchange of necessary information. The anticipated maximum annual yield of the plan is 4 million acre-feet. The supply contractors signed up for nearly 3.5 million acre-feet. The remaining waters are available on an irrigation-demand pattern so long as a surplus exists. State officials have predicted that all available water will be in use by 1981.

The City of Los Angeles already is planning to supplement the California Water Plan. Now using 64 per cent of the Owens River supply, which is delivered through the Los Angeles–Owens River Aqueduct, it has begun work on a parallel aqueduct—a 222-mile-long ribbon of covered conduit and pressure pipeline. This $105 million project will be financed by the city alone and will be completed in 1969. Combined with California Water Plan supplies and its other sources, the project will give Los Angeles enough water to quench its thirst. The Owens and Mono Basin new water should be adequate for a population growth of 750,000 in the city, and this should be the last call for water from the Owens. Basin residents have been assured that they will not be deprived of water necessary to sustain their local economy.

After the turn of this century, southern California will have to look beyond the Feather River for water—to 100 underground aquifers, which have been losing more water than seeps into them, and to desalting ocean waters. Each alternative offers relatively costly water, but unless other sources become available, they are the only ones in sight. LeVal Lund, Jr., executive engineer of the Los Angeles Water System, has calculated that the potential of all current and planned water projects will assure Los Angeles an ample supply for the next 55 years. His calculations are based upon demand for 801 million gallons daily for a population of 4 million.

As this book is written, planners for the state of California are looking to further sources and are campaigning for an $850 million new bond issue. Newest target is the Upper Eel, a far northern California river that could be tied into the California Water Plan. Water engineers see an additional 12 million acre-feet of annual water supply in the region. California will have a population of 56 million in 55 years. In anticipation of this, water men have already studied in detail the potential of other northern rivers—the Trinity, Mad, Van Duzen, Klamath, and Russian.

It is clear, then, that California has water for its fast-growing areas principally because it planned for it far enough in advance. The state recognized the absolute necessity of water for the growth and economic prosperity of southern California. But its success also rests on recognition of two other facts. The first is that obtaining water is a competitive matter, which involves conflicts with other regions as well as between economic groups. This competition intensifies as population expands. The second fact is that it takes many years to plan and build water projects. A 1966 pamphlet issued by "Californians for Water Action" quotes Governor Edmund G. Brown as saying: "There is a gap of 25 years from planning table to the water tap."

It is one thing for the citizens of an area to agree, for example, that water pollution should be abated in a particular stretch of a waterway. It is quite another to get through the conferences, committee meetings, planning sessions, public hearings, and often elections that must take place before the legal and political questions can be cleared away and actual construction of works begun. Even after bids are accepted, it can take several years before works are in operation. We have seen that it took 13 years, from 1922 to 1935, from the signing of the Colorado River Compact until Hoover Dam began to store water, and another 20 years to bring the Upper Basin storage project to near completion.

In 1908, Theodore Roosevelt advocated a "be prepared" concept for the waters of the United States. In that year, his Inland Waterways Commission recommended "prompt and vigorous action" by the state and federal governments to develop comprehensive plans for all our river basins. Americans do not welcome planning as a function of government. Even today, metropolitan government (the proposal to organize political planning authority for our supercities) is denounced by many as more socialistic than the federal government programs they also deplore. Since the proposals of Roosevelt's commission were made, we can point to integrated resource development in only one river basin —the Tennessee. Much worthwhile planning has gone into other river basins. The Colorado, the Rio Grande, the Missouri, and the Ohio are examples. But most of this has been piecemeal. Only the Tennessee has been planned with the goal in mind of developing the full value of the resource. A comparison of the Tennessee development with that of the much larger water resources of the Columbia River demonstrates what can be accomplished through truly comprehensive planning.

Valley of the Tennessee

In a sense, the valley of the Tennessee was the Appalachia of the 1930's. Depressed though the nation was, the valley was even more depressed. Long before the stock market collapse of 1929, the Tennessee Valley had become an area of chronic stagnation and poverty. The sickness of the national economy must have seemed simply one more, and final, blow to an area suffering the misery of eroded lands and poor crops, inadequate roads and water transportation, repeated floods, and high-cost electric power.

The watershed of the Tennessee River covers an area of 41,000 square miles in Virginia, North Carolina, Georgia, Alabama, Kentucky, and Tennessee. The river flows in a giant crescent from Knoxville, Tennessee, 650 miles southwest into Alabama, then northwest to join the Ohio at Paducah, Kentucky, a few miles upstream from the Ohio-Mississippi confluence. The Tennessee Valley enjoys generous rainfall, averaging 52 inches annually. Runoff is heaivest during the winter and early spring.

The fact that the Tennessee Valley boasts the only truly integrated water resource development program in the nation is strong testimony to the power of politics. It took the "Great Depression," plus years of devotion and the application of great political skill on the part of Senator George W. Norris of Nebraska to make it a reality. It is not a water project only, but a comprehensive resource development.

The dream of TVA was born out of the construction of Wilson Dam at Muscle Shoals, Alabama, during World War I. Power generated at the dam was used by two large nitrate munition plants. Following the war, chemical and power compaines, and ultimately Henry Ford, offered to relieve the government of this "burden." Prices offered were ridiculously low. Senator Norris characterized one proposal to turn over Muscle Shoals to a private interest as "the greatest gift ever bestowed upon mortal man since salvation was made free to the human race." He introduced legislation to have the federal government operate Muscle Shoals. Congress passed several of his bills despite denunciations of socialism from private utilities and others. All the Norris measures were vetoed by Presidents Coolidge and Hoover.

In 1933, Senator Norris proposed the basic TVA act, which was passed by the New Deal Congress and joyously signed by Franklin D. Roosevelt. TVA construction brought new jobs and hope to the valley. By 1936, Norris Dam on the Clinch River tributary and Wheeler Dam, downstream on the main river in Alabama, were closed, and their reservoirs began to fill. Pickwick, Guntersville, Chickamauga, and Hiwassee were completed in rapid succession. Hydro plants came into operation and flood control began, as one of the nation's most destructive rivers was progressively tamed.

In 1934, Tupelo, Mississippi, became the first customer for TVA electric power, agreeing to buy for its municipal system as soon as the supply came on the line. Alcorn County, Mississippi, in the same year, became the location of the first Rural Electrification Cooperative. Light had come to the valley, literally as well as figuratively.

"Socialism" on the Tennessee was fought from the outset. It took a Supreme Court decision, *Ashwander* v. *TVA*, to establish the authority's right to generate and sell power. There are those today who would "sell TVA." As the 1964 election results showed, few valley residents would consent to such a sale. There, even the most conservative welcome the project and its accomplishments.

Any TVA "socialism" is well matched by the capitalism represented in the more than $1 billion of private investment in factories lining the river's shores. In 1964 alone, a total of $460 million of new capital was invested in the valley. The area is one of growing cities and prosperous agriculture.

The Tennessee Valley Authority is operated by a three-member board of directors appointed by the President with the consent of the Senate. The TVA has made resolution of conflicting water uses a principal aim. Recognizing the unity in water, shorelines, flood plains, soils, and drainage areas, it has sought to treat the watershed area as an integrated whole. It has sought to unite operations for farm, forest, and city. Concern extends to the raising and lowering of reservoir levels to control mosquitos. Malaria, once prevalent, has been almost eliminated.

In enacting the TVA legislation, Congress called for dams to "control destructive floodwaters in the Tennessee and Mississippi drainage basin," for a navigable Tennessee River from its mouth to Knoxville, and for watershed improvement. In planning the development, the choice was seen as thirty low dams or nine high dams. The bigger reservoirs were chosen to better regulate the waters for navigation and flood control, and take advantage of an electric power potential of 1,651,000 kilowatts. With World War II, dam construction was speeded up, and, by 1942, there were twelve dams. TVA power made a great contribution to meeting the nation's aluminum and armament needs.

By the early 1960's, thirty-one major dams were in place on the Tennessee and its five principal tributaries. In addition, three small private dams had been purchased, and six dams of the Aluminum Corporation of America were part of the system, operating under TVA instructions by agreement with ALCOA. Although the days of new high dams are over, the construction of small dams and reservoirs on tributary streams has just begun. Local initiative will be particularly important in this tributary stream development.

On July 31, 1965, the Tennessee Valley Authority reported that it had repaid half a billion dollars to the U.S. Treasury from electric power revenues alone. Of this, $235 million represented repayment of advances for construction. The Treasury also received $200 million in dividends, $65 million to redeem early bond issues, and $41.5 million

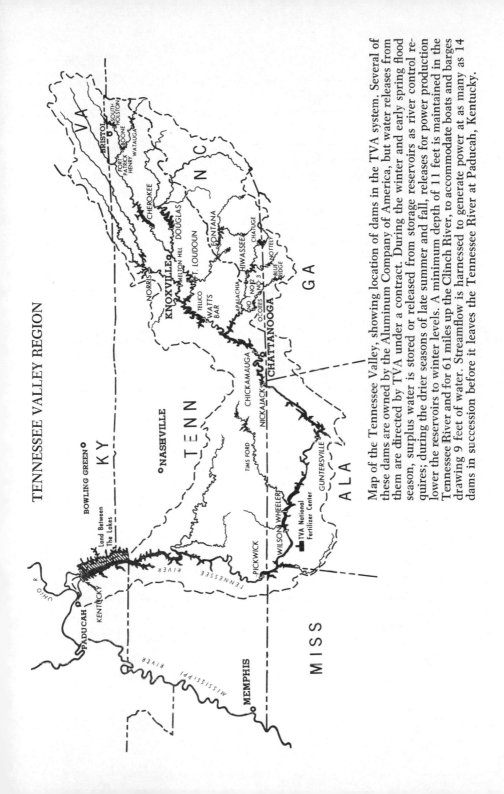

TENNESSEE VALLEY REGION

Map of the Tennessee Valley, showing location of dams in the TVA system. Several of these dams are owned by the Aluminum Company of America, but water releases from them are directed by TVA under a contract. During the winter and early spring flood season, surplus water is stored or released from storage reservoirs as river control requires; during the drier seasons of late summer and fall, releases for power production lower the reservoirs to winter levels. A minimum depth of 11 feet is maintained in the Tennessee River and for 61 miles up the Clinch River, to accommodate boats and barges drawing 9 feet of water. Streamflow is harnessed to generate power at as many as 14 dams in succession before it leaves the Tennessee River at Paducah, Kentucky.

from other than power programs. Although well ahead of schedule, TVA still has years to go before it repays the Treasury for construction costs. But the American people have already been repaid many times over for outlays that started with initial construction in 1934. Repayment has come in the form of rapid economic growth within the Tennessee Valley, cheap electric power, effective flood control, restoration of exhausted lands, improved municipal water supplies, water-based recreation, and navigable waterways. While there is still much catching up to do, TVA has helped raise average per capita income from 45 per cent of the national average in the 1930's to 70 per cent in the 1960's. And it has demonstrated what can be accomplished through a unified watershed policy.

More than a decade has gone by since the TVA last called on tax monies for construction of power facilities. Since the mid-1950's, all additions to TVA's power system have been financed from power revenues or the sale of revenue bonds.

Farm and forest yields have been significantly increased. New and improved fertilizers, developed on the scene, are now widely used in the valley. TVA has paid particular attention to lands within the flood plain of the river, seeking to persuade farmers to plant those crops that will be least harmed by rising waters. It has sought to induce urban communities to employ zoning to reduce construction upon flood plains.

Forest programs of TVA have increased fire protection from half to 95 per cent of the 14 million acres of forest land in the watershed. There has been significant reduction in the number of forest fires, an 80 per cent reduction in the size of forest fires, and a 90 per cent reduction in the annual average burn.

By 1960, nearly 300,000 acres of eroded and otherwise unproductive land had been reforested, while improved practices had been introduced on 2 million acres of privately owned forest lands. The results, as measured on several small watersheds, have been impressive. In ten years, sedimentation was reduced by half on the 85,000-acre Chestuee Creek in eastern Tennessee without reduction of water yield. A badly eroded 1,715-acre area on White Hollow Creek near Norris has been largely restored. Knowledge gained through research is being applied to hundreds of small watersheds.

Examples set by TVA have resulted in the establishment of fifteen organized tributary areas, two chartered by state legislatures. One of these—the Beech River Watershed Authority—has completed seven small dams and reservoirs at a cost of $7 million.

A flood forecasting and river control organization is maintained from which streamflow and rainfall reports are received daily. It has established cooperation with the U.S. Weather Bureau, which provides information to forecast flows and flood stages. Early warnings have been transmitted to communities still vulnerable to flooding. Total investment charged to flood control is $184 million. Savings resulting from floods prevented are estimated at $300 million, or 60 per cent greater than investment.

The act creating TVA called for a nine-foot channel in the river to maintain navigation over the dams. Keeping the channel open and the locks in operation costs a million dollars a year. Navigation is continued year round, supplying and carrying the products of the billion-dollar industry on the banks. Five principal commodities—coal, sand and gravel, grain, petroleum and petroleum products, and crushed limestone—account for three-fourths of the traffic.

As its fame has grown worldwide, tourists have flocked to TVA. Each year more millions visit the dams, many remaining to enjoy boating, swimming, and fishing along the waterway. A very low estimate, based on an expenditure of 75 cents per person per day, placed tourist expenditures in the valley at $34 million in 1964. President Kennedy pointed out that, after New York and Washington, official foreign visitors to the United States most wanted to see the Tennessee Valley. To them, it appeared to be a model upon which their own development could be patterned.

The United States Information Agency has published a booklet on TVA for use abroad. Entitled *Water . . . Wellspring of Progress*, it says in part:

A 10,600,000 hectare (26 million acre) area has been rejuvenated. Thirty one major dams control the waters of the Tennessee and its five principal tributaries. Out of every hundred farms in the TVA region, ninety-five now have electricity, and the new industries TVA power has attracted have created thousands of job opportunities. Fertilizers from big chemical plants make the valley greener and more productive. Manmade lakes cover the swamplands where disease-carrying mosquitoes used

to multiply, and malaria has disappeared. The rivers bear some 3,000,-
000,000 ton-kilometers of freight compared with 53,000,000 ton-kilometers carried before their channels were deepened. Serious floods have
been prevented.

Hydropower development has passed its peak at TVA. The authority
has become the biggest supplier of thermal power in the nation, and
by far the largest supplier of electrical energy. The total system—hydro-
and fossil-fuel—has an installed capacity of over 13 million kilowatts,
making TVA double the size of Pacific Gas and Electric Corporation,
the largest private utility in the nation.

Thermal power at TVA came in with World War II, when existing
hydro facilities proved inadequate to war needs. The first plant was
placed beside Watts Bar Dam on the mainstream less than a quarter
of a century ago.

The new Bull Run steam-generating plant being built on the Clinch
River's Melton Hill Reservoir is more typical of modern TVA operations. The $135 million plant was opened in 1965. Initially, it will
have a generating capacity of 900,000 kilowatts. The plant will burn
316 tons of coal hourly, more than 2.2 million tons each year. The Bull
Run boiler will handle 6.4 million pounds of steam each hour. It will
require fantastic amounts of cooling water—about 400,000 gallons each
minute. Including Bull Run, there are seven steam plants on the Tennessee and its tributaries.

The Tennessee Valley enjoys the cheapest electric power in the nation, and acts as an effective yardstick for power rates. The average
household in the valley pays $4.10 monthly for electric power, but uses
far more than does the average American consumer, who would have
to pay $9.10—more than double—for the same amount.

Despite a record of conservation of resources and restoration of well-
being, one condition in the valley—and one practice of the TVA—
needs correction.

Even TVA planning has not kept ahead of the growth of water
pollution, and the Tennessee River is becoming a contaminated stream,
polluted by the wastes of the industries that cheap TVA power has
brought into the valley. The river contains dye, pickle liquor, chemical
plant and paper-mill wastes. So far, little effort has been made to impose water quality standards. Of the tributaries, the Little Tennessee

is polluted by textile and paper-mill wastes, the Holston by the wastes of various small industries, and the Pigeon by pulp- and paper-mill wastes. Unless checked and reversed, increasing industrial pollution in the basin's river system can ultimately destroy the recreational values of the rejuvenated area.

The effect of TVA coal purchases on Appalachia has been examined earlier. The authority is the largest single buyer of coal in the nation. Although TVA is certainly not responsible for the rise of strip mining, it can exert strong influence on coal-mining conditions. The agency should not maintain low power rates on the basis of a colonialism that holds Appalachia in bondage. Governor Breathitt of Kentucky put his finger on this point when the TVA, in June, 1965, announced an "extra" dividend of $53 million to the Treasury because of higher returns on power sales. At that time, he said: "Certainly the TVA, which is basically a conservation agency, should insist that conservation practices be observed whenever it does business. The conscience of the Authority should not allow the destruction it is today helping to promote."

There is general agreement that it would be far better to hold electric power rates constant and force reforestation clauses into TVA's contracts, and there have been indications that such clauses will be a matter of policy in the future.

It Might Have Been Better

The Columbia of today is a far different river from that discovered by the Spanish sea captain Bruno Heceta, the first white man to gaze upon its waters. Prevented from entering the river by turbulence and unknown channel depths, Heceta reported that the "currents and eddies caused me to believe that the place is the mouth of some great river, or of some passage to another sea."

Known as the Ourigan to frontiersmen, the waterway was given its present name by Yankee skipper Robert Gray of Boston. He sailed upstream in 1792 in his ship, the *Columbia Mediviva*.

Over a hundred years ago, Daniel Webster allegedly roared opposition to annexation of the Columbia Basin because it was an area "of savages and wild beasts, of shifting sands and whirlwinds of dust" and, of course, "worthless." During debate on the House floor only three and a half decades ago, Congressman Francis Culkin of New York rose in opposition to the building of Grand Coulee Dam because there was nobody "to sell power to except rattlesnakes, coyotes and rabbits." Despite Culkin's opposition, work was begun on Grand Coulee in 1935 and was completed in 1941, just before Pearl Harbor. Electricity generated at the great dam powered huge aluminum and airplane industries throughout the war and has since been a mainstay of the region.

The Columbia Basin

The Columbia River is 1,214 miles long. It rises in Columbia Lake, high in the towering Canadian Rockies of British Columbia. Fed by melting ice fields and the awesome glaciers of the Selkirk Range, the Columbia alternately sulks and rages from the mountains to the far-off Pacific. It is a moody and erratic river. The Kootenai and Clark rivers in Canada, and the Boise, Clearwater, Snake, Umatilla, John Day, Lewis, Williamette, Cowlitz and many other streams below the 49th Parallel pour into the Columbia, which in turn pours a volume equal to ten Colorados into the ocean every year. Among American rivers, it is surpassed in volume only by the Mississippi. Although it drains less than half the land area of the Missouri basin, the Columbia's annual flow is five times greater. This huge volume of water falls 2 to 5 feet per mile of flow, providing nearly 40 per cent of the nation's hydroelectric power potential.

Maximum flood stage recorded on the Columbia was the 1,240,000 cubic feet of water that swept past The Dalles, Oregon, in 1894. Lowest flow, in January, 1937, was 35,000 cubic feet of water. For purposes of flood control and navigation, it has become imperative to narrow this 35–1 range. But the power potential of the river has taken precedence over all other resource needs.

The story of Columbia River development began in 1927 when Congress authorized the Corps of Engineers to survey the river for navigation. The Corps proposed ten dams with locks to accommodate deepwater navigation to The Dalles, and river navigation to the 49th Parallel and beyond. Each dam site chosen was at a rapids, where goods moved only via costly portage.

Congress then approved Bonneville Dam, now a famous tourist

THE COLUMBIA RIVER BASIN

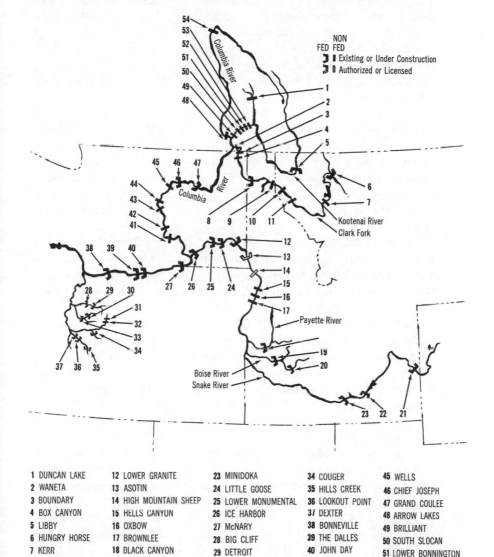

FED	NON FED	
]	I	Existing or Under Construction
]	II	Authorized or Licensed

1 DUNCAN LAKE	12 LOWER GRANITE	23 MINIDOKA	34 COUGER	45 WELLS
2 WANETA	13 ASOTIN	24 LITTLE GOOSE	35 HILLS CREEK	46 CHIEF JOSEPH
3 BOUNDARY	14 HIGH MOUNTAIN SHEEP	25 LOWER MONUMENTAL	36 LOOKOUT POINT	47 GRAND COULEE
4 BOX CANYON	15 HELLS CANYON	26 ICE HARBOR	37 DEXTER	48 ARROW LAKES
5 LIBBY	16 OXBOW	27 McNARY	38 BONNEVILLE	49 BRILLIANT
6 HUNGRY HORSE	17 BROWNLEE	28 BIG CLIFF	39 THE DALLES	50 SOUTH SLOCAN
7 KERR	18 BLACK CANYON	29 DETROIT	40 JOHN DAY	51 LOWER BONNINGTON
8 ALBENI FALLS	19 BOISE DIVERSION	30 GREEN PETER	41 PRIEST RAPIDS	52 UPPER BONNINGTON
9 CABINET GORGE	20 ANDERSON RANCH	31 CARMEN	42 WANAPUM	53 CORA LINN
10 NOXON RAPIDS	21 PALISADES	32 TRAIL BRIDGE	43 ROCK ISLAND	54 MICA
11 THOMPSON FALLS	22 AMERICAN FALLS	33 FOSTER	44 ROCKY REACH	

Bonneville Power Administration

attraction not far from Portland, and construction was begun in 1933. The dam was equipped with a ship lock 500 feet long and 76 feet wide to accommodate deepwater traffic. Bonneville was multipurpose only in that it eliminated the rapids, made river navigation possible, and permitted the start of federal power generation on the river. Fish ladders were constructed to save the famed Columbia River salmon and other migratory fish. Today, tourists watch the fish fight their way upstream.

Bonneville is a low "run-of-the-river" dam with negligible storage capacity. In 1948, huge floods swept over the spillway and wiped out the town of Vanport, Washington. Bonneville was not the first hydropower dam on the stream, although it was the biggest when completed. Enterprising municipalities and private utilities were already drawing power from twenty-one structures on tributaries and one on the mainstream when Bonneville was begun. None stored a significant amount of water.

Largest of the private dams was Rock Island, built by Puget Sound Power and Light Company and completed in 1933. Rock Island, 12 miles south of Wenatchee in east-central Washington, generates 212,-000 kilowatts; Bonneville, 518,400. Rock Island was later bought by the Chelan County Public Utility District.

Public Utility Districts (PUD's) are local public bodies created under Washington state law expressly to generate and market electric power. Most of the hydropower in Washington is generated by the PUD's, which have important rights to power dam sites. They have built huge dams to ensure cheap power, financing the projects with revenue bond issues. The power has a ready market, thanks in part to a huge intertie linking the Bonneville power complex with that of southern California.

Almost all PUD dams are run of the river. Private power companies and the federal government have built similar dams. They generate power, but do little to check flooding or store water for reclamation, flood control, or recreation. Despite the tremendous potential for water storage on the Columbia, the *Water Atlas of the United States* lists but one major storage dam there. That dam is Grand Coulee, authorized as a multipurpose reclamation project and built by the Bureau of Reclamation. Although Grand Coulee backs up lovely Franklin D. Roosevelt Lake to the Canadian border, its total storage capacity of 9 million acre-feet is less than a third that of Lake Mead on the far more parsimonious Colorado.

The water stored at Grand Coulee has reclaimed a vast area. The dry Columbia plateau lies east of the Cascades, which shut off the rain-bearing clouds that drift in from the Pacific to the west of the magnificent range. Formed by lava eons ago, the plateau has almost miraculous fertility when it is watered. During the Ice Age, glaciers gouged out new river beds and diverted rivers into new channels. When the ice receded, the rivers returned to their original beds leaving the plateau scarred by dry-wall canyons, or coulees. The greatest of these is the Grand Coulee, long ago the temporary channel of the Columbia. Grand Coulee is 50 miles long, from 1 to 5 miles wide, and up to 1,000 feet deep.

Both dreamers and practical engineers envisoned the Grand Coulee as a natural channel for excess Columbia waters, which could be fanned out to irrigate the plateau. But those who proposed to lift the waters of the river up to irrigate the plateau were derided as hopeless visionaries. In the early 1930's, the dream captured the imagination of Franklin D. Roosevelt. He allocated $63 million of emergency Public Works Administration funds to start construction of the dam and its associated Columbia Basin Irrigation Project. The initial investment and subsequent allocations have paid off handsomely for the region and the nation.

The dam is 4,173 feet in length and rises 370 feet above the surface of the river. It spans the Columbia 596 miles upstream from the Pacific. Each summer, tourists flock from across the nation to watch surplus water from the melting snow upstream rush over the spillway to create a waterfall twice as high and half as wide as Niagara. Millions now visit Roosevelt Lake to see, camp, boat, and swim.

The primary purpose of Grand Coulee Dam is not power or recreation, but reclamation. Water from Roosevelt Lake is pumped upward 280 feet to the plateau through 6 steel tubes that empty into the Grand Coulee itself, where it is stored in a 20-mile-long reservoir. From the reservoir, the water travels through 288 miles of main canal, 1,623 miles of laterals, and 735 miles of drainage canals to irrigate more than 1 million acres. Irrigation water began to flow to the project lands in 1952. Since then, the area has been transformed into verdant farmlands, whose crops of apples are famous across the nation. Power for pumping is supplied from Grand Coulee Dam hydro stations. Of the installed capacity of nearly 2 million kilowatts, only a fraction is required to pump water up to the ancient river bed. The remainder flows into the Bonneville Power Administration's grid and is marketed with other pooled power sold to consumers at a "postage stamp" rate.

Construction cost of the Columbia Basin Project has been $779 million, an amount that will be repaid from power and water revenues. As on the Colorado, the irrigation would be uneconomical without the power. The lands reclaimed are assuming their true importance as domestic population growth and world food needs have dissipated U.S. agricultural surpluses.

When Bonneville construction was begun in 1933, there were twenty-one dams on tributaries and one on the Columbia's mainstem. The only federal project was Minidoka, the original Bureau of Reclamation dam on the Snake River. Construction before and after Bonneville has been marked by interagency struggle between the bureau and the Corps of Engineers, between the private power companies and the federal government, and between municipalities and PUD's on the one hand and the private utilities on the other.

By late 1965, a hodgepodge of dams spanned the Columbia and its tributaries. There were 84 with a power-plant capacity of 10,000 kilowatts or more. Of 28 federal projects, 20 were built by the Army Engineers and 8 by the Bureau of Reclamation. Others were built by municipalities, Public Utility Districts, and private power companies.

The early pattern of dams chiefly for power has prevailed. Flood waters still cause great damage before running off to the sea. The Corps has built John Day Dam at The Dalles for navigation and power. Lower Monument and Little Goose dams, now under construction, are also run of the river. They will add to power capacity while permitting slack water navigation up to the Snake at Lewiston, Idaho, and Clarkston, Washington, but will do little to reduce flooding.

Thanks to special interests and interagency rivalry, the United States has lost irretrievably a unique opportunity for an integrated river-basin development on the Columbia. This could have resulted in the creation of a super-TVA, treating land, water, power, recreation, navigation, and reclamation as elements of a basin-wide plan. Given this concept, there could be on the Columbia today vast reservoirs to control floods and to be used for export of a portion of the water surplus of the Northwest to nearby and distant arid areas.

Plans for a Columbia River Authority, patterned on TVA, were approved by President Harry S. Truman after Bureau of Reclamation officials and the Corps of Engineers signed a "peace pact" outlining plans for integrated development. Incorporated in the pact were the best ideas of both agencies.

President Truman sent a special message to Congress on April 13, 1949, urging creation of CVA. He acknowledged that valuable and excellent work had been carried out on the river by private interests and federal agencies. He stressed that time was running out on integrated development possibilities, and that only a new single agency could assure use of the full potential of the river. CVA met a wall of resistance, much of it from private power utilities. One bone of contention was a high federal dam at Hell's Canyon in Idaho. Idaho Power Company, backed by other utilities, demanded the right to build low dams on the river.

When CVA was pushed aside by Congress, President Truman countered with a second proposal. He asked joint development by the Corps of Engineers and the Bureau of Reclamation, with Hell's Canyon High Dam as a keystone. He proposed a Columbia River basin fund into which all water and power revenues would flow and from which the federal investment would be paid. Legislation including the Columbia River Basin plan was passed by the House in 1949. But when the measure was reported out of the Senate Public Works Committee in 1950, all reclamation aspects were deleted and only the Corps of Engineers proposals remained. The basin fund was a casualty, as was Hell's Canyon High Dam. An amendment to restore the fund and the Bureau of Reclamation projects, including Hell's Canyon, was defeated on the Senate floor. After this defeat, President Truman fought efforts of the Idaho Power Company to build a low dam on the Snake at the Hell's Canyon site because he believed that the site called for a high dam to ensure more power, adequate storage, and full resource development.

On one side, such an issue has often been viewed as private enterprise against "socialism"; on the other, as private greed against full resource development. Such arguments will continue, but they must not block basin planning. The significant issue is not who gains the right to generate power, but the price of that power, the availability of water, and full development. This need not mean a TVA for every river basin. But increasingly, as our need for water expands, it does mean comprehensive planning that will ensure water protection and restoration.

The Hell's Canyon fight, now history, was lost during the Eisenhower Administration. Five months after President Eisenhower took office, his administration withdrew federal opposition to the licensing of Idaho Power to build low dams. Efforts of Senators Wayne Morse, Frank Church, and others to win Congressional approval of a federal high dam were in vain. Today, two Idaho Power low dams, Brownlee and Oxbow, span the Snake and the third, low Hell's Canyon, is scheduled to produce power in late 1967.

The battle over power rights at remaining dam sites on the Columbia rages without abatement. On the one side is a group of local public agencies, mostly Washington Public Utility Districts, which have banded together to form the Washington Public Power Supply System (WPPSS). On the other is a private power combine, including Idaho Power. Both seek rights to build a dam at the High Mountain Sheep site on the Snake, just above its confluence with the Salmon. An earlier application of WPPSS to build a high dam at the Nez Percé site just below the confluence has been denied by the Federal Power Commission.

The Federal Power Act that grants licenses to build dams directs the FPC to give priority to nonprofit organizations when there is no pending federal claim. The theory is that the rivers are public resources to be developed for the public good. Nonetheless, the FPC has issued a license to the private combine on a technicality. At this writing, the question is before the courts.

Today, the dams on the mainstem of the Columbia—all federal or PUD—have a power potential of more than 10 million kilowatts. This low-cost power is contributing greatly to the development of the region. There can be no question of the worth of the public investment in Columbia River power. Private industry has been among the major beneficiaries. Some 30 per cent of the power supply is sold to aluminum reduction plants owned by big producers. Another 15 per cent goes to private utilities, which resell it to consumers at a profit.

But the Columbia River power race has brought an ironic result to the Northwest. The Columbia's massive volume, together with the lack of sufficient storage capacity to hold the summer runoffs, forces the Columbia dams to spill water into the Pacific unharnessed. Had more storage dams been built, there would be firm power year round to meet the needs of the region and for export. During winter months of low flow, extra water could be released from storage dams to keep the turbines running at full or near-full capacity. Much of the power now generated is not firm power, available on a year-round basis. With its heaviest power loads during the winter heating months, the Northwest has been unable to put the summer surplus to work fully. To solve this problem, and to put the resources of the region to maximum use, the Bonneville Power Administration will link the Northwest by extra-high-voltage transmission lines with the Southwest states of California, Nevada, and Arizona. With their heaviest power demand coming in the summer air conditioning and irrigating season, the Southwest states will put the Northwest's summer surplus to good use. Similarly, winter surplus power in the Southwest will flow north to meet the Columbia Basin's winter peak demands.

Canada, which has done little about the river, will benefit from lack of U.S. planning. It will build three major storage dams to hold water for release when needed downstream. The dams will also prevent downstream flooding and give Canada new hydro capacity, which it is not expected to need for three decades. Canada will obtain its new dams free under the Columbia River Treaty by selling power to U.S. users for 30 years. The new Canadian dams will also provide new firm streamflow to Grand Coulee and make way for the construction of a massive, third power plant there that has been authorized by Congress. This plant will add 3.6 million kilowatts to the 2 million now available. Under terms of the treaty, the United States will also be able to build the long-authorized Libby Dam on the Kootenai tributary in Montana. Libby has not been built previously because it would have backed water into Canada; the new dam will add another 315,000 kilowatts of power to the Columbia complex.

Columbia River development has added much to the wealth of the Northwest and the nation, and it can add more. But what has been accomplished is far less than the potential of the river. It is too late to rectify yesterday's costly mistakes; at least, we should make the most of what remains.

The Way to Planning Is Open

The first recommendation of the Senate Select Committee on National Water Resources was that plans be adopted embracing "comprehensive water development and management for all major river basins of the United States." The committee also called for financial assistance to the states for water planning, and for a biennial assessment of the water supply and demand outlook for each of the nation's water resource regions. As of this writing, the United States has few regional plans—and no national plans—for the restoration and development of water resources.

In 1965, however, one significant step forward was taken, with passage by Congress of the Water Resources Planning Act. The bill was introduced by Senator Clinton P. Anderson of New Mexico, a national leader in water resources development. The act set up three activities of major importance.

First, it provided for consideration of water resource needs—on a national scale—by a high-level group in the executive branch of the federal government. For some years, the secretaries of the Army, Agriculture, Interior, and Health, Education, and Welfare departments had met as an *ad hoc* interagency council to coordinate work in water resources. The Planning Act added to those four the chairman of the Federal Power Commission, and formally established the group as the Water Resources Council. The functions of the council include preparation of a biennial report on the adequacy of the nation's water supplies, and a review of all river-basin development plans.

Second, the Planning Act authorized machinery for the planning of individual river basins. To do this, a "river basin water and related land resources commission" may be created. The complexity of the question with which we are dealing is beautifully illustrated by the history of the authorizing legislation for these commissions and by their membership and operation.

The Planning Act, first introduced in 1963, provided for both federal and state members. Fearful of federal domination, the states asked for more time. For some two years, discussions were carried out, and the Council of State Governments worked diligently to arrive at a compromise acceptable to the states. Finally one was approved by all except the state of Virginia. It provided that all state votes should be cast as one and all federal votes cast as one, thus assuring unanimity before action could be taken.

Before the act was passed, its provisions were altered again, but the unanimity principle was retained. Describing the provisions as simply as possible, the membership of a river-basin commission consists of: a chairman, appointed by the President, who may hold no other federal office; one member "from each federal department or independent agency" that the President considers relevant; one member representing each state "wholly or partly" within the basin; one member appointed by any "international commission" for which representation may be relevant.

A commission "shall submit a comprehensive, coordinated, joint plan" for water and related land resource development for the area, river basin, or portion. However, no time is set for the submission of such a plan. Further, the commission cannot adopt a recommended plan by vote. Instead, "every reasonable endeavor shall be made to arrive at a consensus of all members on all issues." Failing this, each member presents his individual views.

A third section of the Planning Act provides federal money to assist states to do a comprehensive planning job on the waters within their borders. Dams, water supply systems, and factories have been built to take advantage of those supplies of water that have been the cheapest and easiest to get at. Little thought has been given to ultimate costs as our sources of water become more fully utilized. In innumerable cases, it is now necessary to review over-all resource needs to see how remaining supplies can best be utilized and conserved. In the case of intrastate waters, this function can best be carried out by the states. Few, however, have done much water resources planning or have equipped themselves to do it.

We can fervently hope that the Planning Act will be a great impetus to water resources planning in the United States. As pressure for water mounts, the well-being of every city, county, and factory on a river system—and of every fish in it—becomes more dependent on the system's capability to deliver enough clean water. It is obvious that this can be done in a time of dynamic expansion only in accordance with long-range plans.

In the chapters to follow, several methods of reducing water-use waste and of augmenting supplies will be discussed. Before such methods can be put to efficient use, however, each region must decide which ones are practical for it and the extent to which they should and can be relied on to provide water for tomorrow. If the new public awareness of water need is to be translated into productive action, the starting point is the adoption of an up-to-date "California Water Plan" for the United States and for each of its river basins.

CHAPTER XII

Green Fields and Forests

"WE CANNOT COMMAND NATURE except by obeying her."

For disregarding the truth expressed in these words of Francis Bacon, our nation and others have paid a heavy price.

The autumn floods on the Arno River that struck Italy in 1966, battering the homes of thousands, and damaging much of the priceless art of Florence, could not be blamed on heavy rains only. In a dispatch to *The Washington Post*, Leo J. Wollemborg declared the disastrous consequences of the floods were the result of "centuries of neglect and mistakes." And he wrote:

> These have upset the hydro-geological balance of most of the Italian peninsula. Indiscriminate deforestation has hastened erosion, the effects of which have been magnified by the failure to implement coordinated water control programs.
>
> Now, a few days of rain can turn every mountain stream into a raging torrent that sends tremendous amounts of water and soil into the valleys. . . .

This is the penalty of depletion.

To make up for years of "neglect and mistakes" here in America, the United States has mounted great programs to renew croplands, forests, and watersheds.

Two classic cases of depletion are those that led to the creation of the Forest Service and the Soil Conservation Service. The programs of both agencies are essential to the maintenance of the nation's water resources.

Saving the Forests

During much of the nineteenth century, lumbering formed the basis for one of our largest industries. The great forests were logged the cheapest way, without regard for future growth. With the end of the Civil War, the cutting intensified. By 1920, Secretary of the Interior Udall says, only one-fifth of our primeval forests remained uncut.

The story of the founding of the Forest Service is a familiar one. Although agitation for some check on the uncontrolled stripping of the woodlands had gone on for two decades, it really began with the appointment in 1898 of Gifford Pinchot as chief forester in the Department of Agriculture. From that vantage point, Pinchot convinced the nation that his concept of sustained-yield use should be adopted. In 1905, Congress passed a bill transferring the forest reserves from the Department of the Interior to the Department of Agriculture. Pinchot then organized a force of forest rangers to manage the lands.

Forest management must reconcile numerous—often conflicting— uses of the lands, and prevent the many necessary activities, such as timber harvest, road construction, grazing, mining, and recreation, from creating conditions favorable to erosion.

The headwaters of many eastern streams are located in the national forests, and more than half of the water supply of the West originates on national forest land. To maintain and improve these watersheds, conservation plans are developed, based on detailed surveys and analyses. A system of "barometer" watersheds has been established. These are equipped with instruments to measure water yield in relation to precipitation, making it possible to learn the value of planting programs both on the yield of water and the stability of watersheds.

The Forest Service of the 1960's employs some 22,000 persons full time. About the same number work in addition during the field season, which varies in length according to the climate of different regions. Nine regional offices are maintained: at Atlanta, Milwaukee, Denver, Ogden (Utah), Albuquerque, Missoula (Montana), San Francisco, Portland (Oregon), and Juneau.

National forest lands are intermingled with those of the states and private owners. Therefore, much conservation work must be carried out in cooperation with these owners. In the West, such cooperation is directed by the regional foresters. In addition, two area offices are maintained. The northeast area, consisting of the twenty eastern and lake states, is served from Upper Darby, Pennsylvania; the southeast area, stretching from Texas to Virginia, is served from Atlanta.

Conservation work on 460 million acres of western lands, 288 million of them in Alaska, is the responsibility of the Bureau of Land Management in the Department of the Interior. As a consequence of the drought of 1933, drastic action was taken to conserve millions of acres of plains and far-western lands. The Taylor Grazing Act closed the public domain to further settlement and gave rise to the modern concept of a national land reserve to be protected against overgrazing and soil deterioration.

Arid and sparsley vegetated, much of the land administered by the bureau is particularly subject to erosion. Excess salinity in the Colorado River, for example, is due in part to erosion of highly mineralized soils. Watershed stabilization is an important program of the agency, and consists of such measures as contour furrowing, terracing, seeding, deep tillage, brush control, and the construction of small check dams.

The Bureau of Land Management operates in twenty-five states, utilizing the services of 3,500 employees. Operations are carried out from an eastern states office in Washington, D.C., two western service centers, at Portland and Denver, and state offices in Alaska and all of the eleven western mainland states except Washington.

Questions, with both political and economic overtones, frequently confront the Bureau of Land Management and the Forest Service. An example is the determination of the number of cattle or sheep permitted to graze on the public domain. When drought or other conditions reduce the supply of forage, reductions in the number of animals become necessary. Almost always, however, such cuts mean severe economic injury, not only to individual stockmen who have investments in ani mals, equipment, and land of their own, but also to the economies of communities whose principal industry may be cattle and sheep raising.

Saving the Soil

The beginnings of the Soil Conservation Service are associated in the public mind with the drought of 1933 and the "Great Depression." But steps had been taken before that time to bring federal authority and federal tax money into soil restoration.

In 1929, an amendment to the Agricultural Appropriations Act provided $160,000 for soil erosion investigations. Additional money was voted the next two years, and a large amount of information was accumulated. Out of this data came an estimate that is hard to believe: H. H. Bennett, a soil scientist with the Department of Agriculture, stated that every year enough soil was being washed out of our fields and pastures to load a train of freight cars that would encircle the earth eighteen times. The National Industrial Recovery Act provided for actual soil restoration work, in which the Forest Service and the Civilian Conservation Corps also participated.

We are told that passage of the Soil Conservation Act came after the decade's second great dust storm, in 1935, swept a cloud of Kansas soil over Washington, D.C., and other eastern cities. That act consolidated soil restoration activities in the Soil Conservation Service.

After 1935, new soil preservation laws were passed in a steady stream, expanding from one to fifteen the number of programs under SCS jurisdiction. Congress adopted the policy that the actual soil treatment work on private lands should be carried out by the landowners. Soil Conservation Districts were formed. These organizations of landowners supervise the land treatment, with SCS giving technical advice. Cost-sharing is provided through another agency in the Department of Agriculture, the Agricultural Stabilization and Conservation Service.

In 1936, Congress recognized in legislation the need for upstream reservoirs. In 1954, the Watershed Protection and Flood Prevention Act was passed to combine soil and water conservation on the land with control of the runoff through the use of upstream structures. This is a large program. It involves cooperation with states and local governments and other federal agencies, as well as technical, cost-sharing, and credit assistance for various kinds of water conservation projects on watersheds up to 250,000 acres in size. It can be seen at work through a look at the American Fork–Dry Creek project in Utah, which won the "Watershed of the Year" award in 1966.

The American Fork–Dry Creek watershed covers 118,000 acres of productive valley soils, with its upper portion reaching into the rugged Wasatch Plateau. Since the days of settlement it has been troubled by periodic flooding. Waters from sudden downpours in the mountains, or from fast melting snow, plunged down the stream courses, bearing thousands of tons of sediment. The floods attacked bridges, roads, and sidewalks. Sediment blocked irrigation works, covered farm lands, and buried parks and playgrounds.

In 1958, a project was designed with the help of watershed engineers of the Soil Conservation Service. Four debris basins are provided to hold the surging waters temporarily and permit the sediment load to settle. An irrigation reservoir was constructed, for which the water users bear the costs. Its supply is needed to water crops in the late season when other sources are exhausted. The Forest Service made a major contribution by growing plant cover on 44,000 acres of eroded mountain lands that are primarily in public ownership. The project includes wildlife and recreation benefits. Six federal agencies and five state agencies are involved. Total cost of the project is about $4 million. The federal government's share was $1.7 million of the cost of engineering works and a fourth of the $2 million spent for land treatment.

In 1966, the Soil Conservation Service had 15,250 employees, 460 of them in Washington, D.C. Four regional technical services centers employed between 150 and 200 persons each. These were located at Upper Darby, Pennsylvania; Fort Worth, Texas; Lincoln, Nebraska; and Portland, Oregon. The number of employees per state ranged from less than 100 in Massachusetts to 1,400 in Texas.

Information provided by the SCS for the House Agricultural Appropriations Subcommittee in 1964 stated that 136 million acres, or 31 per cent of our cropland, has been adequately treated and that on 7 per cent there is no problem. The report said further:

This is a significant accomplishment, in light of our vast agricultural acreage. But what is perhaps more meaningful is that we no longer have to report large acreages of land destroyed annually by soil erosion, as was commonly done in the 1930's when there were areas in which this was, in fact, happening.

This is not to say that all such problems are solved, for soil erosion, to name just one form of land deterioration, is still a principal problem on an estimated 161 million acres of cropland. But even on the two-thirds of our cropland still needing treatment, scientific research and practical experience have brought into common use methods of land use and treatment that have made it possible for land users to greatly reduce the dramatic and devastating type of soil destruction that was once widespread in this country.

Nearly 2 million landowners and operators, some 75 per cent of the total, were participating in programs of almost 3,000 soil conservation districts.

In 1956, Congress had authorized a Great Plains conservation program. Concerning this, and work in the South and West, the SCS report had this to say:

To date, a total of 10,113 contracts covering 24.5 million acres have been developed to provide for permanent conservation treatment. About one-fourth of the 3 million acres of cropland in these contracts is being converted to grass. This amounts to 7 per cent of the low-grade cropland that needs conversion to permanent vegetation to prevent periodic recurrence of Dust Bowl conditions in these 10 Great Plains States.

Throughout the South, long characterized by a cotton and tobacco agriculture that depleted vast areas, today's predominant picture is one of grass and trees. In many areas, once severely eroded, it is difficult to find even the scars of erosion, covered as they now are by permanent vegetation.

In the range country of the West, where critical problems of erosion and sediment production were once blamed upon overgrazing, privately owned ranges have been upgraded an estimated 25 per cent in the past 30 years, largely as a result of the soil conservation program which helped achieve an improved forage resource as well as improved soil protection.

Concerning the watershed program, it was stated that 1,800 watershed project applications had been put forward, and 816 approved for planning assistance. This covers 130 million acres here and in Puerto Rico. However, a recently completed inventory of conservation needs showed that two-thirds of our watersheds, some 8,300, still need work.

Our cropland and forestland, it is clear, are in inestimably better condition than when the federal government undertook the conservation programs. Difficulties of more recent origin—earth-stripping, for example—remain to be overcome. So do some problems that began years ago, such as wetlands development and drainage, but are only now reaching a critical stage as population increases. Restoration of depleted resources is an extremely complex matter involving many levels of government, numerous influential interests in the community, and remedial methods tailored to fit particular depleting influences.

Wetlands depletion can be stopped by good conservation practices, public acquisition, and zoning. Zoning is up to state, county, and municipal governments, and is subject to the very heavy pressures of real estate developers. The preparation of master land-use plans, which are being encouraged in several programs of the federal government, should help a great deal by informing developers in sufficient time where they are expected to look for building sites.

In most cases, restoring wetlands is all but impossible. Where areas are in public ownership, something can be done, but where wetlands have been drained for development, they are usually gone.

Hope for the Appalachians

The bill enacted in 1963 to benefit Appalachia is economic development legislation, and it encompasses a great deal more than restoration of land and water resources. It will do much to open up the area, much less to repair yesterday's resource damage. Of the $1.1 billion authorized, almost 80 per cent—some $840 million—will go to road construction. About $70 million more was allocated for hospitals, and $16 million for vocational schools. But only $36 million was allocated to reclaim stripped lands.

Six million dollars was included for sewage treatment plants, an insignificant amount for the Herculean clean-up job ahead. Added funds can be provided with matching grants from the 1965 Housing Act and the Economic Development Act, and the 1965 Water Pollution Control Act. But those parts of Appalachia most in need of funds will be least able to match. Sewage treatment and pollution abatement must reach into the sadly neglected mine communities and hollows if the badly polluted waters of Appalachia are to be restored.

The economy of Appalachia is inextricably bound up with the development of its water resources, which, in turn, are bound up with the restoration of the land and its cover. Technology has bulldozed away mountain tops to strip out coal; it can be used to restore the lands and to create water and recreation resources.

With advances in long-line electric power transmission, the day of power plants built at the coal mine has come. Such plants are being built in the West, at points far distant from the markets for electricity. Mine-head plants in the Appalachian Mountains would not be in competition with existing installations. The Edison Electric Institute has estimated that $175 billion in new investment will be needed in two decades to keep abreast of power demands.

Mine-head thermal plants use large volumes of water for steam and cooling. Deep lakes with great capacity for dissipating heat will be required. The valleys of Appalachia offer opportunity to build such lakes, and these also could supply the missing ingredient needed to build a water-based recreation area of great magnificence.

Congress has authorized a study of strip-mining and its consequences, and it is important that such an investigation proceed. Without doubt, such federal interest will spur the interstate pact proposed for the Appalachia coal states and more effective laws in other states. Failure of the states to enact effective strip-mining reclamation laws will be highlighted by a Congressional look, which can also determine whether uniform national standards and federal law are required.

The Tennessee Valley Authority is the largest purchaser of the coal of the Appalachians and bears a share of blame for their depletion. In 1964, it entered into a 15-year contract with Kentucky Oak Coal Company for 50,000 tons of strip-mine coal a week to feed its huge thermal plants. Owners of surface lands stripped are paid a royalty of 50 cents per linear foot.

When TVA entered into its contract with Kentucky Oak Coal, the state of Kentucky had on its books a largely unenforced and toothless strip-mine reclamation law. This law won praise from TVA Chairman Aubrey Wagner, who also held that strip-mining "had done wonders" for the Kentucky mountain area, which, he said, was "just growing trees that were not being harvested" before the strippers came.

TVA director Frank Smith had asserted that the agency "does not propose to buy coal in competition with private power companies except under the same land regulations." TVA had, however, taken some hesitating steps in the right direction and announced that it would require regrading and reclamation provisions in all future contracts.

In January, 1966, Kentucky's Governor Edward T. Breathitt won a significant victory. In the face of mine-operator resistance, the Kentucky legislature enacted the first strip-mine law in the nation requiring effective restoration of the lands. Operators must regrade "spoil banks" to original earth contours in the rolling country of southwestern Kentucky, and terrace and remove scars in mountain stripping in the eastern part of the state.

The new Kentucky law will end the worst abuses of stripping, although it will not restore huge areas already stripped out. And, despite complaints, it is not expected to end coal mining in Kentucky, where the big operators could turn to profitable underground and tunnel mining.

Another hope, also, is that the new law will open the way to an interstate compact establishing similar standards in Ohio, Pennsylvania, Illinois, Virginia, West Virginia, Tennessee, and Alabama. As Kentucky enacted its new "tough" law, Illinois, Ohio, and Pennsylvania were the only other states with legislation of any kind. The Illinois law was weak and largely unenforced; Ohio's law, passed in 1965, is a seriously watered-down version of a proposed law opposed by the coal companies.

Conservation for the Future

An industry view of the need for forest conservation was presented at the December, 1964, meeting of the Willamette Basin Project Committee, which was held in Portland, Oregon. The Oregon forest industry manufactures $1.2 billion of wood products a year, and employs 74,200 persons. Obviously, the industry has a huge stake in watershed and forest management.

C. W. Richen, manager of Northwest Timber Operations for Crown-Zellerbach Corporation, said: "With the availability of an excellent variety of logging equipment for every purpose today, and proposed new logging methods, the forest manager can choose a practical cutting method which can avoid or at least minimize erosion of soil in the logging operation."

He noted that there is a "compatibility in the relationship between growing and harvesting of trees and the production of water and other multiple uses such as forest, wildlife and recreation." And he said that landowners and the forest industry will "invest the necessary labor in the right job in the right place at the right time, provided they are compensated for work which is required in addition to the timber harvest."

What is suggested here is the same point that has been made in relation to abatement of pollution by industry—part of the additional cost of conserving the resource should be borne by the public. It might be that the nation could work out an arrangement with its private forest owners to provide recreation space in return for compliance with minimum standards of land management. Such an arrangement could prove profitable for both.

Land conservation of the scope necessary to protect water resources far into the future could mean a permanent assignment for the Job Corps. Foresters estimate that 275 million acres of timberland need improvement, and 50 million more need replanting to guard against erosion and flooding.

Some eighty Conservation Job Corps camps have been established as one sector of the "war on poverty." Even should that war be won, however, the war against erosion may not be. The pattern of operation of the Conservation Job Corps camps has been established. The money comes from appropriations made to the Office of Economic Opportunity, and the OEO assigns the men to the camps. The camps are directed by the conservation agencies such as the Bureau of Land Management, the Bureau of Reclamation, and the Forest Service. Youths enrolled in the camps spend half their day on conservation work, and half in the classroom. At the same time they get a general basic education, they are taught the fundamentals of surveying, forest-management techniques, pest and weed control, fire control, and equipment operation.

The nation's young people are hungry for involvement in worthy causes; the great conservation job that still faces us could be a real challenge to them. The camp program aids in development of mature citizens as well as protection of natural resources. It could be expanded to include college graduates, because specialized knowledge and technical skills will be more and more needed in conservation and water resource management, just as in other fields of endeavor.

It is inevitable that comparison will be made between the Job Corps and the Civilian Conservation Corps of the Depression years. When first proposed by Franklin D. Roosevelt, the CCC was derided as "just another leaf-raking outfit." But the nation still benefits from the work of the 300,000 young men who annually joined the CCC. They built hundreds of small parks and thousands of roadside recreation areas that still dot the countryside. They built thousands of miles of trails, and thousands of bridges, fire towers, forest roads, and small reservoirs. Few young people today have an opportunity to grow up close to the land. Millions would benefit from a year or two of combined learning and beneficial physical work in the out-of-doors.

When he was a Senator from Minnesota, Hubert H. Humphrey advocated a Youth Conservation Corps of 150,000 members. His bill to establish the corps was twice passed by the Senate but failed in the House. The idea was then incorporated into the Economic Opportunity Act, along with the Urban Job Corps program. The armed services will someday require fewer men than they have since World War II. When that day comes, an expanded Conservation Job Corps could serve both our youth and the nation well.

CHAPTER XIII

Miracle at Santee

ON THE WEEKEND of July 4, 1965, 5,000 Californians on holiday enjoyed boating, fishing, picnicking, and even swimming in what had been an unsightly gully only five years before. Clean water made the difference. But the water that had transformed this piece of wasteland into the mile-long Sycamore Canyon Recreation Area was special.

Santee, an unincorporated suburb situated in an arid valley outside San Diego, had "passed a miracle" by reclaiming its used water. The result was the recreation area, complete with five small new lakes. Water for the lakes had been distilled from sewage by the alchemy of modern treatment and added filtration provided by nature.

On June 3, 1965, nine-year-old Jimmy Lowery had run through a gate and plunged into a new swimming pool that is part of the recreation project. While Jimmy couldn't have cared less, he was making history. A sign by the side of the pool proclaimed: "This swimming facility has opened a new field of recreational opportunity for the American public. It is supplied with reclaimed water." During the summer of 1965, 3,300 persons swam in the lakes, while 50,000 enjoyed fishing and boating. Nobody seemed even slightly concerned about the source of the water, yet every drop had passed through the local sewage treatment plant.

What does Santee's miracle prove? Two things. First, it demonstrates that, under favorable conditions, waste water from our bathrooms can be purified until it as as good as new. Water men are excited about Santee. Los Angeles has expressed great interest in the project. In other places, experiments are being conducted looking to the production of new ground water by injecting sewage effluent into the earth. Borings have been carried out at Pennsylvania State University and in Nassau County on New York's Long Island. But at present there are narrow limits within which such complete purification can be made to take place. For success like that at Santee, a complex set of conditions must be just right. Second, the Santee experience points to one of the ways America is going to overcome its shortage of clean water—by cleaning up and using more of it over and over again.

Chemist Donald E. Carr, author of *Death of the Sweet Waters*, has called the United States the "biggest water hog in the world." Large commercial towns in England use about 50 gallons per person per day, he says, while we use nearly 200.

Senator Edmund Muskie of Maine heads a subcommittee on pollution which, in 1965, held a series of public hearings. When testimony revealed that the Metropolitan Water Board of Southern California brought 1.1 billion gallons of water daily from the Colorado River, and then—after a single use—permitted almost all of it to drain into the Pacific, and to pollute the immediate shoreline, he exclaimed, "They are going to have to find a way to re-use this wasted water!"

No longer can cities like New York, faced with drought, blithely permit hundreds of millions of gallons to go down the drain and out to sea after one use. Neither can hundreds of other cities and thousands of industrial plants.

Re-use of water is intimately tied up with two subjects that this book has already examined—water quality and pollution. For use, it is necessary that water be of adequate quality. Polluting it degrades the quality. If the pollution can be taken out—and thus the quality restored—it can be used again. But it is even better if contamination can be kept out in the first place. This chapter takes a look at two subjects—keeping waste from getting into our waters and taking pollution out.

The Santee story began six years before the day Jimmy Lowery dived into a new swimming pool. It started when a suburbs developer approached Roy L. Stoyer, manager of Santee County Water District.

The real estate man needed water for a new golf course. Stoyer agreed to supply him treated sewage effluent if he would let the town use an ugly gully that ran beside the housing development. The developer agreed, and today is furnished water for his golf course that would otherwise have cost from $40,000 to $50,000 a year.

Santee takes its water from the Colorado, some 200 miles distant. But the area has no nearby river, lake, or ocean in which to dump its waste water. At first the waste was allowed to seep into the ground. But in 1959, the state of California enforced a regulation against the practice. Santee was faced with the choice of hooking into the San Diego sewer system at a cost of $160 daily, or of finding an acceptable alternative.

Stoyer pushed hard for a $700,000 bond issue and won voter approval for a plan to solve the waste problem by creating pure-water recreation lakes. He then consulted water experts, who helped design the project. Sewage effluent is fed into a quarter-mile-long pond, where it stays for a three-week period of aeration and oxidation. Then the water is pumped uphill to the formerly dry 30-acre gully and permitted to trickle downhill toward town through a layer of sand 12 feet deep.

"Somehow," Stoyer explained to a reporter, "it worked. What came out at the bottom was clean enough to make a lake."

The lake was stocked with bass, bluegill, sunfish, and catfish, all of which thrived. Boating and fishing were permitted in late 1961, with the stipulation that fish caught would not be eaten. Then the other lakes were created.

The water was tested and found to be germ-free after chlorination. Fearing infection from filterable virus, water engineers called for further tests. Dr. Beatrice England, San Diego Health Department virologist, injected Sabin polio vaccine into the water as it entered the old riverbed. Examination of that which emerged some 400 feet downhill showed that it was virus-free. From then on, swimming was permitted and fishermen were free to take their catches home to eat.

In August, 1965, Santee's kids temporarily lost their right to swim when an accumulation of iron and manganese stimulated bacteria growth and threatened to end the local miracle. But all was under control again by October.

Dilution by Flowing Streams

Processing wastes, using water over again, and treating water, have been going on in the United States for years. But most of the water we re-use has been diluted by flowing streams. These streams are generally polluted beyond their ability to purify wastes themselves. Nevertheless, sewage effluent taken directly from treatment plants contains from ten to twenty times the impurities found in such running streams or in lakes. The Ohio is the most used and re-used river in the nation. Each use further contaminates the stream, but it is still much purer than highly treated sewage effluent.

Here it must be re-emphasized that one of the major uses of water is for removal of waste. This is true both in the home and in industry. Drinking, cooling, and lawn watering account for far less water use than home cleaning, laundering, dish-washing, bathing, and disposal of human excreta. Industry consumes little water, but must use large quantities for cleaning and cooling.

Water itself does not "wear out" and, in theory, could be used any number of times. Under present conditions, however, continued re-use builds up harmful properties. The principal limiting factor is the inability of treatment facilities to remove all pollutants. Most treatment methods take out 70 to 90 per cent of suspended solids, but little nitrogen or phosphorus. Complex chemicals, such as gasoline, defy treatment by presently known economical methods.

Chicago uses as much Lake Michigan water for pollution abatement— to send its treated effluent down the Illinois River—as it does for consumption. Water for pollution abatement is a major need of the nation. Nothing purifies wastes better than a river, provided that there is sufficient oxygen in it to accomplish the task. It is true that a high degree of treatment reduces the dilution requirement for dissolved oxygen in the water, but the higher the degree of treatment, the greater the need for clean water to dilute algae, which produce the nitrogen concentrations.

Treatment of Wastes

In the chapter on water quality, it was noted that nature does three things to purify water—aerates it, settles out solids, and decomposes organic wastes through the action of oxygen-using bacteria. In sewage treatment the objective is the same, but processes must be tailored to fit the quantity and "balance" of pollutants in the water, which are different from nature's.

Depending on the degree of purification obtained, sewage treatment is classified as primary, secondary, and tertiary.

A well-designed primary plant removes up to 40 per cent of decomposable organic matter. In this process, sewage first passes through a screen that removes large objects such as rags and sticks. Next it flows into a grit chamber where sand and silt settle out. The effluent then goes into a large settling tank where suspended solids sink to the bottom or rise to the top. The effluent between top and bottom is then drained off, chlorinated to kill bacteria, and permitted to enter the stream.

Secondary treatment expands removal of organic wastes by addition of a process of bacterial action. In one method, sewage is slowly sprayed on a bed of coarse stones about six feet deep. Biological growths developing on the stones catch the sewage and oxidize it, after which it is passed into large tanks where it is "digested" by microbes. The effluent is then chlorinated and discharged into the stream. A more modern secondary plant may remove 85 per cent of biologically decomposable matter.

Tertiary treatment of effluent is now being considered as a means of further reducing contamination and as a needed step in reclaiming water. This involves processes such as trickling the output of secondary treatment plants through crushed coal or some other form of activated carbon, and means of disposing of salt compounds through chemical precipitation, or even the extreme of distillation or membrane treatment. So far, there is little tertiary treatment, although plans are developing for a tertiary process for Washington, D. C.'s modern Blue Plains plant.

For waters that are in heavy use, primary sewage treatment—or partial treatment—is entirely inadequate. Before 1966, it was feared that Lake Tahoe, once considered one of the world's three purest lakes, could become a rival of Lake Erie as one of the nation's filthiest. Lying high in the mountains astride the Nevada-California border, Tahoe was a drowsy summer resort for a few thousand residents. Between 1956 and 1964, it exploded into a gaudy tourist mecca attracting 6 million visitors a year. Despite several expansions, the sewage treatment plant at Bijou, California, remained seriously overtaxed.

In the hope that it would filter into the lakes as clean water, effluent from the treatment plant was sprayed on forests. Stands of trees died; ponds of effluent gathered and polluted nearby streams that feed the lake. The lovely blue waters of Tahoe were becoming infected with an ugly growth of algae, which fed on the nutrients carried by the waste water.

Finally, a solution was agreed upon. It included construction of a mammoth treatment plant that would filter the water to drinking standards, plus the building of three pipe lines to carry the water out of the Tahoe Basin to be used to irrigate lands in Nevada and fill a recreation lake in California.

Philadelphia gets its water from the polluted Delaware and Schuykill rivers. In 1963, about half of the city's supply came through its ultramodern Torresdale plant. Although not typical, the Torresdale operation illustrates the degree of treatment increasingly needed to ensure pure water.

The Delaware carries human sewage, dead vegetation, chemical and industrial wastes, and other impurities. Solid wastes are screened out at intake pipes, which lead into the water purification plant. As the screened water enters, it flows into a mixing chamber, where it is given a preliminary chlorine treatment. The water is then piped into a huge sedimentation tank, where remaining larger solid particles sink to the bottom.

Next, the water is pumped into a chemical building. There it is treated with chlorine to further destroy bacteria and organic matter, with lime and alum to form "snowflakes" and lessen pipe corrosion, and with carbon to destroy disagreeable odors and tastes. At this stage the water is mixed, first rapidly, then slowly, before it is permitted to settle for two and a half hours while the alum-lime snowflakes carry remaining impurities to the bottom.

Finally, the water is filtered through ninety-four sand beds, and treated again with chlorine, fluorine, and phosphates. The phosphates are added to inhibit pipe corrosion. The water is then ready to be piped to users throughout the city.

At Lebanon, Ohio, a pilot plant of the U.S. Public Health Service takes a portion of waste water produced by the community of 7,000 and recycles it into pure drinking water. The sewage effluent normally runs into nearby Turtle Creek, which has long had its carrying capacity overtaxed by partially treated sewage wastes.

A portion of this treated effluent is fed into white, powdery diatomacious earth to remove remaining suspended solids. Following this, the waste water trickles through cylindrical tanks containing activated carbon—highly porous charcoal. The water at this stage is essentially pure except for a high mineral content. Treatment by electrodialysis removes these impurities by forcing them through membranes.

The process is still expensive, although less than desalination. Public Health Service researchers estimate that if a 10-million-gallon daily plant were built, pure water could be produced at about 40 cents per 1,000 gallons. This is an economical cost for some water-short communities, and may be an alternative to excessive ground-water pumping for municipal purposes.

The water produced by the Lebanon pilot plant is fed back into Turtle Creek for pollution abatement purposes. A larger plant is planned to produce from 1 to 5 million gallons of pure water daily.

When America was a less industrial and less crowded land, the city sewer offered a relatively inexpensive way of carrying off offensive and dangerous wastes and removing them from sight, smell, and conscience. During the nineteenth century, most streams were still able to take care of waste disposal without excessive pollution of their waters. But streams and lakes have become overloaded with waste until today every bit of effluent or untreated sewage dumped into most water courses aggravates pollution and sends poor quality water downstream.

At the turn of the century, only 950 cities had sewers; they served a population of 24.5 million persons. Sixty of these cities provided some treatment for their sewage. The municipal wastes reaching our streams had a polluting impact of raw sewage from a population of 24 million. By 1963, 11,400 communities had sewer systems; they served a population of 118 million. Of these, 9,300 communities had primary or secondary plants, serving 102 million people. But, despite the progress in building treatment plants, the municipal pollution load on our waters increased almost 5 times between 1900 and 1964. This was due to familiar factors—population growth, increased use of water in homes, the huge growth of industrial wastes, and limited treatment of sewage. In the 1960's, some 2,000 communities with a population of more than

16 million still send untreated sewage through their sewer pipes directly into streams and lakes. Over 50 million Americans still depend on septic tanks and cesspools, which overflow and poison earth and water.

The treatment plants of an average community of 100,000 daily discharge into nearby waters 17 tons of organic suspended solids, 8 tons of inorganic solids, and 60 cubic feet of grit. Chicago has a very efficient sewage disposal system. Yet waste discharged at the output pipes of its treatment plants is equal to the untreated sewage of more than a million persons, and solid wastes sent down the Illinois River each day amount to 3,400 tons.

Many Americans don't know how a sewer operates, although, for pleasant living, few pieces of home equipment are as important. To get to the sewer, the wastes from an individual home or factory are carried away in a small pipe, which joins other pipes from other homes and plants. As these are combined, the pipes increase in size until they become or join a main trunk line. The sewage flows downhill by gravity because of the slope of the pipes. Sewage from the trunk is fed into the treatment plant.

Most of the nation's sewer systems were designed and installed years ago, before water courses were so badly polluted. To save money, storm and sanitary drains were combined, causing the runoff from rains to enter the sanitary sewers. When the total of storm runoff and municipal waste water became too great, the treatment plant was by-passed and the combined waters ran untreated into the receiving stream. This occurred because a weir or low dam was used to divert the flow of wastes from the trunk sewer into an interceptor sewer that led to the treatment plant. When the rains came, part of the flow ran over the dam and emptied into the river through an overflow drain.

Treatment plants were usually designed to handle twice the normal dry weather flow. But this was in the day when unpaved walks and roads absorbed water. Runoff from paved surfaces has greatly increased flow into sewers during storms. With the added municipal waste that has entered many sewers, even light rains may overflow. A single rain of 0.08 inches at Buffalo was recorded as having brought a four-hour overflow into Lake Erie, depositing floating solids equal to a normal accumulation of one and a half days. Following storms, beaches in many cities must be shut down until the flood of pollution abates.

In 1963, the Senate Committee on Public Works reported on the runoff overload of sewer lines and the result of many tons of raw sewage being dumped into water courses to be conveyed to the downstream user. "This problem confronts more than 1,900 communities with a total population of nearly 40 million," it was said.

The report added that, by 1970, municipal wastes of 85 million persons and the equivalent of 210 million more from industrial organic wastes would be dumped into our increasingly dreary waters. It noted that this "does not include the pollution occurring from mineral and chemical origin."

In 1965, the Public Health Service estimated that the cost of separating storm and sanitary sewers into two systems would fall between $25 and $30 billion. In some cities, new storm sewers could be built and present systems blocked off for sanitary purposes alone. But aside from direct costs, there would be the massive indirect costs, such as relocation of telephone and telegraph conduits and gas and water mains.

Storage of sewer overflows has been proposed. Excess waters could go into storage basins for later treatment at municipal plants during nonstorm periods, or preferably, into special treatment plants. Because the raw sewage carried is highly diluted by storm waters, it might be possible to reclaim it for industrial or other use. One obstacle is that outlet pipes are usually located in crowded areas where land values are high and sewage storage undesirable. Storage has also been termed a very costly operation requiring construction of conduit systems to carry the overflow to available sites for storage or treatment. Yet, during the drought of the 1960's, the intake pipes of Philadelphia's Torresdale plant were extended upriver to avoid salt intrusion. Temporary piping was mounted on barges. The development of inexpensive plastic pipe may make storage feasible.

For the past four or five years, the state of Michigan has required, that, in a combined sanitary and storm sewer system, storage basins must be constructed to catch rainfall exceeding the minimum amount that the system can handle through the treatment plant. The rainwater discharges are later released, at a low rate, into the sewer that goes to the treatment plant. As much as 85 per cent of normal rains could be retained for later release. New York City, with a combined sewer system, has also begun the installation of holdover storage basins.

Industrial Practices and Processes

Expanded treatment and sewer improvements for our municipalities will add significantly to our capability to re-use water in the United States. But the greatest opportunity to obtain large supplies from this source is dependent on industrial practices and processes.

In 1965, the nation had more than 150,000 water-using manufacturing plants. Many of these are located along streams, although 125,000 use municipal sewer systems for disposal of waterborne wastes. The 25,000 plants that discharge their wastes directly into streams are generally huge installations—and they cause more pollution than all the others.

In numerous cases, industry provides waste treatment. The Toms River Chemical Company, at Toms River, New Jersey, manufactures dyestuffs, synthetic resins, and chemical specialities. The company's manufacturing processes produce 5 million gallons a day of waterborne wastes containing acids, organic by-products, and various organic substances in solution. The nearby Toms River is used to carry off the waste, which must be highly treated to comply with the standards established for the river by the New Jersey Department of Health.

The company states that there are five distinct steps in its purification process. The first is equalization, which means running the discharges into lagoons to "smooth out" variations in quality and quantity so that treatment processes will apply uniformly. The next step is neutralization —necessary because the plant wastes are high in acidity, which is overcome in an agitating tank into which lime is fed. The third step is clarification, which takes place in a two-step process that utilizes settling tanks and takes a total of three hours. Biological oxidation is the fourth operation. Its purpose is to reduce the organic content of the waste so that a minimum of the oxygen of the Toms River will be used. In this step, the effluent and compressed air are pumped through 94 jets lying on the bottom of lagoons, thus providing both aeration and circulation of biological material. The last step in the waste treatment process is chlorination. The plant operates 24 hours a day, 365 days a year.

Under pressure of water supply or cost factors, industry has shown what can be done in the way of re-use and conservation.

Bethlehem Steel's facility at Baltimore is a case in point. Here, there has been a big saving of water through intelligent re-use, which has also resulted in reduced cost. The steel plant needed water for cooling. It had been drawing ground water, but salt-water intrusion from Chesapeake Bay threatened corrosion of equipment. Instead of reaching farther for fresh water or buying it from the city at a higher price, Bethlehem Steel decided to try treated effluent from a sewage plant.

The firm now takes about 125 million gallons of effluent daily from the Back River sewage treatment plant of the city of Baltimore. The company installed added treatment works and also chlorinates the effluent. The important fourfold results are: adequate quality water for the steel plant at a price below city water or that resulting from development of an independent source; no additional demand on the city's already hard-pressed system; added revenue for the city of Baltimore; disposal of effluent that would otherwise pollute Chesapeake Bay.

Edmund B. Besselievre, a water engineer, has stated that in his view the most important advantage is that the city of Baltimore is not being called on to supply water needed for other purposes. "Due to this re-use and lessened demand," the water expert said, "the records of water usage in the city have shown a decrease despite the increase in population."

The Kaiser Steel plant at Fontana, California, re-uses its supplies so efficiently that water intake per ton of steel is 1,100 gallons, against a national industry average of 65,000 gallons.

A roller-bearing plant in Ohio slashed its water withdrawals two-thirds by installing a recycling system involving a cooling tower and pond. At Santa Rita, New Mexico, a copper plant uses septic-tank effluent as process water twice over. The second use is in the copper-precipitating process.

In the Kanawha Valley in West Virginia, I. E. DuPont de Nemours Company operates 12 chemical manufacturing plants and employs 25,000 persons. Some 40 outfalls are used to return waste to the river. Through agreement with other private firms and in cooperation with the West Virginia Water Resources Department, goals of waste reduction were set up that resulted in a decrease of 90 per cent in biochemical oxygen demand.

Water Management in West Germany

A very successful water quality program embracing an entire river basin protects the Ruhr region in West Germany. Containing 8 million people and 40 per cent of West Germany's industrial capacity, the area is watered by five small rivers—the Ruhr, Lippe, Wupper, Emsher, and Niers. Together, their average annual flow is less than one-third the lowest recorded flow of the Delaware, yet they satisfy the region's needs.

Responsibility for water management is held by *Gennossenschaften* (fellowships), which are cooperative groups established by law and to which membership is compulsory for cities and industries. In 1897, a voluntary fellowship—the Ruhrtalsperrenverein—was formed. It brought together the larger water users on a program to manage reservoirs and water supply. In 1913, the Ruhrverband—an organization of river polluters—was set up by law. Members include 250 towns and 2,200 industries. Instead of imposing water quality standards, the organization levies a fee for discharging of wastes. The fee goes up as the level of pollution goes up in a factory's or a city's discharge. This fee system has led to widespread clean-up of wastes before discharge and has provided funds for construction of many wastes-treatment works. The heavily used streams are suitable for swimming and boating and are used for drinking water with moderate treatment. In 1938, the Ruhrtalsperrenverein was given legal status, and it and the Ruhrverband were put under a single management.

Steel mills along the Ruhr have built internal recirculation systems that permit them to re-use water over and over again, taking from the river only enough to replenish unavoidable losses. It once required 130 cubic yards of Ruhr water to make a ton of steel; it now takes only 2.6 cubic yards.

Accomplishments of ORSANCO

The most extensive river-basin antipollution operation in the United States is the Ohio River Valley Water Sanitation Commission (ORSANCO). It was established in 1948 by interstate compact and, as required for such compacts, approved by Congress. The area covers some 154,000 square miles, and embraces parts of Illinois, Indiana, Kentucky, New York, Pennsylvania, Virginia, and West Virginia. Industries and communities are not members but are governed by the applicable laws of the states. The organization is financed by appropriations made to it by the states. ORSANCO has made impressive gains in abating pollution and has developed interesting and effective methods for monitoring water quality.

When the organization was formed in 1948, only 1 per cent of the region's population was served by sewage treatment plants; in 1965, the figure was 90 per cent. More than 90 per cent of the industrial plants on the Ohio and its tributaries maintain at least minimum quality standards.

A central robot in Cincinnati inquires once every hour about the condition of the water of the Ohio River. Its question goes out over long-distance-telephone lines to thirteen robot monitors submerged along the river system. These monitors constantly test the quality of the water flowing through their sensing units. The robot in Cincinnati records the answers on an automatic typewriter and on tape. The quality-monitoring program also includes reports from seventeen stations operated by water treatment plants and eleven operated under contract by the U.S. Geological Survey. The system enables the commission to alert affected cities or industries at once if pollution on the river becomes hazardous.

Although continuous monitoring is the most significant part of the surveillance program conducted by ORSANCO to supplement the efforts of the states, inspections are also made from the air and from boats.

ORSANCO has attacked and partially solved a staggering problem. By 1948, the Ohio had reached the point where it was a health hazard to millions of Americans and could not continue to serve the needs of industry. Since then, more than a billion dollars has been invested in sewage treatment plants and additional millions by industry for waste disposal. Still, there are many industries that do not comply with the standards. Further, it is charged that minimum quality standards are below what they should be. The mine acid problem has not been solved. Pleasure boats and commercial craft both dump sewage and litter into the stream.

Certainly, industrial spoilation like that along the Mahoning in the Ohio steel belt cannot be tolerated. In effect, the system was threatening to leave Youngstown stranded for lack of water as coolant for the big—and wasteful—mills. Use of Mahoning waters for steel-mill and thermal

ORSANCO MONITORS WATER QUALITY ON THE OHIO.

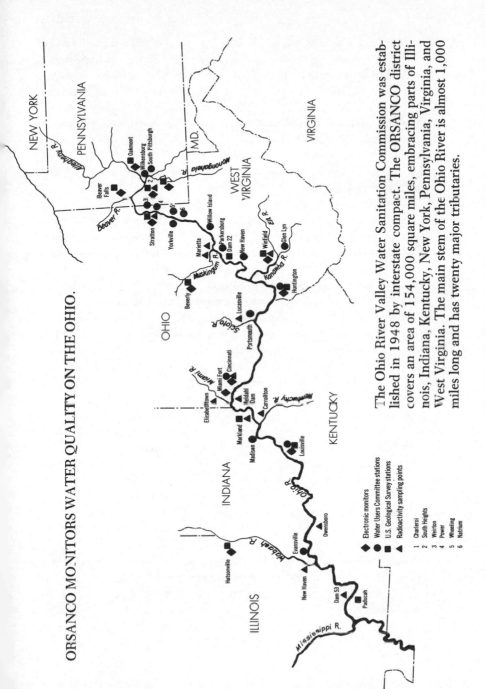

The Ohio River Valley Water Sanitation Commission was established in 1948 by interstate compact. The ORSANCO district covers an area of 154,000 square miles, embracing parts of Illinois, Indiana, Kentucky, New York, Pennsylvania, Virginia, and West Virginia. The main stem of the Ohio River is almost 1,000 miles long and has twenty major tributaries.

Reprinted with permission from *Power*, June, 1966. Copyright McGraw-Hill, Inc., 1966.

power-plant cooling had killed all the fish in the river and rendered
the water unfit for further cooling. The river temperature had registered
137° F. during a summer period of low flow at 175 cubic feet per
second. Even at 500 cubic feet per second, the temperature averaged
104° during summer months. The "hot Mahoning" was highly polluted
because the heat had driven out the dissolved oxygen, without which
organic wastes will not break down.

On the Illinois, heat pollution caused by thermal power plants had
produced a pollution equivalent double that from organic waste flushed
downriver from Chicago.

If heat pollution could not be controlled in 1965, heroic action indeed
will be required to control it in the years ahead. The Senate Select
Committee predicted that it could be expected to increase at a very
substantial rate for forty years from both industrial and power-plant
sources. "Industrial activity is projected to increase between five and ten
times the present rate, the heat pollution from this source can be expected to increase accordingly," the committee reported.

Heat on the Mahoning illustrates the point that if re-use is to be
expanded significantly, river basins—particularly those in areas of high
industrial concentration—must be treated on a "systems" basis. As with
the Ruhrverband, all cities and industries using the river must be parti-
cipants in the system. Cleanliness will result only from uniformity of
use regulations. In a market economy, voluntary compliance is an illu-
sion. It amounts to providing a competitive advantage to the most
wasteful use of water. We do not rely on voluntary compliance in place
of meat inspection; we cannot rely on it for pure water.

Within practical systems, improved treatment and recirculation could
make waste water into a tremendous new supply for the nation. C. H.
Scherer, in charge of water for Amarillo, Texas, has pointed out that a
gallon of raw sewage contains only one-twentieth of an ounce of contaminants. "Considering the small amount of waste, we have made very
small use of these very large amounts of water," he said.

Amarillo sells 4 million gallons daily of sewage effluent that is not
pure enough to drink to industrial users and another million gallons to
farmers. This sale brings in $100,000 annually to the city, enough to
pay 60 per cent of the cost of running its sewage treatment program.
The waste water sold to farmers is used to irrigate 2,000 acres of grain
sorghum crops. Health hazards prevent its use in growing root vege-

tables such as potatoes and carrots. But grain farmers near large cities may yet find added water for irrigation in treated effluent. Ironically, carefully controlled use of effluent for such purposes can help reduce stream pollution because the effluent would no longer be dumped into the watercourse.

In many instances, the progress that has been made in the re-use of water is impressive. The need is for continued improvement of sewage treatment and industrial water-use methods and for adoption of the best methods for use in all our water courses.

CHAPTER XIV

The Race Is On in Research

APPEARING BEFORE the Senate Air and Water Pollution Subcommittee in 1963, Senator Gaylord Nelson (then governor of Wisconsin), offered in evidence pictures of "mountains of foam." The mountains were detergent suds floating on polluted waters. Those suds are now gone; the story of their elimination is an informative illustration of the application of research to water problems.

Detergents appeared on the market shortly after World War II. They were cheaper than soaps and washed clothes and dishes cleaner and faster. They soon captured 75 per cent of the household market.

Soaps break down readily in water and decompose rapidly in sewage treatment plants and by natural bacterial action. As originally produced for market, detergents were highly stable and resistant to breakdown. Even the most modern treatment plants rarely decomposed more than 50 per cent of surface-active ingredients in detergent water. Just as home washers are damaged by excess suds, so foam damaged and cut the efficiency of treatment plants. Milwaukee reported that detergent foam raised disposal-plant maintenance costs between $50,000 and $100,000 a year.

It was not long before suds appeared as foam on rivers and lakes. Some running streams resembled the inside of churning washing machines. Rock Creek, flowing through the lovely park of the same name in the District of Columbia, often carried clouds of foam, which bedecked rocks and banks at low flow.

Detergent foam floated downstream to other communities, appearing in water supplies and sometimes coming out of water taps. Complaints of suds backing up in apartment-house plumbing became common. Water supply systems in some communities developed detergent tastes and odors. Septic-tank problems multiplied, and detergents soon polluted ground waters. Of 600 wells studied in the Long Island area, 35 per cent contained detergent along with other sewage residues. In Wisconsin, 32 per cent of some 2,100 shallow wells contained measurable detergent pollution.

Pressures mounted to "do something." In Germany, where a similar problem had appeared earlier, the Bundestag enacted a law requiring the use of a "soft" type of detergent. Similar legislation was proposed in at least thirteen states, and in the U.S. Congress in 1963. One proposal would have made the sale of "hard" detergents illegal after June 30, 1965.

The type of detergent depends on its basic sudsing ingredient. Most widely used in hard detergents was a chemical compound known to the trade as ABS (alkyl benzene sulfonate), which resisted biological breakdown or biodegradation. A new "soft" detergent called LAS (linear alkylate sulfonate) was developed in a cooperative study by seventeen laboratories. LAS breaks down relatively readily in sewage treatment plants and in normal bacterial levels in water. Studies also revealed that the new "soft" detergent cleans better.

Despite mounting public clamor, U.S. detergent makers took the position that they couldn't meet the June 30, 1965, deadline and that, in any case, there was no need for legislation. But three weeks after the deadline was included in a bill introduced in the Senate, the industry announced that it would voluntarily switch all production to the soft LAS detergent by December 31, 1965.

Having made up its mind, the industry raced to produce the soft and better detergent. Some $100 million was spent to modernize plants. By mid-1965, the change-over was complete. In 1962, the industry produced and sold 4 billion pounds of hard detergents, containing about

560 million pounds of ABS. Industry spokesmen announced that not a pound of the ABS type would be made after June 30, 1965, the cutoff date in the Senate bill.

The industry deserves high praise for its voluntary conversion to soft detergent production. Assistant Surgeon General Gordon E. McCallum noted that the detergent industry's action was the "first time that a product change-over of this magnitude has been made—solely to resolve a water pollution problem."

After the first year's use of soft detergents, it was plain that foam from detergents had been reduced. However, there is some evidence that soft detergents deposit substances harmful to fish life.

Public health experts agree that even hard detergents in the nation's inland waters presented no major hazard to human health. Detergents are odorless, tasteless, and nontoxic at the concentration at which foaming takes place. The Public Health Service has reported that even prolonged consumption of drinking water containing higher than acceptable levels of ABS "led to no significant evidence of intolerance."

Nevertheless, the PHS warned in 1962 that foam billowing from sewage-treatment aeration tanks contained a bacterial count twenty times greater than the liquid sewage from which it came. The PHS reported that foam blown from sewage tanks represented a "significant health hazard." Among other cities, El Segundo, California, was forced to install an $83,000 spraying system to combat contaminated sewage-bred foam blown on its sand dunes.

Hard-detergent pollution has not been responsible for fish kills but has been toxic to other forms of marine life. PHS found that tests with eight detergents showed all of them "toxic to eggs and larvae of clams and oysters at concentrations of 0.6 parts per million or less." Although phosphates in detergents promote algae growth, these chemicals also enter from other sources, and there is no evidence that the elimination of hard detergents would alter the growth of unsightly and harmful algae.

Geological Survey researcher Cooper H. Wyman has noted in the *Bulletin of the Atomic Scientists* that "initial studies suggest that detergent water pollution . . . would be reduced, but not eliminated, if soft detergents are substituted for hard detergents, and if secondary [sewage treatment] facilities be available." At least 40 per cent of the nation's

200 million people are served by sewage systems without secondary treatment.

Mr. Wyman also pointed out that tests in Long Island homes with septic tanks showed that the use of soft detergents over several months failed to cut detergent pollution in underground waters. Even the optimistic detergent-manufacturing industry has issued a word of caution. John P. Moser, president of the Soap and Detergent Association, pointed out that "there will not be an immediate end . . . to the appearance of foam in waste discharges," although "in time, episodes of foaming traceable to detergents will be rare, except where treatment is inadequate."

There now is an effort being made to develop a "supersoft" detergent to clean better and with suds that break up and disappear in a day or less when flushed into water containing normal bacterial count.

It must be stressed that detergents have accounted for less than 10 per cent of the pollution in water. When a sea of suds appeared, it was usually because of other, hidden, and far more dangerous deterioration in water quality. There is even some danger that the reduction of foaming in our waterways will reduce public concern.

Important as it is, detergent pollution does not loom very large in the whole field of water problems. The questions to which water research must be applied are appallingly numerous and complex. Research must show how to control many types of pollutants at lower cost, how to use water more efficiently in a variety of industrial processes, how to restore ground waters, and how to expand water supplies in arid regions. Much more must be learned about water usage by specific crops and the action of soil moisture.

Water resource planning of the future will require use of modern methods of systems analysis, as all river basins put to use increasingly complex multipurpose projects and larger, more involved systems. The ecological impact of expanded water development on watersheds must be understood. Despite the thousands of dams that have been built, much remains to be learned about efficient construction of water-storage and diversion structures.

The need to know more about the nature and action of water was officially recognized as early as 1830, when Congress authorized research on steamboat navigation on the Mississippi River. In 1836, members were expressing interest in weather modification. During the 1880's, the Geological Survey began water resource investigation. Before the turn of the century, the Department of Agriculture was conducting irrigation research.

An 1893 Forest Service bulletin, *Forest Influences,* called for a program of research as a basis for improving streamflow and controlling erosion on forest lands. To these ends, the Wagon Wheel Gap Watershed Experiment was begun in Colorado in 1910 and the Great Basin Experimental Range was established in Utah in 1912.

Since then, water research has been a steadily enlarging activity. By the 1960's, five federal departments—including twenty-two bureaus or equivalent units—and three independent federal agencies were operating water research programs. The states were operating similar programs equal to about half the federal effort. Private industry, too, has long conducted major water research programs, which are related principally to the use of water in manufacturing processes and the efficiency of equipment manufactured for sale.

Despite these efforts, well-informed citizens have recognized that we have been expanding our water knowledge too slowly. The Senate Select Committee recommended that the federal government undertake a "coordinated scientific research program" to include basic research, applied research for increasing water supplies, and applied research for conservation.

In 1964, Congress enacted a bill to create the Office of Water Resources Research in the Department of the Interior.

The act provided $11 million annually for federally supported water research. Under one part of the law, each state can receive financial support for the operation of water-research study centers at land-grant universities and colleges. Under another provision, $5 million each year was authorized to be matched by states developing research projects approved by the Secretary of the Interior.

In 1966, Congress enacted a bill to enlarge the research program by authorizing $5 million—to be increased $1 million a year to $10 million —which can be spent yearly on grants, contracts, or other arrangements with educational institutions, private foundations, and individuals to conduct water research projects on aspects "not otherwise being studied."

The 1964 act directed the President to create a center to catalogue current and planned water research by all public and private agencies and to coordinate these responsibilities with those of federal agencies.

More than 3,900 projects have been catalogued. The act also makes available to the public without charge the use of all patents, and processes developed under federal research grants.

The Clean Waters Restoration Act of 1966 stepped up pollution research by authorizing funds for studies on several specific problems. Examples are handling and disposal of industrial wastes, waste discharges from boats, and household waste disposal systems.

The present level of federal financial support for water resources research is over $100 million a year, of which some $75 million is expended by the Department of the Interior, $16 million by the Department of Agriculture, $5 million by the Department of Defense, and $3 million by the Department of Health, Education, and Welfare.

The Federal Council on Science and Technology has appointed a committee to develop a balanced long-term plan for water resources research.

Previously, water research has been done mostly by hydrologists, geologists, soil scientists, microbiologists, and chemists. Therefore, most of the knowledge gained has concerned the scientific aspects of water. Although these aspects must not be neglected, expansion of research is needed in water economics, administration, and law.

The two best-known water research programs are discussed at length in the next two chapters. These programs are the search for cheaper methods to take the salt out of sea water (desalination) and the search for ways to modify the weather. But many other fascinating and significant questions are being probed by our water scientists.

In the fall of 1964, the U.S. Geological Survey reported a precious find that may have important implications for the Eastern Shore of Maryland. An underground water channel was discovered near Salisbury, Maryland. It was said to be a legacy from the Ice Age, when the Atlantic was a smaller ocean, and geologists expressed the opinion that the underground fresh-water channel could extend inland for 60 or 70 miles. *The Washington Post*, commented in an editorial that "from the long-range point of view, the discovery may be far more valuable than a similar finding of oil or gold," and expressed the opinion that there is far too little research and survey work being done on this subject. Maryland maintains a geological survey unit that is working with the federal agency in searching out underground supplies. Few states have such an agency.

Underground reservoirs collect water during wet periods and store it for use during dry seasons. Water so collected is not subject to the evaporation that steals so much of the moisture precipitated on the land.

Where man has overdrawn his ground-water account, new ways must be found to restore the underwater resources and fill up exhausted natural aquifers. Runoff of floods and heavy rains can be used to recharge ground waters through spreading. This process involves the development of a system of lateral channels and ditching.

The Water Quality Act of 1965, which established the Water Pollution Control Administration, authorized $20 million annually for four years to create demonstration projects to develop new methods of minimizing pollution dangers resulting from combined sanitary and storm sewer systems.

As discussed previously, most municipal sewer systems were built years ago and combine storm and sanitary drains. When large volumes rush in after storms, they overflow through "safety valves," where the storm water and raw sewage are mixed. These mixtures by-pass treatment plants and pour into lakes and streams through sewer outlets. The ideal solution of this problem is two systems: a sewer system to channel storm waters directly into streams, and a sanitary system that delivers sewage to treatment plants. The road block is cost; an estimated $30 to $40 billion would be required to separate all combined sewer systems in the United States.

Researchers have long concerned themselves with the elimination of "phreatophytes," the water-stealing vegetation that robs the West of much precious water. Phreatophytes are long-rooted plants that literally suck up ground and river waters. The word, taken from the Greek, means "well plant." These plants prefer stream banks, where their capillary roots fringe just above the water table. They occupy about 15 million acres of western land and stand out a lush green in contrast to the gray of desert vegetation. It is estimated that they use some 25 million acre-feet of water annually in the western states—enough to supply the needs of nearly 100 million persons.

Transpiration of water by plants—plant consumption—is greater than evaporation from bare land surfaces and reaches to much greater depths. Elimination of phreatophytes could do much to restore depleted ground waters. High plant consumption has been one reason that New

Mexico has had difficulty in delivering water to Elephant Butte Reservoir, as required by the Rio Grande Compact.

A few phreatophytes, such as alfalfa, have a major place in the nation's agricultural economy. Most—saltgrass, salt cedar, willows, mesquite, and cottonwoods—offer man no benefit and would be better replaced by useful or equally esthetic vegetation using less water.

One of the chief water thieves is the tamarisk, called "salt cedar" in the American West. This fast-growing, bushy plant covered only 10,000 acres half a century ago, but has spread rapidly to cover more than a million acres. When the Colorado River flow is low, as in 1966, the sandbars are exposed only a few days before they are covered with a carpet of thousands of salt-cedar plants and take on the appearance of newly planted lawns. Each acre of phreatophyte swallows up 4 acre-feet of water annually. It compounds flood hazards by growing so densely along waterways that rising waters are blocked and so dig new channels.

A 10-year experiment to rid 9,000 acres of salt cedar was begun along the Gila River near Phoenix, Arizona, in 1962. The $1.25 million experiment, carried out by the Geological Survey, aims to clear out this plant by cutting off roots 18 inches below the ground. Ground-water flow will be measured carefully at the start, during, and at the conclusion of the experiment. As the useless plants are removed, beneficial vegetation will be planted in their place. As part of the proposed Pacific Southwest water plan then pending in Congress, researchers had developed plans to save 100,000 acre-feet of water lost annually to phreatophytes on the lower Colorado between California and Arizona. The Bureau of Reclamation has estimated that the $4 million cost of clearing 40,000 acres of phreatophytes would be repaid many times over by added water supply.

As we have seen, 60 to 70 per cent of the nation's precipitation is used by plant life, or otherwise returned to the atmosphere through evaporation. Evaporation of snow, soil moistures, and water from the earth's surface accounts for perhaps half of this loss. Basic research to reduce such evaporation is going forward.

Snows falling on western forests are evaporated from tree branches at a far faster rate than from the ground. Experiments with scientific thinning of evergreens and the substitution of trees that lose their leaves during the winter have resulted in significantly less evaporation of snow moisture.

The largest potentially controllable evaporation loss is that from the surfaces of rivers, canals, irrigation ditches, lakes, and reservoirs. Such losses in the arid western states are estimated at 24 million acre-feet every year. Twenty-five billion gallons of water a year evaporate from New York City's reservoirs. Reduction of this loss could significantly assist the city in a battle against future drought.

Research has resulted in the development of two wax-like anti-evaporants, one named "hexadecanol." These are similar to substances used for three decades to slow evaporation in perfumes and other cosmetics. They are monomolecular—producing films 1 molecule thick—and have reduced evaporation significantly when spread over lakes and reservoirs. The substances act as shields, preventing water molecules from escaping into the atmosphere. Made of fatty alcohols, they are nontoxic, inexpensive, colorless, odorless, and nonrigid. The shield of monolayers tends to heal itself even when broken apart by waves or the passage of boats. Experiments at Saguaro Lake, near Phoenix, and Lake Cachuma, near Santa Barbara, California, resulted in a 22 per cent reduction in evaporation losses. Experiments at Utah Lake using an airplane equipped for crop dusting demonstrated the feasibility of spreading the chemical from the air.

So far, at least, the use of monomolecular antievaporants has not gone beyond the experimental stage. One major problem inhibits use: Winds tend to blow the material into piles on the shorelines. Experiments at Lake Hefner, near Oklahoma City, were largely unsuccessful because fifteen-mile-an-hour winds blew the antievaporant from the surface of the lake to the shores. New tests are aimed at overcoming this problem by using the winds themselves to spread the monolayer over the surface.

Despite problems in the use of these antievaporants, many experts are optimistic. Professor Abel Wolman of Johns Hopkins, water consultant to New York City, believes that "evaporation suppression" offers great promise. Victor K. LaMer, a Columbia University researcher, has asserted that "suppressing evaporation from large water storages by monolayers is the most economical of all methods of conserving water that are now available." He has noted that, in laboratory tests, evaporation has been reduced from 50 to 70 per cent at a cost of 10 to 12 cents per 1,000 gallons of water saved.

Consideration has been given to trying evaporation suppression on New York City reservoirs. The hope is for a saving of 5 million gallons of water annually, equal to 5 days' supply (and the amount saved through the 1965 conservation program, which included a ban on air conditioners and lawn watering).

The Bureau of Reclamation is looking forward to at least limited use of antievaporants in the West between 1965 and 1970. According to one spokesman, the goal is a 25 per cent reduction in the rate of evaporation by 1970. If antievaporation research should be that successful, present water resources of the region could last several years more than previously anticipated.

Technicians at the U.S. Water Conservation Laboratory at Tempe, Arizona, feel they have made a breakthrough that will contribute significantly to the future of the water-short West. They seek to capture water from desert rainstorms through "water harvesting."

Tests have shown that more than 90 per cent of a quarter-inch rain can be "harvested" from ground surfaces treated with silicones at a cost of $250 per acre. Most of this moisture is now lost through evaporation. The water-resistant silicone enables the water to be gravity-drained into reservoirs. Asphalt can also be used for treating ground surfaces, but it appears that its costs will be higher.

One drawback to this harvesting process is erosion resulting from runoff. "If we can only stabilize that silicone to resist erosion, the cost of harvesting water will be much lower than our earlier estimates," Lloyd Myers, director of the laboratory, has said.

Seepage of water in irrigation ditches and stock ponds causes a yearly loss of 20 million acre-feet of water in the seventeen western states. Many irrigation canals in these states are lined with concrete to halt loss through seepage. But concrete cracks with weather variation, requiring expensive repair or replacement. Researchers at Tempe have developed a modified asphalt that can be sprayed into the cracks at small cost.

Most of the foregoing examples touch on major areas of water research, which, if successful, could add substantial quantities to the nation's supply of usable water. They represent only a fraction of a complex and extensive national program. In 1965, the Office of Water

Resources Research listed 1,546 federally supported projects, classified in eight categories: nature of water, water cycle, water and land management, development and control, qualitative aspects, re-use and separation, economic and institutional aspects (including water rights and law), and engineering works.

For the water research effort, the nation is utilizing the same structure that is used for most federally supported research—a large number of projects operated by individuals or departments at universities and other institutions. The wide range of subject matter and geographic location of research supported by the Office of Water Resources Research can be shown by these examples: urbanization and its effect on water resources (Rutgers–The State University, New Jersey); conjunctive use of ground water and streamflow in the Humboldt River Basin (University of Nevada); economic evaluation of pricing water supply in Illinois (University of Illinois); effects of pulp-mill effluents on the growth and production of fish (Oregon State University); effect of low-flow hydrologic patterns on water quality management (University of North Carolina).

Some students of water research believe that the federal effort should not be so dispersed. Donald E. Carr, mentioned earlier as the author of *Death of the Sweet Waters,* has called for a concentration of effort in a new "Manhattan Project" for water. Whether such concentration is undertaken is likely to depend on how fast the program in effect produces results.

During the early 1960's, the nation's water research efforts have been expanded to more nearly meet the need. However, increasing pressure on water resources and the development of new chemical substances and compounds and new industrial processes call for a constant expansion of knowledge and technical capability in the water field.

To paraphrase H. G. Wells' remark about education, American civilization may well be a race between water research and disaster.

CHAPTER XV

From the Ocean Shore

RESIDENTS OF COALINGA, California, a town of 6,000 near Fresno, draw their water from faucets marked hot, cold, and good. Hot and cold comes from brackish wells, the only local supply.

"Good" water is cheaper than it was before the town built the nation's first municipal saline water-conversion plant in 1959, but it still costs about $1.43 per thousand gallons. Before the plant was constructed, water was brought in by tanker truck at a cost of $7 per thousand gallons.

Coalinga still uses local unconverted water for most purposes. Containing 2,000 parts per million of mineral salts, it is considerably less salty than sea water, which has about 35,000 parts per million. Coalinga's electrodialysis plant reduced the salt content of its "good" water to 290 parts per million. The capacity of the Coalinga plant is 28,000 gallons daily—about 5 gallons for each resident, or just about enough for drinking and cooking purposes. Coalinga waters its lawns, washes its cars, and does most of its other water-using chores with brackish supplies.

Of all the scientific solutions to America's water problems, desalting sea water is probably the one to which the public looks with the highest hopes. There are good reasons for optimism. Man has known how to distill fresh water from salty supplies for centuries. Anyone who has seen steam from a tea kettle condense into drops of water when blown against a cold windowpane is familiar with the basic process.

When Thomas Jefferson was Secretary of State, someone brought him a plan for distilling salt water over a wood fire, and he had instructions printed on the backs of all papers used aboard ship. Before radio communication was so highly developed, some U.S. airmen were equipped with kits that would distill about a pint of fresh water. Ocean liners are equipped with sea-water distillation plants because space is more valuable for passengers and cargo than for stocks of fresh water.

In February, 1964, Fidel Castro cut the water line running to our Guantanamo Naval Base on Cuba. An experimental desalting plant at Point Loma, California, was dismantled, transported to the island, and reassembled, rendering the base entirely independent of Cuban water. The cost of the new supply runs about $1 per thousand gallons.

In the once desolate nation of Kuwait, lawns are kept green with desalted water; the cost is more than offset by the oil riches of the Persian Gulf sheikdom.

Representatives from 29 nations drank converted sea water at an Office of Saline Water demonstration plant at Freeport, Texas, in the summer of 1965. The plant had been turning out a million gallons of water daily for four years. The cost runs about $1.25 per thousand gallons. The water is sold at $1.20 a thousand to users of less than 2,000 gallons, and 30 cents a thousand to users of more than 65,000 gallons monthly. Dow Chemical Company is the chief user of the Freeport plant's converted supplies.

Like any distilled water, that produced at Freeport is flat to the taste. Both Dow Chemical and home owners use the converted sea water to dilute brackish supplies from local wells. Drinking water is somewhat salty but potable and cheaper than the desalinated water by itself.

The diplomats visiting the Freeport plant expressed amazement both at the process and the results. They were guided from a point where they could see fish, eels, crab, and squid in the intake pipe to a tap from which they could draw warm, flat, fresh water for drinking. It was predicted that most of the nations represented on the Texas inspection trip would be converting sea water or brackish water for themselves within a decade. Desalination is here, and American firms advertise desalting plants for sale. There are over 550 desalting plants operating in many parts of the world, with a total capacity of nearly 126 million gallons daily. The Dutch island of Curacao has several, with a total capacity of 4.8 million gallons a day.

Following "extensive research, plus designing and building a scale-model desalting plant," Westinghouse Electric Corporation, in 1950, installed 18 submerged tube evaporators in Kuwait. By 1961, the plant had been augmented to include 24 units with the capacity to produce 4.7 million gallons of fresh water a day. At that time, William E. Rub-loff, manager of Westinghouse's heat transfer department, estimated worldwide capacity of sea-water conversion apparatus at 20 million gallons a day. Later, the Kuwait plant was expanded to a 7.2-million-gallon capacity.

For this book, the significant questions are: What quantities of water may we expect to obtain from desalination, and for which water resource regions? The answers will depend on delivered costs compared to those for water from other sources. Problems of plant operation—such as waste disposal—also will have to be considered. Obviously, for the factory, community, or country with other assets and no fresh water (Kuwait), or where considerations of state are paramount (Guantanamo), desalting solves the problem. But reliance on this source for major quantities of water is another matter.

The average national cost of desalted water without credit for power is about $1.08 per thousand gallons. Brackish well water desalted by electrodialysis costs between 90 cents and $1.00. This compares with the 27 cents per thousand paid by the average consumer for municipal supplies delivered from conventional fresh-water sources. Industry pays about 6 cents per thousand for its water; the farmer, to irrigate his land, 3.5 cents per thousand.

The average user of municipal supplies might pay more without material effect on his living standard, particularly if less wasteful practices were enforced. With adequate conservation measures, industry might be able to pay more without increasing prices significantly. But higher costs for irrigation water would ruin much of the nation's agriculture. Under present circumstances, desalted water is still too expensive where other supplies are available.

Dr. Maynard M. Huffschmidt, former director of the Harvard University Water Project, has stated that conversion plants built so far are uneconomic even for delivery to coastal towns. Dr. Huffschmidt has pointed out that while costs have been significantly reduced in the past decade, "small-scale plants are still costly in terms of water—say two to three times the cost of conventional means."

This water expert is of the view that until large plants are built "and the many uncertainties in cost were determined by experience, it's very rash to say that the price could be brought down to something even close to conventional means"—even at sea level.

"I don't see in the near future that anything yet demonstrated can make it feasible for a community to use this type of water supply in contrast to others available to them. Certainly this is true of New York in relation to the Hudson River or a combination of other sources," Dr. Huffschmidt said in the fall of 1965.

Inevitably, opinions as to costs of water produced by plants of different sizes, and by plants employing different processes of salt-separation, have varied widely.

To try to bring down costs—and assemble firm cost figures—a desalination program was launched by Congress in 1952. It passed the Saline Water Act, which established the Office of Saline Water (OSW) in the Department of the Interior. A sum of 2 million dollars was authorized for a five-year-period to start a program:

> to provide for the development of practicable low-cost means of producing from sea water, or from other saline waters, water of a quality suitable for agricultural, industrial, municipal, and other beneficial consumptive uses on a scale sufficient to determine the feasibility of the development of such production and distribution on a large-scale basis, for the purpose of conserving and increasing the water resources of the nation.

To make it possible to accomplish this ambitious program, the Congress has followed the original act with a series of enactments to extend and accelerate it. Through the fiscal year ending June 30, 1966, $81 million had been appropriated. The appropriation for the Office of Saline Water for the ensuing fiscal year was nearly $30 million.

The OSW has adopted a three-point program, based on short-range, intermediate-range, and long-range objectives. The purpose of the first has been to "produce desalting water at the lowest possible cost at the earliest possible date." The intermediate-range goal is the provision of second- and third-generation desalting processes in the time frame of 1970–75.

The long-range program is centered in basic research. Research is carried out by five divisions within the OSW. It is divided into four categories: properties of water, separation processes, interactions at boundaries of water systems, and properties of brackish waters, salts, brines, and by-products.

To attack the problem of producing low-cost desalted water, the OSW established five pilot demonstration plants, each to employ one of the five most promising processes. These are: long-tube-vertical (LTV) multiple-effect distillation process, multistage flash distillation, electrodialysis, freezing, and forced-circulation vapor compression.

The first demonstration plant was built at Freeport, Texas. It uses conventional thermal power (coal) and employs the "long-tube" distillation process. Because fresh water has a lower boiling point than salt water, the two can be separated by boiling. Cooling converts the steam to fresh water. Chemicals are employed to prevent the formation of excess scale inside the converting equipment. The Freeport plant has been modified several times, substantially increasing its capacity.

The Point Loma (San Diego) plant transported to Guantanamo initially had a million-gallon daily capacity. By using new methods to combat scale formation, it was possible to increase the operating temperature of this flash-distillation plant from 190° to 250° F. resulting in a 40 per cent increase in output and only a small increase in operating cost.

In flash distillation, sea water is heated under great pressure and fed into lower pressure tanks where it "flashes" into steam rather than becoming boiling water. The Point Loma plant uses a refinement of this process—"multiflash." Sea water is heated under even greater pressures, and then "flashed" into steam. Any leftover superheated brine is then "flashed" through thirty-six more chambers until nearly every drop that can be converted to steam is wrung out.

Most saline-conversion plants now use the multiflash distillation process. To reduce costs, the steam produced is used to drive turbines before being converted into fresh water. The electric power thus generated is sold, and the savings are reflected in lower costs for water.

Like the municipal plant at Coalinga, California, the Office of Saline

Water's brackish water conversion plant at Webster, South Dakota, uses the electrodialysis process. Its capacity is 250,000 gallons daily. As reported in early 1965 by Kenneth Holum, Assistant Secretary of the Interior, the plant has "achieved all reasonable expectations" but faces such technical problems as the "plugging up" of membranes by small amounts of organic matter.

Water entering the Webster plant contains mineral salts that are "ionized"—split into their components—by a direct electric current that carries the ions to two different electrodes. The process is interrupted by selective membranes that filter out the fresh water. High costs for energy and membranes have conspired to keep this process in the experimental stage. Desalination experts believe that, with lower membrane costs, the electrodialysis process may become economical for conversion of local municipal supplies where only branch water is available.

The fourth process, freezing, is based on the different freezing points of fresh and salt water. A pilot plant contracted for by the Office of Saline Water has experienced serious technical difficulties. Because of these problems, a demonstration plant intended to produce 250,000 gallons of fresh water daily by the freezing method has not been built. In its stead, a larger pilot plant—with an ultimate capacity of 200,000 gallons daily—has been placed in operation at Wrightsville Beach, North Carolina.

In the freezing process, ice formed on the water's surface is taken off and melted into fresh water. Because the ice can be used to lower costs of refrigeration, the process has great potential. The principal unresolved problem is economical separation of fresh-water ice from a salt crust that forms underneath.

"Our technical people," Mr. Holum reported, "tell me that there are definite theoretical advantages inherent in the freezing process but as yet we have been unable to solve the mechanical problems."

The fifth process—vapor compression—is under study at the OSW plant at Roswell, New Mexico. It is a million-gallon plant, but it has been plagued with process and operating problems and has not operated at designed capacity. A principal difficulty has been the nature of the brackish waters being converted. Apparently, unique problems are presented by the diverse waters found at various inland locations, making specially developed processes necessary.

Jellyfish ingest pure water from the saline water they inhabit through an osmotic process. Science has sought to steal this "reverse-osmosis" patent from the jellyfish. The method requires a membrane that rejects salt; originally, cellulose acetate was used. Salt or brackish water is applied to one side of the membrane under pressure, and fresh water filters through to the other side. Obstacles have included high costs for power and for membranes.

In March, 1966, however, Frank C. DiLuzio, then director of the Office of Saline Water, reported:

> Reverse osmosis is one of the most promising of all desalting processes. Although we are just making some of our first tenuous steps to advance the process through the engineering phases of its development, we are very excited about its possibilities. First of all, it is a liquid-to-liquid process, and as such it eliminates the costly phase change of liquid to vapor and back to liquid required by distillation processes, or from liquid to solid and back to liquid as required by crystallization cycles. Since it only requires simply pressure for its operation, the key to the process is the efficiency of the reverse osmosis membrane itself.
>
> We are supporting a broad and active program to improve the membranes in order to provide greater flux, longer life, and cheaper casting methods. Progress in any one of these areas will substantially improve the promise of the process.

He announced awards of two contracts, one for a 10,000- and one for a 50,000 gallon per day reverse osmosis pilot plant. Extensive tests will be conducted on a variety of waters, including polluted waters, brackish waters, acid mine waters, and, eventually, sea water. Mr. DiLuzio stated that "based on the present status" of the process, its first economic application would be brackish waters.

A major attack on the desalting problem is underway around the globe. Nations, states, communities, industrial firms, water authorities, all are at work on proposals, investment projections, and cost estimates.

Converted sea water could help to keep peace in the Middle East, where trouble threatens to explode over diversion of the Jordan River's meager supplies. Israel will be using all available fresh water by 1971 and must find more if its growth is to continue. It has sought low-cost desalted water for a decade, and has long experimented with the freezing process. The OSW has entered into a research contract with Hebrew University in Jerusalem for study of ion transport in salt water and of bacteria in the Dead Sea. Israel has signed a treaty with the United States for desalination cooperation. As a result of that agreement, the United States has signed a feasibility study contract with Kaiser Engineering, looking toward construction of a nuclear-powered desalting plant at Ashod, on the Mediterranean.

Britain has designed a nuclear-powered desalting plant capable of producing 60 million gallons of fresh water daily. It would utilize the multiflash process and be powered by an atomic reactor. The plant would sell water at 50 to 60 cents per thousand gallons for a 60-million-gallon plant using a 600-megawatt reactor. With a 1,000-megawatt reactor, a 30-million-gallon plant could produce fresh water at about 50 cents per thousand.

In October, 1965, delegates from fifty-eight nations, world-famous scientists, and representatives of leading industrial firms attended the first world conference on desalination in Washington, D.C. They heard more than a hundred papers on desalination progress and problems. Delegates came from both sides of the Iron Curtain, and included representatives of nations unwilling even to talk to each other under most circumstances.

Officials of New York City conferred during the summer of 1965 with federal officials regarding a plant to provide a daily supply of 150 to 250 million gallons, equal to 10 per cent of the city's needs. Its cost was estimated at $500 million. An act of Congress would be required to obtain federal funds for the project.

New York's Governor Rockefeller authorized a state demonstration plant built on Long Island Sound at a cost of $3.5 million. The plant would be nuclear powered and would produce a million gallons daily by 1968. The water would be purchased by the town of Riverhead at 35 cents per thousand gallons, and 45 cents after 11 years. Although atomic power produced by the plant could be sold to help defray costs, the water price to Riverhead would reflect a state subsidy. At this writing, the project is held up because no federal participation in construction cost has been forthcoming.

New York City estimates its water cost at 15 cents per thousand at the reservoir. Its citizens use an average of 154 gallons daily. The head of New York state's Atomic and Space Development Authority has estimated that a $500 million plant would bring down costs to 15 cents per thousand at the plant, but the estimate does not take delivery costs into account. (It is also based on sales of power and of isotopes for medical and food preservation.)

Professor Abel Wolman, retained by New York City as a water adviser, does not see converted sea water as the city's answer. The Johns Hopkins professor, an internationally recognized authority on water, finds the answer in intelligent management and re-use. Professor Wolman looks to the Hudson, with an average flow of 11 million gallons daily, as a better source for the city's needs than desalination, and has also pointed to the upper watershed of the Susquehanna as a largely unused source. He has stated that "economic justification" of proposed desalting plants has not been explained, pointing out that

> New York gets its water, delivered by gravity flow to the city, for only about 15 cents per thousand gallons (and many customers are charged only 12 cents).
> The lowest predicted cost for desalination, assuming a plant with a capacity of 250 million or more gallons, is a highly optimistic 30 to 50 cents per thousand gallons. Since a desalination plant would be at sea level, it entire output would have to be pumped; storage and conveyance together would add about 20 cents per thousand gallons to the basic pro duction cost.

In Dr. Wolman's view, it would be cheaper to bring water from the St. Lawrence, a distance of 270 miles, "if Canada would give its consent." And whatever the international problems, New York City has relatively nearby Lake Champlain, as well as the Hudson and the Susquehanna. According to Dr. Wolman, the Hudson and Susquehanna, together with present Delaware supplies, should be adequate for New York until at least the year 2000.

Desalting has been hailed as the next major industry for the United States. An Interior Department spokesman has been reported as saying that a firm order for metal tubing "for one moderately large desalting plant would take up the present idle capacity of all the tubing manufacturers in the United States for the next three years."

Edmund B. Besselievre, a Fellow of the American Society of Professional Engineers, assailed desalination as "pound foolish" in an interview in *Industrial Water Engineering* in February, 1965. Mr. Besselievre has designed or played a role in designing 850 water, sewage, and industrial waste plants throughout the world. He served as consulting engineer in the construction of the desalting plant at Freeport, Texas.

Mr. Besselievre agreed that desalting costs decline as volume rises. But he seriously questioned the ability of a 50-million-gallon plant to produce water at 34 cents a thousand, and questioned the method of assessing fixed charges, amortization, and interest costs in plants then under consideration.

This water expert put the cost of treating fresh water to meet potable standards at about one-fifth that of producing potable water from the sea. Nonetheless, he stressed that "nothing in this interview should be construed to mean that I am averse to desalination in its proper place." He pointed out that in most places where the economics of scale are applicable in the United States, desalination is not required because of available fresh water. In small installations, according to Mr. Besselievre, costs will remain high even at tidewater.

The answers to many cost questions may come when the proposed 150-million-gallon-per-day plant at Bolsa Chica Island begins producing water for the Metropolitan Water District of Southern California. At this writing, the plant, proposed by the Bechtel Corporation, is going forward, with the financial and technical assistance of the Department of the Interior and the Atomic Energy Commission.

The 43-acre man-made Bolsa Chica Island is to be located some 2,800 feet offshore from Orange County. The desalting plant will be combined with an 1,800-megawatt power plant with energy supplied by two nuclear reactors. The water produced will be sufficient to meet the municipal and industrial needs of a city of 750,000 persons, and the electricity produced will exceed that generated at Hoover Dam.

The Colorado River Association, of which the Los Angeles Metropolitan Water District is a member, has reported that the project would deliver water to the Los Angeles filtration plant at a cost of from $87.99 to $114.06 an acre-foot (325,872 gallons). The engineering and economic feasibility study shows an average cost of 22 cents per thousand gallons at the plant and 27 cents per thousand gallons delivered into the system.

Electric power production is included in the operation for two purposes. First, the plant itself will require several hundred megawatts to satisfy its own internal power needs—for example, to pump water. Second, the desalting process produces large quantities of steam, which can be used to drive turbines, produce surplus electric power for sale, and thus lower the plant costs that must be charged to water. In the case of the Bolsa Chica plant, the economics of production are such that producing the full 1,800 megawatts of power enables production of both water and power most cheaply. The electricity will be integrated into the region's power distribution system by a pool of power companies.

In considering desalination, we are inclined to concentrate attention on our greatest reservoir of water, the sea. But the value of these processes goes beyond that. As we have seen, experimentation is under way to purify brackish inland water, which has unique composition depending on the ground characteristics of the area from which it comes.

It was the intent of Congress that the saline program include conversion of brackish water supplies, which are substantial in the Midwest and Southwest. Plants were established at Roswell, New Mexico, and Webster, South Dakota, expressly to develop technology to purify brackish waters. (For many years, brackish river water has been purified by water evaporators before being fed into the boilers of steam-turbine electric-generating stations.) The technology employed in the purification of brackish water is also applicable to water contaminated by various pollutants and to waste waters.

Inland areas have had another hope from expanded desalination: that coastal locations could obtain enough water by this method to release supplies now drawn from inland. For example, if southern California could obtain significant supplies through desalting, some of its Colorado River allotment could go to such states as Colorado, Utah, Nevada, New Mexico, and Arizona. This action, however, would require desalination on a scale hardly thought of as this is written. Also, it would require renegotiation of existing interstate and interbasin compacts.

Many proposals for desalting plants include the use of nuclear reactors to provide the energy. But it must be emphasized that the only advantage nuclear power can offer is lower cost. Frank C. DiLuzio has said that a desalting plant "doesn't know—or care—where its energy comes from; it is only interested in the availability and cost per million BTU of that energy." Joint studies with the Atomic Energy Commission have indicated that dual-purpose nuclear reactors will provide the lowest cost energy for very large plants, but that fossil fuel will prove advantageous for those in the size range of 1 to 25 million gallons per day.

There are other considerations beyond cost in the construction of

large-scale nuclear-fuel conversion plants. Not the least of these is disposal of atomic wastes. Research is badly needed in such disposal, particularly of wastes with a high level of radioactivity. At present,
lower-level wastes are placed in concrete-coated steel containers and
dropped into deep sea waters. Highly active wastes are buried in desolate areas, at least until their radioctivity is partially dissipated.

So far, ocean burial has proven safe, although ocean bottom studies
may reveal hazards. Recent studies by government geologists showed
that gigantic underwater landslides take place on the ocean floor about
100 miles off Hawaii. Similar slides elsewhere conceivably could crush
and open waste barrels containing radioactive waters.

Salt-waste disposal is also a serious problem for all desalting plants—
a problem that increases with the size of the plant. Great quantities of
heat are generated, and great quantities of concentrated brine must be
disposed of. Brine and heat must be dissipated quickly into the surrounding sea, or ecological balances on the valuable continental shelf
may be drastically altered. One result could be growth of seaweed and
algae, which might destroy beaches and seascapes of great beauty.

In a discussion of the saline water conversion program at a nuclear
energy symposium held at the University of Arizona in March, 1966,
Director DiLuzio emphasized the long lead-time necessary for the development of water projects and the necessity of water management
planning. He said:

> The lead-time between the glassware of the laboratory and the hardware
> of a commercial desalting plant is long and arduous. It is unrealistic to
> assume that cheap desalting plants or processes to meet the great variety
> of requirements in terms of plant sizes, types of water and different
> processes will burst upon the scene like the first bright rays of the rising
> sun. The facts of life are that plants and processes will be produced as a
> function of time and effort, in a broad spectrum, and they will be ini-
> tially economically viable only for selective application. As experience
> and knowledge grow, the application of desalting technology will be in
> direct ratio to the lowering of product water costs and the increased cost
> of providing fresh water from conventional sources of supply. Then and
> only then will desalting come into its own in ever-increasing measure.
>
> The greatest single need to solve this Nation's water problems is to
> (1) provide better institutional water management techniques and (2)
> provide the basic technical and economic data on the wide range of al-
> ternatives from which to choose the best alternative or combination of
> alternatives.

CHAPTER XVI

Change the Weather

MARK TWAIN was wrong. Someone *is* doing something about the weather. Satellites are peering at it; computers are "memorizing" uncounted bits of information about it; scientists in many nations are even giving it a nudge now and then. In the fiscal year beginning July 1, 1966, American taxpayers spent $7 million on studying the weather with an eye to making changes. We are aiming to reduce storm losses, bring extra water to arid and drought-stricken areas, and possibly avert unpleasant consequences that it is feared could come from warming up the atmosphere.

In Riverton, Wyoming, four housewives did something about the weather just for fun. Nine days later, they heaved sighs of relief when it finally quit raining. The ladies had built a rain-making machine from such junkyard material as rusted auto fans, clutch plates, gears, and an old irrigation pump. The pump was fitted over a contraption—filled with dry ice and water—that gave off volumes of vapor. A "cannon" made of a chrome drillstem six feet high was loaded with black powder and pieces of newspaper. When fired, the "cannon" blew smoke three stories high. Everything was mounted on a 100-year-old buckboard, and the grotesque monster entered in the Fremont County Fair parade.

The cannon was fired often throughout the parade, which was hardly over before the clear blue sky became heavily overcast. Later in the evening, it started to rain. For nine days, the skies remained cloudy, and rain fell several times. Snow fell at Shoshone Lake. Fourteen inches of precipitation were recorded in the Sweetwater area south of Riverton.

Mrs. Sali Freese, one of the "inventors," received a call from an irate farmer who told her to take the rain maker apart, "or I'll take you apart." The arrival of the sun saved the contraption—and the four collaborators decided to keep it around because "you never know when a drought will come."

No doubt the farmer's fears were foolish, and the precipitation a coincidence. Still, with rain making you never know. Gunpowder, water, and dry ice have all been used before, sometimes with apparent success.

Mankind's oldest gods are those of the weather. All peoples, ancient and modern, have dreamed of changing the weather and have sought to propitiate the gods with rites or prayers, or to outthink them with airplanes and dry ice.

Yucatan is a land almost without rain. It is green with jungle growth because of a huge subterranean stream. The long-dead Mayan civilization, centered in the Mexican peninsula, dug deep wells and brought water to the surface with wind-driven water wheels of the type still used in the ancient land. The wells of the Mayans were considered sacred. At Chichen-Itza, where the magnificent ruins of a once-great Mayan city still stand, offerings were tendered to the Rain God, Yum Chac, lest he cause the wells to run dry. Most exotic among the offerings was the sacrifice of virgins grandly bedecked for their rendezvous with the god.

Some four decades ago, Don Eduardo Thompson, American Consul at Yucatan's capital, Merida, hired four Greek sponge divers to plumb the holy well at Chichen Itza. The divers brought to the surface a great assortment of bones and baubles, estimated to be worth half a million dollars. Thompson promptly shipped off the booty to the Peabody Museum at Harvard. So far, at least, Yum Chac has not retaliated by changing the weather in either Yucatan or Massachusetts.

Among North America's most colorful rites are the rain dances of the American Indian, which can still be seen—a strong reminder of man's traditional dependence on a capricious nature.

Even modern man turns to the supernatural in his search for water. A "dowser" using a forked stick has long been employed to find locations at which water would come to a well. Nobody has an adequate explanation for the wand's "magic" in the hands of the water finder.

In California, Stephen Reiss, a water expert, won a new trial in his suit for $187,292 against the San Bernardino Valley Municipal Water District involving three wells drilled for the district under a 1959 agreement. The wells produced water, but the district refused to pay on the ground that the real source was the Santa Ana River. Reiss has an unusual view on the source of ground water; he believes that it is produced by chemical action deep within the earth and is not dependent on the hydrologic cycle.

Reiss' theory is hardly more novel than others appearing during periods of prolonged drought. One such caught the fancy of Mayor Robert Wagner of New York, who dispatched a team of investigators to California for a first-hand look at an experiment of a startling nature, saying, "Our need for water is so great that I favor looking into suggestions from any responsible source, no matter how unorthodox these suggestions may be."

The rain-making experiment in question was being carried out by responsible parties, and the mayor's view was fully understandable. In 1964, at Escondido, California, under the auspices of the Vista Irrigation District and the Escondido Mutual Water Company, two scientists from the New York Central Railroad's Cleveland Technical Center had developed a technique to clear snow from railroad tracks. They used 6,000 feet of uninsulated wire, one-hundredth of an inch in diameter, carried by poles set 300 feet apart. A 50,000 volt direct current was flashed through the wire, creating a corona of ions in the atmosphere to melt snow. In theory, the technique could induce rain clouds to drop their vapor.

Despite New York's eager searchers, their city remained as dry as before, but Mayor Wagner announced that the city would continue its search for artificial rain making. He termed the problem national in scope and urged greater federal research in rain production.

The Escondido plan is no more far-fetched than other recent proposals. These have included the towing of icebergs from the Arctic to anchorages outside drought areas. Theoretically, the moisture from the melting 'berg would permeate the atmosphere and bring rain. Unfortunately, several factors appear to make the proposal futile. First, tremendous energy would be required to melt an iceberg rapidly. Second, it is likely that prevailing winds would blow the moisture out to sea. Third, the comparative warmth of the surrounding sea would soon melt the iceberg from underneath.

Despite all the disappointments, however, and after thousands of years of hoping, man may at last be at the point where rain making will be translated from a joke to a scientific reality.

The year 1966 marked a turning point in the views of many scientists as to the possibilities in weather modification. Two groups, the nongovernmental National Academy of Sciences and a special commission of the National Science Foundation, came to virtually the same conclusions and made the same recommendations. Their optimism was based on two points: the accumulation of evidence that rain making and other control experiments have been more successful than previously thought and the possession of new tools, such as computers and weather satellites. Without question, these tools will make possible the accumulation of a vast amount of knowledge in a very short time and will open a new era in weather forecasting.

These are exciting possibilities, but the subjects being examined in this book limit the questions asked about weather modification to a few very specific ones. Many aspects of weather control could affect water supply. However, weather control in relation to water resources in the 1960's means one thing: increasing precipitation. Questions here relate to the amount of water we might expect and how soon we might expect it. Can precipitation be increased by a specific percentage in any region? If so, by how much can it be increased? How soon can such increases be counted on? What would be the effect of rain-making activities in one water resource region on other water resource regions? For our purpose, advances in the science of weather modification must be examined with these questions in mind.

Seeding of clouds has so far proven to be the most practical method of rain making. Speaking precisely, the process increases or induces precipitation. Normally, clouds drop about 1 per cent of the moisture they carry; seeding proponents claim that the process can double the yield. Under most weather conditions, seeding produces no results. Given certain types of cloud formations and a near-precipitation point, seeding will produce snow or rain. Surveys of the American Meteorological Society have concluded that cloud seeding acts to trigger the release of moisture under conditions which usually would produce rain naturally.

Whether particular cloud formations are right for seeding depends on a complex of weather factors that began far away and many days before. The evaporation-precipitation cycle has no real beginning or end, but it can be viewed as starting in a belt near the equator. Here, the hot sun evaporates vapor from the seas and causes the warm moist air to rise. This air flows outward from the equatorial belt at high altitudes. Because of the earth's rotation, the air moves in a generally northeasterly direction in the northern hemisphere. When it reaches the latitude of New Orleans, the air loses heat and sinks. At the earth's surface, some moves back toward the equator, while the rest continues its northeastern journey into the temperate zones.

Meanwhile, cold air moves in a cross direction—down from the northwestern polar regions toward the southeast. This air warms up as it moves and, at about 60° latitude in Canada, most turns back toward the polar zone. When this colder air breaks out into the temperate zones, it forms a high front. The low, warmer front from the equator meets the polar-generated high and tends to rise above it. When the moisture-laden low reaches a high enough level, it forms clouds. Some moisture in the clouds crystallizes into droplets around dust particles and other impurities in the air. As these droplets condense, they release heat, which causes the moisture-laden clouds to rise further. At dewpoint, enough moisture crystallizes into raindrops or snow for precipitation to fall.

Three kinds of rainstorms originate within the general movement of the earth's atmosphere. Cyclonic storms result from the meeting of equatorial and polar air masses to produce general rains and cloud masses over broad areas. Convectional (or thunder) storms result from uneven heating of air over a locality. They generally produce heavy rains over small areas. Excessive heat may center over a city where streets and rooftops are warmer than the surrounding countryside, or it may result from differences in temperatures between open sweeps of land and surrounding forests or nearby lakes. Orographic (or mountain) storms, result from warm moisture-laden air being lifted up a mountainside until cooling takes place at the precipitation point.

Cloud seeding would not be as useful as it is if all vapor-bearing formations brought precipitation. But droplets of water within clouds

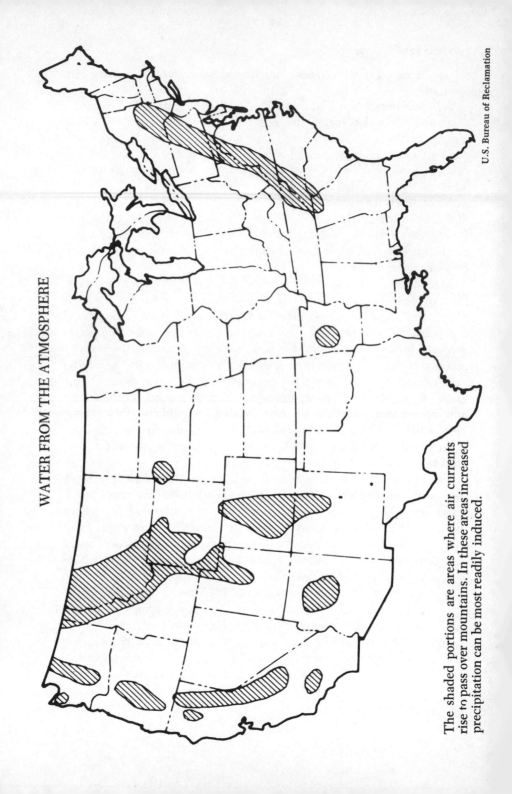

WATER FROM THE ATMOSPHERE

The shaded portions are areas where air currents rise to pass over mountains. In these areas increased precipitation can be most readily induced.

U.S. Bureau of Reclamation

are often evaporated before falling. Lush clouds, giving hope to farmers with parched crops or cities suffering drought, often disappear into the atmosphere without producing a drop of rain.

Artificial rain making began in 1946 when Dr. Vincent J. Schafer of General Electric produced precipitation with dry ice released from an airplane. Shortly thereafter, Dr. Bernard Vonnegut, also of GE, used silver iodide released from ground generators. Theory has it that the minute crystals are sucked into the upper atmosphere where they lower cloud temperature and provide a nucleus around which water droplets can crystallize. Seeding elements used from airplanes include water, carbon black and silver iodide particles, as well as dry ice (carbon dioxide). Seeding by airplane is considered too expensive for wide use.

Seeding of massive cyclonic cloud layers is generally considered futile; too much energy is required to affect them. Seeding of convectional, or thunderstorm, clouds produces precipitation under favorable circumstances. But there is scant evidence that rain would not have fallen in any case.

Seeding is often successful on the windward side of mountain slopes where clouds form in abundance at temperatures low enough for precipitation. Experiments conducted in the Colorado Basin by the Bureau of Reclamation showed that "cap" clouds—those gathered around the tops of mountains—can be made to produce snow almost every time. The scientists are not yet certain, however, that additional precipitation has resulted, or, if it has, how much was caused by seeding. There is some evidence that seeding of winter storm clouds in the mountains has resulted in an increase of 10 or 15 per cent in precipitation. Programs have been begun that will attempt close control of experiments to seek more precise answers to these questions.

Some have described weather modification as already a "reality." Some have spoken of a "break-through." Our scientists have recommended an expansion of weather-modification spending from the present $7 million to $40 million by 1970, which some believe will enable them to move into a new era of weather control. Many nations—notably France, Italy, and Russia—are increasing interest and experimentation in the weather. In 1967, the World Meteorological Organization will begin a "World Weather Watch" making use of Tiros and Nimbus satellites and a network of 250 land and sea stations. It is proposed that more advanced weather-probing devices, and even weathermen, be shot into the sky.

An accurate description of these developments, however, would be that they are increasing weather knowledge and advancing the science of weather prediction, not physically modifying the weather. With the exceptions of inducing precipitation under favorable conditions, dispelling fog, and perhaps pulling the teeth of some storms, anything that could be regarded as "commercial" weather modification is still in the discussion stage.

More accurate weather prediction, of course, is of immense practical value. Hurricane "Betsy," one of the most destructive ever to hit the Gulf Coast, was tracked by satellites, and loss of life was substantially reduced by an early warning system, although mammoth property damage could not be prevented.

As Betsy gathered force, some 900 miles east of the Florida coast in 1964, scientists with "Project Storm Fury" flew to Puerto Rico to decide whether or not to seed the storm with silver iodide crystals. The seeding was not carried out because Betsy did not enter an area prescribed by the Weather Bureau. Borders of the area have been so drawn that, if a hurricane enters, the scientists are certain that it will move out to sea. Otherwise, seeding could lead to the breakup of the huge mass of energy into several dangerous storms, which could strike the U.S. land mass.

Despite Betsy's erratic course, it was possible to keep track of it until it degenerated into a tropical storm over the land. The hurricane was first sighted east of Barbados in the West Indies by a weather satellite, Tiros 10. Three other satellites, Tiros 7, 8, and 9, joined Tiros 10 in the lookout.

The next storm rivaling Betsy in fury was "Inez," the hurricane that threatened the United States from September 21 to October 10, 1966. Inez also did not enter the prescribed area, so again seeding was not attempted. It did great damage in the Caribbean and in Mexico but did not turn into a tropical storm over the U.S. mainland. Gordon E. Dunn, head of the Weather Bureau's National Hurricane Center in Miami, has reported his view that a plateau has been reached in hurricane control theory. He believes technology's greatest contribution has been the early warning system.

Radar is a new tool, which gives the forecaster a view of changing weather conditions and permits him to trace the direction and intensity of storms and cloud masses. Without radar weather observation to provide advance alerts of rain or heavy storm, air travel might still be very hazardous.

More accurate weather prediction is also one of the forerunners to large-scale attempts to modify the weather. Almost nothing is known about the effects that weather modification—even cloud seeding—over one region may have on another. The National Science Foundation report points out that excess rainfall could adversely affect the balance of nature. Wild plants and animals have taken on special characteristics in response to particular environments. Habitat destruction can come from too much rain as surely as from drying up of a creek. A growth of sagebrush brought to Washington, D.C., by a Westerner in the early 1960's lived in his garden for a year or two but eventually died from too much moisture. A hurricane contains the energy of 150 hydrogen bombs. No one knows what would happen if an attempt were made to prevent such a storm from forming or what would happen if one were broken up. Interference with a typhoon in the South China Sea could alter storm and precipitation patterns on the coasts of China and Japan or in far-off India.

Assessing in advance what might happen when we tinker with the weather is one of the advantages expected to arise from the use of high-speed computers. As knowledge grows, more and more facts can be stored in a computer's "memory," and increasingly detailed and sophisticated evaluations made of the effects of any weather-changing action.

Some aspects of weather modification can be of great significance from the standpoint of the total environment. Many scientists believe that man may be altering the weather unknowingly by changing the carbon dioxide content of the air through the burning of coal and oil and through the discharge of other chemicals into the atmosphere. One of these is Dr. Walter O. Roberts, director of the Center for Atmospheric Research in Boulder, Colorado. He has proposed increasing weather-gathering data tenfold through a satellite-balloon system that would use 6,000 to 10,000 balloons to relay findings from several atmospheric levels.

"We must know the details of the behavior of the atmosphere before we tamper with it," Dr. Roberts has pointed out. "It is beyond man's

capability to alter the tides of the atmosphere, but climatic changes of
the past may have been triggered by relatively small forces."

A second forerunner to large-scale weather modification should be
in the area of the law. There is nowhere a body of law—either statutory
or common—governing weather modification. There are a few state laws,
mostly making it illegal to seed clouds or otherwise induce rain. The
question of who owns the moisture carried by the clouds has hardly been
raised, let alone resolved. The National Science Foundation report
stated that scientific and technological progress is running ahead of
man's legal, social, and political arrangements to deal with the consequences. (This observation is true of every field that affects our environment.) Recommended was a single agency to direct the nation's
weather modification program, either the Environmental Science Services Administration of the Department of Comerce or a new agency.

Weather modification on a grand scale would involve decisions opening a new field in international relations. The foundation urges beginning the assessment of the legal aspects of weather modification damage,
as well as regulation of those who engage in changing the weather. Also
recommended is issuance of a "basic statement of [U.S.] views on the
relationship of this national effort to the interests, hopes, and possible
apprehensions of the rest of the world."

Another point should be made relative to the movement of water in
the sky. We are told that changes in the jet stream affect the amount
of precipitation that falls over a particular area. Changing the weather
could well mean altering the jet stream to produce unusual or desired
patterns of precipitation. If it is morally right to alter patterns of moisture in the sky, a strong case can be made for the rightness of altering
the flow of water on the ground. Weather control could be used to
increase precipitation for some regions; redistribution could also be
used to increase water supplies for the same regions.

The weather modification effort of the federal government is part of
the National Atmospheric Sciences Program. In 1958, the National
Science Foundation identified an area of scientific research as the atmospheric sciences, and, to insure an adequate research effort, a continuing program was established.

It involves sixteen departments and agencies and will cost more than
$230 million in the fiscal year which began on July 1, 1966. Most of
the work, however, is directly related to primary responsibilities of the

agencies. For example, the largest amount—one-third—goes to the Department of Defense for research on the effects of the environment on our weapons systems.

Weather modification will receive about 3.5 per cent of the total, to be allocated as follows: $3,750,000 to the Department of the Interior (Bureau of Reclamation); $900,000 to the Department of Commerce (Environmental Science Services Administration); and $2,300,000 to the National Science Foundation. Smaller amounts will go to the National Aeronautics and Space Administration and the Department of Agriculture.

The question remains: Can any water resource region in the United States include weather modification as an element in planning its water supply program for the years ahead? As this is written, the answer must be "No."

In the mountainous areas of the West, cloud seeding may one day be counted on for a calculable increase in precipitation. Beneficial results might also be obtained in another drought like that in the Northeast in the 1960's. In such a situation, clouds might be induced to drop their moisture over the land, as they normally do, rather than carrying it out to sea. For the distant future, the outlook is optimistic. The new tools will rapidly increase our knowledge. Research will unlock many secrets. Someday, there is little doubt, we will be able to tap the moisture the sky holds.

But today's water planners must look for firm available supplies. They are to be found on the ground and under it.

CHAPTER XVII

From the Frozen North

THE ANCIENT ROMANS took their water where they found it. The famous baths of Rome were supplied through aqueducts that reached hundreds of miles into the mountains. Thanks to advanced water resource development, the ancient city enjoyed a constant supply of 300 million gallons a day.

The principles of water resource development have not changed much, but modern engineering skills, and the materials and techniques of construction, enable modern states to do things undreamed of by the Romans. In addition, the conversion to electric power of what the engineers call the "gravity-stored energy" in water makes it economically practical to build projects that the richest emperor would not have attempted. An example is use of the power generated at Grand Coulee Dam on the Columbia River to pump water to the high coulee, whence it flows to the farmlands of eastern Washington.

Like the Romans, the North Americans have taken their water where they found it. To our forefathers, the water resources of the continent seemed boundless; to them, wasteful development was economical.

Now the United States must meet a prodigious demand for water with supplies that are badly contaminated. Even the Canadians—with one of the greatest water reserves in the world—have vast areas of waterless prairie. They share with the United States the problems of pollution and lowered levels of the Great Lakes.

NAWAPA: Water for a Continent

In northern Canada and Alaska, enormous quantities of fresh, clean water flow unused into the Arctic seas. Inevitably, the possibility of transporting a portion of it to meet the needs of the continent's populous centers has been considered. But such consideration involves continent-wide planning.

For a variety of reasons, such planning has not been done until recently, and even now is not done by any public agency. One barrier has been the use of political borders—rather than natural ones—to assert authority over rivers and lakes. Another barrier to continent-wide planning is the separated responsibilities among federal agencies and among provincial and state governments.

The need to cross political borders in water resource development gave rise to the device of the interstate compact, such as that in use in the Colorado Basin. The same need gave rise to the cooperation between Canada and the United States on the St. Lawrence, the Great Lakes, and the Columbia River. But no over-all policy has guided these development efforts. Now, such a policy is needed to guide future planning. That policy must take into account the use and preservation of the total water resources of the continent and the ultimate needs of all the people on the continent.

Although no public agency has taken a look at the total water resources of North America, such an examination has been made—by a private engineering firm. This is the Ralph M. Parsons Company, which is based in Los Angeles and does work in all parts of the world. Its water resources-planning engineers have taken a technical and economic approach to continent planning, leaving the problems of relationships, jurisdictions, and organization to the social and political specialists.

The product of their effort is a concept of resource development, power generation, navigation, and water distribution that would benefit one territory and seven provinces in Canada, thirty-seven states of the United States, and three states of Mexico. Looking forward to a possi-

NAWAPA—

Planning on a Continental Scale

Ralph M. Parsons Co.

ble organization to sponsor such an undertaking, the Parsons people named the project the North American Water and Power Alliance, commonly called NAWAPA.

Others, also, have proposed extensive water diversions to meet supply and pollution problems. Because the NAWAPA concept is the most comprehensive and has received the most attention, it is examined here in some detail.

The real significance of NAWAPA is that a competent engineering firm has found that it is technically feasible and economically realistic to collect and distribute water on a continental basis. Parsons says NAWAPA could be built with today's technology, costing on the order of $100 billion and producing $4 billion in annual revenues. With operating costs of between one-half and one billion, it fits into the framework of conventional financing of water resource projects. The work done on NAWAPA has been in the nature of an in-house research and development job by the Ralph M. Parsons Company. The concept is based entirely on published topographical and hydrological data. The firm points out that many variations are possible and suggests great changes might be indicated by field studies. The report published in 1964, has been stimulating and provocative—and encouraging.

To get a feeling for the grandeur and potential of such continental-scale thinking, it is worth tracing the NAWAPA concept from Alaska to Quebec and Mexico. In the following sections of the chapter, the routing is traced largely by the major river courses followed. There are hundreds of miles of tunnels and canals. Along the way, the flowing waters generate 100 million kilowatts of electricity, using nearly a third of this for pumping purposes but leaving two-thirds for sale. The salable product is an economic advantage the ancient Romans didn't have.

Alaska to Quebec

The Parsons engineers proposed collecting 15 to 18 per cent of the excess runoff from the high-precipitation, medium-elevation areas of south-central Alaska and the upper Yukon river basin. Throughout the continent, the NAWAPA concept deals with *surplus* water. Optimal flows would be maintained downstream in all collection areas and flood peaks leveled.

The upper reaches of the Copper, Susitna, and Tanana rivers in Alaska would be joined by a system of reservoirs and tunnels with the upper Yukon waters in the Yukon Territory of Canada. In northern British Columbia, these waters would be raised to an elevation of 2,400 feet in a pump station just south of Atlin Lake and combined with waters brought in from the Dease and Liard rivers, thence flowing south via the Nass and Stewart rivers to a junction with the Fraser River at Prince George in central British Columbia.

North and east of Prince George, Canada presently is building one of the greatest hydroelectric installations in the hemisphere. This is the Portage Mountain project, at the point where the Peace River flows through the gap in the Rocky Mountains. It would be integrated into the NAWAPA plan and fully utilized. By extending the reservoir behind the Portage Mountain Dam, which could be done by raising the height of the main dam or building smaller dams upstream, the Peace River could be connected with the Fraser.

The NAWAPA designers envisioned this interconnection for both supply interchange and navigation. By canalization of the Fraser from Prince George down to Vancouver, and of rivers to be interconnected across the Prairie Provinces, Canada could have a navigable waterway from the Great Lakes to the Pacific. Let us trace the networks eastward across Canada.

The route across the Prairie Provinces, for waterborne commerce and great new supplies of water, would be from Peace River to Lesser Slave Lake, thence via the Pembina, North Saskatchewan, and Battle rivers to a junction with the South Saskatchewan River in southwest Alberta. From here the flow would be via the Que Appelle and Assiniboine rivers to Lake Winnipeg. Connection to Lake Superior would be via the English River and the network of lakes in western Ontario.

Construction of NAWAPA would make Winnipeg the only four-way port on the continent, since in addition to the passage to the Pacific via Peace River, the project would canalize the Nelson River while developing its power potential between Lake Winnipeg and Hudson Bay. The eastward connection to Lake Superior would permit use of the St. Lawrence Seaway to the Atlantic and the Mississippi River waterway to the Gulf of Mexico.

Hudson Bay Watershed

A glance at the map will show the water-collecting capacity of the James Bay watersheds in northern Ontario and northwest Quebec. The NAWAPA concept would develop the full power potential of the half-dozen rivers flowing into James Bay, providing a barge canal across central Quebec to the headwaters of the Hamilton River near the Labrador border. It would also permit diversion of some of this water via the Ottawa River and Lake Nipissing into Lake Huron, thus providing a second supply point for the Great Lakes. The augmented supply for the lakes means stabilized navigation levels and power flows for the St. Lawrence.

The megalopolis from Quebec and Montreal via Toronto to Detroit and Chicago is developing into the principal axis of population and economic activity of the North American continent. The Great Lakes form its lifeline. Neither Canada nor the United States can afford the continuing deterioration of the quality of the lakes. Although abatement of the contaminants being poured in by cities and by industry is essential to the restoration of the lakes, new water can and will be very important.

The Canadians recognize this as well as we do. At Sudbury, Ontario, Thomas W. Kierans has developed a plan quite independent of, and separate from, the NAWAPA concept to use the Great Lakes as a great distribution manifold for waters to be brought from James Bay. Since James Bay is salty, Mr. Kierans would make fresh water reservoirs out of the estuaries of the six or seven major rivers flowing into the bay. Barriers would be installed to prevent the mixing of the fresh with the salt water.

A feature of importance claimed by Mr. Kierans is that his plan avoids diversion and permits water in the James Bay rivers to do its full work before he removes it from the estuarine reservoirs. Tremendous amounts of power generated in the downflow of these rivers would be necessary to pump the water all the way back to the lakes, over the 900-foot divide between the James Bay basin and the Great Lakes basin. (I don't know whether this makes economic sense or not. It certainly points up the fact that the value of water goes up and up, and the megalopolis along the Great Lakes may be willing to pay the price.) Both the Kierans and the NAWAPA plans would utilize James Bay watershed runoff; both rest on the premise that there is plenty of unused water there, which can better be used if moved to where people are.

Proponents of the NAWAPA idea and the Kierans proposal are careful to avoid presenting the plans as competing alternatives. They simply urge that the principle be studied. Whatever judgment the governments of Quebec and Ontario and the federal government at Ottawa may form on the basis of studies of NAWAPA and the Kierans plan, the fact remains that vast amounts of water are now pouring unused into northern seas and are irretrievably lost.

Perhaps it is too early for broad jurisdictional studies by an international body, such as the International Joint Commission, since both Canada and the United States have a lot of internal work to do to form a basis for joint continental planning activities. But it is not too early to begin work in earnest on the possibilities of augmenting the supply of water in the Great Lakes.

The question is of growing importance because, as Mr. Kierans and the Parsons engineers point out, the lakes are a great natural reservoir and can be used as a distribution manifold for supplementing the water supplies of the entire northeastern United States. Since publication of the NAWAPA report in 1964, the system has been extended to incorporate the New York state barge canal as a distribution channel to carry water direct to the Hudson Valley and the New York City system. Provision is also made for a tie-in with the Susquehanna and Delaware rivers. The proposed Ohio River–Lake Erie connection also becomes more interesting, with plenty of water available to Lake Erie.

The experience gained in working out an equitable arrangement for adding water to the Great Lakes and redistributing it for the benefit of both countries would point the way to a much broader arrangement for a continental distribution system similar to NAWAPA. The Great Lakes are already a shared water system, as are the Columbia and St. Johns rivers. A treaty for coordinated development of the Columbia was signed in 1964, and negotiations are currently underway for similar development of the St. Johns River in the Northeast.

British Columbia to Tamaulipas

Following the flow of water in the NAWAPA network from Prince George, B.C., southward, the Fraser River would be dammed where it leaves the Rocky Mountain Trench. More than half of this great natural defile along the continental divide would be closed by other dams, which would be built at the gaps of the Thompson, Columbia, and Kootenay rivers. A pump station at the Fraser River dam would raise the water to 3,000 feet in the trench reservoir. All of the projects now authorized for development of these rivers would be incorporated in the NAWAPA plan.

The proposed Rocky Mountain Trench reservoir is a major feature of the NAWAPA concept. The four dams—on the Fraser, Thompson, Columbia, and Kootenay rivers—would raise the water level sufficiently to flood over the divides between the headwaters of these rivers, thus creating a fresh-water lake 500 miles long and 5 to 15 miles wide. There are many questions about such a project. Dr. Raymond L. Nace, research hydrologist of the U.S. Geological Survey, says the possible ecological impact of the huge artificial bodies of water created by NAWAPA must be thoroughly studied. Even then, he says, we cannot be sure of the long-term effects of such vast changes in the hydrological patterns of the continent. Parsons, however, says there are other ways of doing the job if the Trench reservoir proves unfeasible or undesirable for ecological or other reasons.

The Rocky Mountain Trench reservoir would discharge into Flathead Lake in Montana. The latter would be tied into another vast collection system centered on the Montana-Idaho border, with pump stations to raise the waters to 5,000 feet at the Sawtooth Mountain Reservoir in Idaho. The lower Snake and Clearwater rivers would be fully developed, generating power for pumping as well as for sale, and permitting control of flow into the lower Columbia. Since the flow into the upper river from the Trench reservoir could also be controlled, the Columbia could be stabilized at optimal flow for power, irrigation, and navigation.

From the Sawtooth Mountain Reservoir, water would flow through a tunnel 80 feet in diameter and 50 miles long to the Great Basin Waterway, which would cross the upper Snake, with an interchange connection, just below American Falls. The route would then cross the extreme northwest corner of Utah to Lake Nevada, a huge reservoir to be built northeast of Shafter.

The Trout Creek Diversion south of Lake Nevada near Ibapah, Utah, divides the main waterway. One course, the Colorado Basin Aqueduct, leads by gravity flow across southern Nevada to California. A branch from Lake Vegas, north of Las Vegas, would lead due south to Mexico, with interconnections to the Colorado at Lake Mead and at Yuma, supplying Baja California and Sonora. Southern California would be supplied from the Panamint reservoir to be built north of Barstow.

The other course from Trout Creek would lead diagonally across Utah, employing pump-lifts and tunnels to get through the Wasatch Mountains. It would cross the Colorado, with a siphon interchange twenty-five miles above Glen Canyon Dam, and would serve most of Arizona. Two supply lines lead into Sonora, with a cross connection to the Colorado at Yuma.

Southern and eastern New Mexico would be served by an aqueduct carrying water east to the Pecos River, permitting augmentation of flow of the Rio Grande by an interconnection at Elephant Butte. From the Pecos Reservoir, near Roswell, water would be pump-lifted and passed through tunnels to supply eastern Colorado via the Purgatoire River. This north-flowing East Slope Canal would permit adding water to both the Canadian and Arkansas rivers.

The Staked Plains area of north Texas would also be served from the Pecos Reservoir, and the flow of the Pecos and Rio Grande rivers would be stabilized. Aqueducts parallel to the lower Rio Grande would extend irrigation on both the American and Mexican sides, utilizing the Amistad Reservoir now under construction. The additional supplies of NAWAPA water would greatly enhance the value of existing reservoirs as well as those outside of NAWAPA. The end of the line for NAWAPA water would be the coastal flatlands of Tamaulipas. In all, Mexico could receive sufficient water to irrigate seven or eight times as much land as the Egyptians will reclaim from the Aswan High Dam.

Moose Jaw to Minneapolis and Other Links

The United States and Canada would have still another NAWAPA link in the form of a barge canal connecting the Prairie Province Waterway with the Missouri and Minnesota rivers. A new waterway called the Dakota Canal would start near Moose Jaw, Saskatchewan, and extend southeastward across the two Dakotas and Minnesota. A connection at Garrison Dam would permit low-flow augmentation of the Missouri. The Dakota Canal would provide both supply and navigation for the Dakotas and Minnesota, tying into the Mississippi at the Twin Cities.

This Moose Jaw–Minneapolis link was proposed by the Parsons engineers as a 12-foot-draft barge canal, consistent with the standard of the U.S. inland waterway system. The trans-Canada waterway from Lake Superior to Prince George and thence Vancouver was proposed as a 30-foot-draft canal to permit passage to the west of any vessels that can use the St. Lawrence Seaway. The feature has been criticized as unnecessary, although many Canadians like the idea of the waterway just for recreation purposes. A New Orleans sportsman noted that he could fish from Louisiana to Alaska on his own boat.

The key to NAWAPA is the use of gravity-stored energy of water picked up at high elevations to move the water to where it is needed. The NAWAPA plan would bleed off, or "overboard," as the engineers say, some of its collected water in order to generate power for pumping. This is the reason why, on the one hand, the system appears to be self-financing, even at this early stage. The delivery capability of the NAWAPA system, on the other hand, could be expanded any time by substituting nuclear-powered stations for pumping energy. That simply means taking advantage of the fact that water may become more valuable than the energy needed to make kilowatts.

Recognition of the NAWAPA concept, or rather of the objective it seeks, dates from the studies made in 1964 by the Senate Subcommittee on Western Water Development. The subcommittee made a rough comparison of the NAWAPA plan with an inventory of all the water resource development projects anticipated by federal agencies over the next twenty years. The general conclusion was that for about 25 per cent greater cost, the NAWAPA approach could provide twice as much water as all of the other projects put together.

The subcommittee's review admittedly was hasty. The degree of refinement of the NAWAPA design at that time did not warrant more detailed study. It is now time to study the NAWAPA idea seriously, not so much because of the additional work done in the meantime by Parsons but because our eyes have been opened to the possibilities.

Important as they are, the water links between Canada and the United States and Mexico may not be a bit more significant in the long run than the bonds of mutual benefit from trade in water. Despite our many ties to Canada, there are people in the United States, and especially in government, who oppose NAWAPA on the basis that it would make the United States dependent on a foreign country for our most precious natural resource.

One way to get work started on concepts of such magnitude is to select the most critical elements for individual study. For example, there is no use going further into the NAWAPA scheme if the plan would do unacceptable damage to the beautiful rivers of the Montana and Idaho Rockies. Perhaps the initial plan could be improved to reduce such impact. The engineer who laid out the original routing points out that many factors, such as geological data, may call for scores of changes.

Some of the major questions such as ecological impact of diversions and the economic and geological problems of creating artificial lakes as big as Lake Erie, which the Rocky Mountain Trench reservoir would be, can be studied separately before time and money is spent to check out the whole plan.

Canada and the United States have a long history of constructive joint work on the Great Lakes. What has been learned in dealing with the lakes and other shared watercourses such as the Columbia and the St. Johns rivers, can be applied to continent-wide planning.

The countries of North America can hardly be any more separate in their utilization of the continent's water resources than they are in the defense of the continent. There is complete military cooperation.

Americans and Canadians want to live in constructive peace on this continent for many centuries to come. They can't do it unless they take care of the unparalleled natural endowments of North America. Certainly, the United States will not expect the people of Canada to enter into any arrangement for trade in water unless it is demonstrably in Canada's best long-range interest.

It appears to be to Canada's long-range economic and social advantage—and natural resource advantage—to serve the U.S. market with both water and hydroelectric power in order to develop her own northland.

Canadians have argued against trying to bring the water to the people, and urge moving the people to the water. Somehow, man just doesn't behave in such a logical way. If he did, Canada would not be confronted with the problem of having such a high proportion of its population congregated along the U.S. border. The investment required for works like NAWAPA, however, will do much to settle and develop the great expanse of Canada to the north, now so thinly populated.

One student of NAWAPA says Canadians are divided, like Gaul, into three parts on the subject of water export. There are those who say NAWAPA is Canada's great opportunity, "Get on with it." Then there is a second part made up of those who say "Never!" Millions of kilowatts they would export, and uranium and natural gas and other depletable resources they would sell, "but not one gallon of our precious birthright water."

Finally, there is the third part (presumably the largest), made up of those serious-minded Canadians who say that something like NAWAPA could be of great advantage to Canada, and may even be inevitable in the interest of sound growth and development of the two countries. They say, however, that they need from five to ten years of intensive survey and appraisal work in order to develop an adequate technical base for the essential policy decisions. Clearly, this estimate is reasonable.

The United States has much of the same kind of homework to do. Our country is hardly more ready to talk about importing water than Canada is to talk about exporting it. One of the first things to be done is to study the manner in which we could interconnect our own river basins in order to distribute the imported water. For example, the United States is a long way from using efficiently the water it has within its own borders. The Canadians like to point this out to us. The Columbia, they say, pours more water into the Pacific, unused, than any other river on the continent except the Mississippi and the Mc Kenzie.

Utilization of Columbia River waters to supply the arid Southwest has long been a contentious issue in the United States. The NAWAPA proposal, of course, makes transfer of some of the Columbia water an agreeable proposition, because the additional water from the north assures ample supply for all needs in the Columbia basin. There are a number of routes not so agreeable as the NAWAPA proposal because they do not provide for back-up supplies to the Columbia.

One modification of the NAWAPA plan should be looked into with a view to reinforcement of the Columbia. This is the collection of water in south-central Alaska and direct transfer to the Columbia basin without any input of Canadian water. It has even been proposed that this water could be brought down by a plastic pipe to be suspended in the Pacific Ocean. It would make more sense simply to ask Canada to grant a right of way across British Columbia to provide a connection from Alaska to the contiguous states of the United States. The eco-

nomics seem far less appealing than the combining of waters envisioned in the NAWAPA idea, but the possibilities should be considered.

The proposals for gigantic diversions of northern water are encouraging as well as provocative. They are encouraging because they indicate clearly that if we are wise, and if we apply the technical knowledge
we have to the problem, the whole of the North American continent
can be assured of an adequate supply of good water for as long as we
want to live here.

An appealing element of these proposals—and possibly their greatest
value—is that they have focused attention on the things we ought to
be doing to care for our water resources. NAWAPA is not just a huge
engineering job. It would require the greatest continuous and most
intensive conservation effort ever thought of. The mere mention of
$100 billion makes everybody look to the things we ought to do first,
before we commit ourselves to such an expenditure, and the things we
ought to do to protect the investment once we make it. This means
conservation, pollution control, expanded and more efficient distribution, and disciplined use of water.

Canada is already looking into the conservation aspects of programs
like NAWAPA. For example, Professor E. Kuiper of the University of
Manitoba, one of the world's great authorities on water and author of
an important book called *Water Resource Development*, has started a
graduate-school study program to establish some of the parameters and
basic requirements of giant collection and transfer work. Care of the
watersheds, he points out, is the most important.

America and Canada must work together on these concepts. The
United States should seek a rapport with the Canadians permitting
joint continent-wide conservation and development studies of water
resources. The additional development that could be made possible
within Canada should extend the producing lifetime of Canada's water-
harvest areas.

Common sense and prudence dictate that the two countries, while
doing their respective homework on water resources, keep an eye on
the continental system possibilities. Water resource development projects
on both sides of the border should be examined to make sure they would
not interfere with a whole-continent system. And, in the meantime, let
Canadians, Americans, and Mexicans keep open the channels of communication that can lead to intelligent decisions as to our true long-
range interests in water resource development.

PART THREE

We, the People

CHAPTER XVIII

The Great Partnership

THE BIG OBSTACLE to restoring the Hudson Valley, it was charged in 1965, is "bureaucracy." *Newsweek* magazine, which expressed that opinion, reported: "More than fifteen federal agencies from the Coast Guard to the Department of Commerce (which maintains its mothball fleet of cargo ships in Tompkins Cove) tangle with New York state departments of Conservation, Health, Public Works and Commissions for Fish and Game, Parks, Water Resources and Motor Boats, to name a few. And few of these are under any obligation to consult with each other or a higher authority."

Although Americans want new cars every two years, they move slowly to bring their agencies of government up to date. In few places is this more evident than in the area of water management.

A question vital to this book is whether the programs necessary to restoration of America's waters can be carried out within the framework of existing governmental structures. Are the federal, state, and local agencies of the 1960's *capable* of effective water management? Experience indicates that they are not, and that significant changes are essential.

257

The importance of crossing state lines to make the river basin the unit of water management has been mentioned frequently in these pages.

Lieutenant General W. K. Wilson, Jr., former head of the U.S. Army Corps of Engineers, has expressed this opinion: "Comprehensive, basin-wide planning is probably the process by which most future development . . . will be conceived."

With its issue of June, 1966, the magazine *Power* published a special report on water in which an "engineering view" of a successful attack on water-management problems was described: "Our waters must be handled as *systems*—with many sources and uses, pollutants and treatments. . . ." In most cases, the article continued, the system will be a river basin: "In some it may be a region embracing two or more small basins. But in any case, the first step must be to define the system and then, on that basis, evaluate the alternatives available for the most effective development—or restoration—of the water resources in the area. We thus applaud recent legislative emphasis on river-basin planning, and urge its vigorous prosecution."

Even should authorities be successfully established for every river basin, however, many will be interrelated. Precipitation, pollution, and water use in one basin can vitally affect others. Coordination in their development and management is essential.

Of equal importance is the effect that federal water programs have on the programs of basins and states. For example, if large quantities of water are to be diverted from the Columbia Basin into the Southwest, or massive quantities from the Arctic into the West and Midwest, these projects will dominate the water programs of many basins and states. Ideally, we should have a national long-range plan for management of the water resources of the United States. The national plan would then be the starting point for the formulation of regional and state plans, which would, in turn, provide the foundation upon which counties, communities, and industries could make their plans. Expanded federal leadership is therefore necessary.

But the federal government has not—and cannot—provide either the requisite leadership or the necessary planning. It is not organized to do so. Natural resource management has been entrusted to a maze of agencies scattered throughout the government. At best, they operate in splendid isolation, often pursuing contradictory policies and objectives. At worst, they engage in open warfare.

Two major governmental changes are called for. The first is a strengthened interstate arrangement—a solid basis for the establishment of river-basin authorities to encompass all phases of water use, quality, conservation, and regulation. The second is the placement of all federal water-management agencies under one head. In addition, cooperation in resource management must be improved all along the line—between cities, counties, states, and the federal government.

An examination of the history and accomplishments of governmental agencies in dealing with water problems shows how necessary these changes are.

The United States is a unique experiment in federalism. Authority has been divided among many segments of government, commonly called "levels." The basis of the division is that matters of local concern are the responsibility of the cities and counties, those of state concern the responsibility of the state capitals, and those of national concern the responsibility of Washington. (There are also interstate or regional authorities usually organized within a water basin.)

Although the authority of the central government is limited to interstate matters, federal money can be used to support and stimulate regional, state, and local action. Our public schools are administered by local boards, but they have long received state aid, and, since enactment of the Elementary and Secondary School Act, are eligible for federal financial help. Not only is federal tax money used for such purposes as municipal sewage treatment plants, but entirely federal projects are built for navigation, flood control, irrigation, electric power generation, and water storage. Even with this federal involvement, however, a great deal of the responsibility for water resource management has remained with states and localities.

In seeking to combat the northeastern drought of 1965, President Johnson, pointed out that although he had directed every federal agency "to do all that should and can be done," the problem of water supply was "first of all, a great responsibility of our local governments."

"It is imperative," the President said, that "we proceed toward the goal of 'drought-proofing' our metropolitan areas and their agricultural regions."

By "we" the President meant the federal government acting in partnership with state and local governments.

While serving as chairman of the Senate Select Committee on National Water Resources, the late Senator Robert S. Kerr of Oklahoma asserted that needs in water resource development were so great that "meeting them will require the combined efforts of federal, state and local governments and private enterprise, working together with their efforts coordinated to a high degree."

For many localities, the rapidly rising pressures on their waters have created unbearable financial burdens.

In the summer of 1965, the attorney general of New York state brought suit against two small upstate communities for failure to cease polluting local waters. Summoned were the villages of Silver Creek in the western part of the state, and Waterloo, on the Seneca River in the famed Finger Lakes area.

Waterloo had been ordered to cease dumping raw sewage into the river, and to construct a new sewage disposal plant. The village attorney retorted that the state wanted the community to build a plant costing $450,000 and commented that "a village of this size doesn't have that kind of money."

About the same time, the state's assistant commissioner of Environmental Health Services told a citizen's meeting that the predicament of the two small villages was not unique and that paying the bill for pure water would require "an effort of local, state and federal government."

New York state's voters have since approved the billion-dollar bond issue to help communties build treatment plants. The expanded federal program will also help communities like Waterloo and Silver Creek.

Drought, pollution, and rising demand have created a greater sense of urgency on the part of the nation, but the "great partnership" which is essential to the successful management of water resources is beyond the horizon of the mid-1960's. As has been shown, governmental policies have too often been determined by the politics of regions, localities, economic interests, and agencies, rather than by water management requirements.

Texas became the first state to notify the Department of Health, Education, and Welfare that it intended to comply with the Water Quality Act of 1965. The "special to *The New York Times*" that reported the event carried the following lead: "Texas moved this week on two fronts to hold tightly to its right to regulate the pollution of its rivers and bays."

The action meant higher quality water for Texas—but it was taken with the backing of the Texas Manufacturers Association to hold off the imposition of federal standards. The mayor of one important coastal city and a leading state legislator complained that proposed state regulations would permit serious pollution in a ship channel where heavy industry is concentrated. The mayor (of Baytown) pointed to six kills that had left thousands of dead fish on the shores, and had created a local health hazard.

The Texas action was hardly in the spirit of the great partnership that must be created if water pollution is to end. Nor was an earlier action of the state legislature that stripped the Texas Water Pollution Control Board of its authority to regulate disposal of salt water resulting from oil and gas production.

If federal action has been required for pollution control on the Great Lakes, the intervention was forced by the negative attitudes of the states. In Ohio, the State Pollution Control Board has been prohibited by state law from disclosing the sources and nature of industrial pollution without the express consent of the industries affected. Initially, both New York and Pennsylvania informed the federal government that their cooperation was not essential to a cleanup on the lakes.

Both states contended that an attack upon lake pollution by the Water Pollution Control Administration would mean federal domination of state pollution control agencies. In virtually the same breath, Governor Nelson Rockefeller applauded payment by the federal government of 30 per cent of all state pollution clean-up costs, and called for special income tax incentives to industry for cleaning up its mess. He said that, "there would be no benefit to New York in terms of its intrastate pollution problems from federal enforcement," and added that federal enforcement would "only serve to duplicate and hinder state action and diffuse responsibility, and thus delay the achievement of the real goal—clean water."

State-federal cooperation is much easier to come by in water development than in pollution abatement, because development means expenditures and more business while abatement often means new restrictions and higher costs.

An example of strong cooperation came in late 1965 when voters in seven counties in Utah gave approval and local financial support to a federal water program that will result in construction of the key Central Utah Project, a vast irrigation and water conservation program.

The Central Utah Project was authorized by Congress as a "participating project" of the huge Colorado River Storage Project in the Upper Basin. But before reservoirs and other works could be built, prospective users had to agree to repay costs allocated to water supply. The people of the counties voted 13 to 1 for a repayment contract for the Bonneville Unit of Central Utah, which will provide 23,000 acre-feet of irrigation water, 79,000 acre-feet of municipal and industrial water, and 6,500 acre-feet for fish conservation. Under terms of a contract between the Central Utah Water Conservancy District and the Secretary of the Interior, repayment of the $324,600,000 project will take place over forty years at 3.5 per cent interest. Power revenues will account for $194 million of repayment costs. Water to be made available will support a population increase of 300,000.

The states, of course, have always recognized the interstate nature of waters, and compacts dealing with water predate the formation of the Union. A listing published by the Council of State Governments traces the first interstate compact back to 1783, when New Jersey and Pennsylvania agreed on jurisdiction over certain islands in the Delaware and took action to improve navigation.

Most state river compacts since have also been concerned with boundary questions and navigation. Even today, states negotiate with each other over river boundaries, sometimes because of shifts in channels and sometimes because of long-standing disagreement. The joint boundary commission of the states of Minnesota and Wisconsin began talks in January, 1966, dealing with Mississippi boundary questions, as well as land use and water quality.

The modern interstate river compact came into being in 1923, when the seven states of the Colorado River basin reached agreement on apportionment of that river's waters. The Colorado River Compact was a necessary first step to construction of the reclamation projects that today regulate the river's flow. It also heralded an expansion of federal-local partnership.

The interstate compact needs Congressional approval because nine compacts were required to resolve state boundaries before the Constitution could be drafted. Article I, Section 10, of the Constitution states:

"No state shall without the consent of Congress, enter into any agreement or compact with another state, or a foreign power."

With the Colorado River Compact, the idea spread, and states turned to this kind of negotiation in lieu of litigation to settle rights to water allocation. The device was soon extended to bridges and tunnels over or under interstate waterways, and to port facilities.

In 1932, Congress approved the first interstate pollution abatement compact, which involved New York, New Jersey, and Connecticut. This was followed by other similar multistate compacts, as states sought to meet immediate problems arising from common-boundary rivers.

Congress attempted to encourage the use of compacts among states in the 1936 Flood Control Act, which contained a provision giving advance consent to states to negotiate compacts to avert flood. The 1948 Water Pollution Control Act sought further to stimulate joint state effort to abate growing befouling of the nation's waters.

Devices other than compacts have been used to bring about cooperation with individual states and among the states. With state cooperation, the U.S. Geological Survey and the U.S. Public Health Service have created a network of water-monitering stations. Because of the nature of its activities, the Fish and Wildlife Service has sought to promote interstate cooperation. Federal pollution control work has necessarily called for multistate agreement.

The Department of Health, Education, and Welfare has issued a "suggested" uniform State Water Pollution Control Act, but the federal government can do little more than suggest.

Despite some solid accomplishments in pollution abatement, major gains through interstate compacts have been made in the area of water allocation. Compacts have had small or no effect on watershed improvement, and other conservation activity, although one laid the foundation for reclamation work on the Colorado. In general, the compact approach has been inadequate to solution of flood control and pollution problems. The Council of State Governments is a natural advocate of the multistate compact. Yet, Frederick L. Zimmerman and Mitchell Wendell, two authorities in the area, wrote in a 1951 volume (The Interstate Compact Since 1925) published by the council: ". . . to date agreements which rely for enforcement entirely upon the officials of the separate states have not worked well."

The weakness of the interstate compact as an antipollution weapon is that it is often tailored to the lowest common denominator acceptable to the negotiating states. Although a low standard might be better than none, it is usually not good enough to maintain water fit to swim in and otherwise protect the public interest. The very passage of the Water Quality Act of 1965 is eloquent proof that the interstate compact is a weak instrument.

The Ohio River Compact, which created the Ohio River Sanitation Commission (ORSANCO), is in some measure an exception and, as noted elsewhere, its accomplishments have been impressive, even though the river remains badly polluted. In their treatise *The Administration of Interstate Compacts* (Louisiana State University Press, 1959), Richard Leach and Redding S. Sugg, Jr., attribute the measure of success to the commission's "decision to rely mainly on education and persuasion."

But it is likely that ORSANCO has worked as well as it has because most of those using the Ohio's waters recognized the critical condition into which they had fallen, and these people have had the intelligence and the sense of community responsibility to be willing to carry a share of the load. A measure of success on the Potomac may be attributed as much to White House influence and Congressional nearness as to "education." Even here, quite helpless District of Columbia officials were criticized in 1965 by the Senate Appropriations Committee for short-sightedness in water planning.

The interstate compact has sometimes been used as a device to thwart federal water programs. It was such a gambit that caused Franklin D. Roosevelt in 1942 to veto the Republican River Compact involving Colorado, Kansas, and Nebraska. In his veto message, the President said:

It is unfortunate that the [original] compact also seeks to withdraw jurisdiction of the United States over the waters of the Republican River for purposes of navigation and that it appears to restrict the authority of the United States to construct irrigation works and to appropriate water for irrigation purposes in the basin. The provisions having the effect . . . would unduly impede the full development of the basin and would unduly limit the exercise of the established national interest in such development.

The compact was subsequently revised and limited to allocation of water to the three states—after which came federal approval.

Under authority of the Flood Control Act of 1936, Connecticut, Massachusetts, New Hampshire, and Vermont agreed on a compact to abate flooding on the Merrimack and Connecticut rivers. They sought to vest in themselves all hydroelectric power authority and provided a state veto of federal projects. This attempt to reverse federal policy had the support of utility and other business interests. President Roosevelt frustrated the take-over by announcing his opposition, which killed the proposed pact.

In 1961, and again in 1962, the effort was repeated. The four states proposed that Congress authorize a Northeastern Water and Related Resources Compact for all six New England states. Senator George Aiken of Vermont indignantly told a Senate committee that the proposed compact "is without doubt the worst that has ever been proposed. . . ." He charged that it had been prepared by an "expert experienced in the art of spreading confusion and obfuscation," and that it was opposed by virtually every federal agency concerned with soil and water conservation.

This opposition from Senator Aiken, and from others who traced ties between the sponsoring New England Council and private interests, again killed the compact. Nonetheless, the fight for the instrument has seriously delayed integrated development of the region's water resources. Until 1965, when Congress authorized the Dickey and Lincoln School dams on the St. Johns River in Maine, New England was the sole region of the nation without a federal project having a hydroelectric component.

A historic experiment in federal-state water resources cooperation was begun in 1961 when Congress approved the Delaware River Compact, which created the Delaware River Commission. Members of the commission include the governors of each of four states and a federal representative. The commission is charged with preparing, approving, and implementing a single long-range program for development of the Delaware's waters. This will mean harmonizing the interests of 43 state, 14 interstate, and 19 federal agencies—and those of hundreds of enterprises depending upon the river's waters. The Corps of Engineers studied the river and proposed the commission's comprehensive plan. In signing the compact, the four affected states—New York, New Jersey, Pennsylvania, and Delaware—waived the right to take disputes over water allocation to the U.S. Supreme Court and gave the commission full authority to allocate water.

A severe strain was placed on the Delaware River Compact by the drought of the 1960's. As described earlier, New York City's use of water threatened to cause salt-water intrusion into the water intake pipes of Philadelphia and Camden. An emergency meeting of the commission directed New York to decrease its take from the river and release more water from its reservoirs. The strain was eased as the result of the compromise arranged by federal officials.

The Delaware River Compact may open new roads to state-federal partnership because of its novel structure and broad purposes. Nonetheless, it was almost rejected by the Kennedy Administration because it lacked the historic "preference" clause, which gives city-owned plants and nonprofit cooperatives first chance to buy the hydroelectric power produced at federal dams. Committees of the House and Senate dealing with the question took what they termed a "neutral" position. They stated that the preference clause should apply on the Delaware, but concluded that "in the future when we write the legislation to authorize projects will be the time to deal with the preference question."

Stronger federal-state cooperation may also result from the Water Resources Planning Act of 1965. In October of that year, the new Federal Resources Council acted on a request from New England governors and approved formation of the New England River Basin Commission, the first to be formed under the act. The commission will serve areas in the New England states plus a portion of New York state within the drainage basin of the Housatonic River. The commission is authorized to coordinate plans for long-range water resource development, establish construction priorities, and work on a comprehensive regional water plan. However, it is forbidden by law to study interbasin transfer.

Federal-state cooperation including recreation has been emphasized in the interim report on the Potomac prepared jointly by a federal task force and the Potomac River Basin Advisory Committee representing Virginia, Maryland, West Virginia, Pennsylvania, and the District of Columbia. It calls for the vast Potomac Valley historic park and three upstream reservoirs, and could lead to a compact similar to that on the Delaware.

Federal-local partnership for flood control was authorized by Congress in 1936. Federal grants helped to build local levees on the upper Mississippi, but lack of a unified program resulted in tragic loss of life and property in the angry flood of 1965. Only St. Paul and a handful of towns at the lower end of the upper basin have completed works capable of holding back the massive recurring floods.

Some cities, such as Mankato, Minnesota, have turned down federal aid and have built their own levee systems. Other cities, fearful of recurrence of the 1965 floods, have asked for help. Those floods led to the creation of the Upper Mississippi Flood Control Action Committee, which favors real federal partnership in a planned program involving local funds and participation.

Although improvement was coming, by the end of 1966 much remained to be done to bring either interstate cooperation or the great partnership of federal, state, and local government to the point of efficiently administering the nation's water resources. Meanwhile, the federal government had failed to put its own house in order in the natural resource field.

One who is familiar with the operation of federal resource agencies is not surprised to learn that the Agricultural Stabilization and Conservation Service in the Department of Agriculture for years paid a bounty to Dakota farmers for draining potholes and wetlands, while the Bureau of Sport Fisheries and Wildlife in the Department of the Interior entreated their conservation. More appalling is the result of conflicting policy in the Florida Everglades, where the National Park Service of the Department of the Interior has come into headlong conflict with the Army Corps of Engineers. As described previously, the Engineers have built massive levees to contain runoff from Lake Okeechobee and have constructed 1,400 miles of drainage canals in the name of flood control. Park Service officials complained bitterly that the Engineers drained Everglades National Park almost dry in their efforts to halt flooding in the wetlands area and to reclaim 'Glades country for agriculture.

Flood control advocates have backed the Engineers and their work with the assertion that this reclamation is for people while Everglades Park is "for the birds." Yet, as National Park Service director George

Hartzog, Jr. has pointed out, the real question isn't people versus birds at all. "The park," Director Hartzog has stated, "was created for people —and the real question is whether we will preserve something of tremendous value to the people, or sit by and see this great possession destroyed."

Conflicts like these, of course, can be found in many places in government, and in nongovernment institutions as well. They are interesting and of some significance, but their real importance lies in the fact that they may be symptoms of major sicknesses.

Our sickness in water administration is easily diagnosed: No one is in charge of the federal effort. As of January, 1966, the major water resources responsibilities were fragmented among four Cabinet-level departments: Defense; Health, Education, and Welfare; Interior; and Agriculture.

Following these four came two important independent agencies with key water responsibilities. The jurisdiction of the Tennessee Valley Authority is limited to a single river basin, but it is all-encompassing there. The Federal Power Commission, which decides who shall build dams at particular sites and under what terms, has assumed major river-basin-planning functions.

On the basis of expenditures, the most extensive federal activity in the water resources field is conducted by the Department of Defense through the Army Corps of Engineers. Established in 1802, the Corps was given responsibility for maintaining navigable channels on the Ohio and Mississippi in the rivers and harbors legislation of 1824. This was the start of a long-term lease on work on navigable waterways that has gradually been expanded to include dam construction for flood control, power, and other purposes. The Corps is a highly efficient construction organization. But there is at least an element of truth in the contention that it has been more interested in dam building than in river-basin development, more concerned with water movement than with watershed care.

The Corps operates in every state. Although commanded by Army officers, it employs thousands of civilians. Because its connection with the Department of Defense's major mission is tenuous, the Corps has operated with almost complete independence in carrying out its chief domestic duty.

The position of the Engineers in water resource management was strengthened after the Civil War, during the administration of Ulysses S. Grant. Continued flooding on major rivers caused Congress to create a commission to study flood problems under the guise of navigation needs. Small sums for flood control were included in its navigation appropriations from 1879 until 1917.

Disastrous Mississippi floods brought the first clear-cut federal flood control legislation in 1917, during the Wilson Administration. But it was not until Congress approved the Jadwin Plan in 1928 that the Corps of Engineers became at least as concerned with flood control as with navigation. The Jadwin Plan studies remained relatively academic until floods took 450 lives in 1936. In his second term, Franklin D. Roosevelt called for action. Congress responded with the first significant flood-control legislation—which also marked the start of a major bureaucratic tangle.

Prior to 1936, the Bureau of Reclamation had had almost sole federal authority to harness rivers for storage and electric power. Lodged in the Department of the Interior, the bureau was created by Congress in 1902 to reclaim land in Arizona, California, Colorado, Idaho, Kansas, New Mexico, Montana, Nebraska, Nevada, North Dakota, Oklahoma, Oregon, South Dakota, Texas, Utah, Washington, and Wyoming. The bureau's authority remains limited to these states although it has become a major instrument of federal conservation policy. In 1906, the bureau was authorized to build dams for hydroelectric power as well as for irrigation. But it remained largely an irrigation agency until passage of the Boulder Canyon Act in 1928. The building of Hoover Dam established its prowess as a master buillder of massive water projects.

By 1936, three major agencies were hip deep in water development—Army, Interior, and TVA. In 1936, legislation brought the Department of Agriculture into the picture by authorizing the construction of small upstream and tributary check dams, and small watershed restoration, reforestation, and related soil-conservation projects. This program, although essential, has often been in conflict with that of the builders of the big dams.

The 1936 legislation nonetheless marked a significant departure in federal water-resource development. It clearly recognized the federal responsibility for flood control; it authorized 250 projects, allocated relief funds for conservation, appropriated money for survey and research work, created a mechanism for federal-state-local cooperation in flood control, and established a policy that federal water projects must create economic benefits greater than costs.

The federal tangle was further complicated by 1944 legislation which provided that water projects—particularly those designed for flood control—be multipurpose wherever possible. This brought the Corps of Engineers all the way into irrigation, power generation, and recreation.

Because the Corps had no marketing facilities for water and power, Congress turned to existing facilities in the Department of the Interior, providing that:

> Power produced at hydro plants built by the Corps of Engineers would be marketed by Interior.
>
> Surplus water from Corps projects in the seventeen states served by the Bureau of Reclamation would be sold by Interior.
>
> All Corps projects costs attributable to flood control, navigation, and recreation would be paid from federal tax monies. Costs attributed to power were to be repaid by Interior from power sales revenues.

Like all organizations, federal bureaus seek to justify themselves by reaching out for new functions. Once created, these functions rarely dissolve, and few agencies willingly divest themselves of authority or staff. By 1955, the second Hoover Commission Report listed ten agencies with water resource responsibilities in the Department of the Interior alone: the Bureau of Reclamation, three separate power-marketing agencies, the Bureau of Indian Affairs, the Bureau of Land Management, the Fish and Wildlife Service, the Bureau of Mines, the Geological Survey, and the National Park Service.

Since 1955, the Office of Saline Water, the Office of Water Resources Research, and the Bureau of Outdoor Recreation have been added—and Fish and Wildlife has been elevated to bureau status. Water resource functions are coordinated through an assistant secretary for Water and Power, but the assistant secretaries for Public Land Management and Fish and Wildlife also have major roles in water resource decisions.

Increased pollution of our rivers and lakes brought the Public Health Service of the Department of Health, Education, and Welfare into the water picture in 1956 when the first antipollution legislation was passed. The Water Quality Act of 1965 increased HEW's role by creating the Federal Water Pollution Control Administration within the department under a new assistant secretary. (This administration has since been transferred to the Department of the Interior.)

The Department of Agriculture's involvement in water resources has grown as its programs have proliferated. As already noted, the Soil Conservation Service builds small dams and seeks to restore small watersheds. The Forest Service builds check dams and concerns itself with pollution, storage, and other water resource programs in the national forests where it holds jurisdiction. Both the Agricultural Stabilization and Conservation Service and the Farmers Home Administration provide aid to farmers for projects related to water resources. Agricultural Research and Economic Research Service are involved in water research programs. The Rural Electrification Administration is concerned with hydroelectric power generation and marketing.

The Department of State is concerned with water allocation, pollution, and related problems through such agencies as the International Boundary and Water Commission (United States and Mexico), the International Joint Commission on the Great Lakes (United States and Canada), and through treaties such as the one governing the development of the Columbia.

Further muddying the water picture is a multiplicity of state and local agencies with responsibilities that overlap as much as those of the federal agencies. As noted earlier, efforts to clean up the Hudson River may be impeded or even frustrated by the tangle of overlapping agencies.

As the chapter on planning made clear, the desperate need for coordination of the efforts of all the federal agencies has been recognized. The Interagency Committee on Water Resources was formed at the Cabinet level years ago. Partially as a result of its activities, the Bureau of Reclamation and the Corps of Engineers executed a "treaty" at the start of the Kennedy Administration. The Water Resources Planning Act followed in 1965. But there has been no single department with prime jurisdiction in the natural resource field. Natural Resources should be a department comparable to Defense or Agriculture, or the newer departments of Housing and Urban Development or Transportation.

The creation of a Department of Natural Resources is long overdue.

Population increases and technology geared to ever-rising living standards are exerting massive pressures upon the nation's limited store of natural resources. Not only water, but land, mineral, and forest reserves—and even the air we breathe—are seriously threatened by malpractice and the seemingly insatiable appetite of modern industrial society. More urgently than ever, a unified national policy is required to prevent heedless spoilation and to husband diminishing supplies.

Resources for the Future, a Washington-based conservation research authority, has projected:

> a tripling of requirements for both energy and metals by the year 2000, almost a tripling for timber, and almost a doubling for farm products and for withdrawal depletions of fresh water. . . . Increasing demands for land space for outdoor recreation, urban growth, highways, airports and perhaps forests by the year 2000 will far exceed any relief provided by possible reduction in land needed for crops and the amounts of now unused land that can be pressed into service . . . land requirements, if each use is counted separately, would add up to 50 million more acres than the country has, and this assumes no increase whatsoever in forest land.

Water is the natural resource most beset by bureaucratic multiplicity; it is also the resource that has suffered actual deterioration in the past two decades. But the management of the nation's lands, and of its increasingly important outdoor recreation resource development program, suffer similar ills.

A paper published by the *Natural Resources Journal* of the New Mexico School of Law declared that the confusion stems from "the administrative organization of federal agencies and not from lack of good will or devotion on the part of the agencies concerned. There are no heroes or villains in this story," it said. The article also pointed out that "In nature, the resources of soil, water, forests, wildlife and minerals are a closely interrelated whole. . . . A symphony orchestra composed of outstanding musicians each dedicated to producing beautiful music will produce only discordant noise in the absence of a conductor."

As long ago as 1949, the first Hoover Commission tried to end the federal resources tangle by creating a Department of Natural Resources. And ten years previously, Secretary of the Interior Harold Ickes had proposed that Interior be transformed into a Department of Conservation.

In 1965 and 1967, I introduced into the Senate bills to create a Department of Natural Resources. The description of departmental changes that follows below is based on the provisions of those bills and suggestions I have made in connection with them. This is a controversial measure because it steps on bureaucratic toes and would change long-established methods and prerogatives. But the tremendous pressure on our natural resources has made such an agency regrouping highly essential to the national welfare.

Although a Department of Natural Resources would include all federal agencies with major resource responsibilities, only those relating to water need be discussed here. Water and power would be the direct responsibility of an under secretary for water and power. Reporting to him would be two assistant secretaries.

The first of these assistant secretaries would direct the planning and construction activities of the Bureau of Reclamation, the civil functions of the Corps of Engineers,* the operations performed by the Soil Conservation Service under the Watershed Protection and Flood Prevention Act, the Office of Water Resources Research, the Office of Saline Water, and the Water Pollution Control Administration. Water resources plans of the Federal Power Commission would conform to river-basin authority plans or, where none exist, would be subject to approval by the Department of Natural Resources.

The second assistant secretary would direct all federal activities in the field of power generation, transmission, and marketing now exercised by Bonneville Power, the Southeastern and Southwestern Power administrations, the Bureau of Reclamation, and the Corps of Engineers.

In May, 1966, President Johnson took a major step toward placing all federal water resources management functions in one department. He transferred the new Water Pollution Control Administration from the Department of Health, Education, and Welfare to the Department of the Interior. (Recently, another proposal aimed at improved natural resource management has been advanced, by Senator George McGovern of South Dakota. It would create a Council of Resources and Conservation Advisers within the executive office of the President,

* The Corps of Engineers need not be split up. Policy direction could be in the Department of Natural Resources in peacetime, and in the Department of the Army in wartime, in the same way that the Coast Guard moves from Transportation to Navy and back.

and a Select Committee on the Resources Conservation Report in the Senate and House.)

The creation of a Department of Natural Resources would not abolish the many agencies concerned with water, or the differences of opinion between them, nor would it eliminate the necessity for coordination of their activities. But it would assure a unified policy at the secretarial level, in the same way that we have a unified defense policy at the Department of Defense level. It would give to one department both the responsibility and the authority to present to the President and the Congress a national program for the conservation and development of our natural resources.

The establishment of river-basin authorities and the creation of the Department of Natural Resources would give the nation the governmental machinery without which sophisticated management of our waters could hardly succeed. One would enable the resource regions, through viable authorities, to manage their waters; the other would enable the federal government to carry out its responsibilities of national leadership.

CHAPTER XIX

Toward a National Policy

THERE IS GENERAL AGREEMENT that the nation is in the midst of a perilous water crisis. At least, that fact is well understood by numerous local, state, and federal officials, by many members of Congress, and by many journalists, scientists, educators, and industrialists. The people of the United States want to restore and preserve their waters, but they have adopted no national policy to accomplish that end. The lack of such a policy is the major reason that water deterioration has been permitted to go as far as it has.

Policy can be defined as the course of action that has been decided on by an individual, an organization, or a society. There is no such course of action in relation to water on which the people of the United States are agreed and to which they are committed. There are many great water conservation and development projects underway, but they do not yet add up to an adequate national program. Putting an adequate program into effect will require two quite different kinds of action.

The first includes application of what have been called the "scientific solutions" to water problems. Broadly, these are the remedies that the scientists, engineers, and technicians can be expected to provide. Examples are dam construction, sewage treatment, desalting, and research.

The second is determination of public policy. This means the decisions "we, the people" must make—through government—to manage our waters in the national interest. This category includes enforcement of water quality standards, the organization of government agencies, and preservation of "wild rivers."

A good example of a policy matter is what Washington, D.C., has labeled "no new starts." The name had its genesis in the Truman Administration, when, as an economy measure, it was decided to build no more federal dams until the Korean War was over. During the second Eisenhower Administration (or so its critics claim) the "no new starts" policy was reinitiated for federal economy, only to be dropped quietly during Eisenhower's last year in office. This did not mean that dam construction was not going forward; after 1956, the great Colorado River Storage Project was under construction, and millions were being invested in it. The policy meant only that no new projects were begun.

It is easy to see that the more new starts there are, the faster the water storage needs of the nation can be met. Of course, new starts cost mony. But ultimately the public must decide: How fast is the dam building program to move?

The vital importance of the citizen's role in the restoration of the nation's waters will be clarified by a brief review of where we stand in relation to water problems and improvement programs.

Pollution is the water problem of concern to most Americans. The rapid growth of population and the remarkable expansion of industry in the United States have increased the use of rivers and lakes for waste disposal at a rate far faster than corrective measures have been organized. In addition, the many new chemical substances being developed each year produce exotic pollutants beyond the capability of sewage treatment plants to neutralize. The two great sources of water pollution are cities and industries. But, for many reasons, the problems posed by industry are the more difficult to solve. These include: the greater volume, variety, and complexity of industrial wastes; the political difficulty in inducing prominent industries to adopt more expensive processes; and the federal financial incentives, which have been available to communities but not to private business.

Some have said that America would have plenty of water if it were taken care of. This optimistic statement does not apply to the West—

some 40 per cent of the land area of the nation. There, shortage of water is chronic, and it poses a definite limitation on growth.

In the East, the drought of the 1960's demonstrated that the narrow margins of reserve in many areas make water shortage an eastern problem as well. Further, it appears that international management will be needed to maintain sufficient good water in the nation's greatest reserve, the Great Lakes.

Variability reduces the capability of many river basins to supply sufficient water, and it imposes large flood losses. Great flood control works, both upstream dams and downstream levees, have sharply reduced the amount of flooding, but the continued development of dwellings and industries on flood plains keeps losses high.

Urban expansion imposes new strains on watersheds with resultant erosion and flooding. Real estate development also encroaches on precious marshlands and shorelines. The results of overgrazing, strip-mining, timber cutting and other destructive practices of years ago continue to plague watersheds and the waters they store.

The volume of water wasted is extremely hard to measure. But billions of gallons a year are wasted—both through water that flows unused to the sea and water that is used only once. Much water is lost through evaporation both from surface reservoirs and "water-stealing" plants.

As of the end of 1966, the status of water resources programs could be summarized briefly in seven classifications as follows:

Land Conservation. Millions of acres have been restored through long-standing programs conducted by government and through citizen-government cost sharing. Figures compiled in 1964 showed that 30 per cent of all U.S. cropland and 25 per cent of Great Plains acreage had undergone restorative treatment. The over-all cropland included much in the South that had been depleted by cotton and tobacco agriculture. Approximately one-third of the nation's watersheds have also been treated.

Re-use. There is widespread recognition—both in government and industry—of the necessity for improved treatment of water. Demonstration programs of the Public Health Service and the treatment programs of many cities and industries are showing the way. But expansion of the best methods to all operations is a tremendously complex and expensive task. Federal expenditures on municipal sewage treatment for fiscal year 1967 will amount to some $230 million. This is about 30 per cent of the total to be expended.

Research. Research is the key to increased efficiency for every category of water management. The federally supported research program alone involves more than 3,200 separate projects on all phases of use and conservation of water. Expanded underground storage, improved handling of pollutants, and reduction of evaporation losses could mean large water savings.

Desalination. American industrial firms offer desalination plants for sale, and there is a worldwide attack on the problem of cutting the cost of removing salt from sea water. Use of desalted water, however, is still limited to areas without traditional sources. The federal research and demonstration program, plus the building of some huge atomic energy plants, will provide more reliable cost figures and performance data. Without doubt, desalting will grow substantially, as will purification of inland brackish supplies. The extent of that growth depends upon costs (including cost of pumping from sea level) in relation to other methods of providing water, and the management of waste disposal.

Weather Modification. Precipitation of water has been induced in particular instances where favorable conditions exist. Changing the weather is considered a reality from a scientific point of view. However, this source cannot be counted on to provide firm supplies for any water resource region.

Redistribution. Interbasin transfer of water is taking place, and it offers hope to arid regions. But neither political nor resource-planning foundations have been laid to permit transfers of water in the quantity many believe necessary to solve major national water problems.

Planning. As water management grows more complex, the need for wise planning becomes more acute. It is essential for the efficient application of available technology—of re-use, desalination, or diversion of water—in particular water resource regions. Consideration of water supply development in relation to expanding suburbs, highways, and industries is only part of the problem. If the environment is to be protected and enhanced, and provision made for recreation needs and wildlife habitat, projects must be considered while there is yet time and space to apply alternate solutions.

280 THE WATER CRISIS

Passage of the Water Resources Planning Act has given a needed impetus to planning. It enables basin-planning authorities to be established where they are desired and where agreement can be reached. Two basin authorities have been established, and three more are near that point.

To restore the nation's waters and assure a sufficient supply for all uses, the corrective measures listed above must be applied—in proper proportions—to all river basins. This will not be done, however, without overcoming the conflicts and politics of pressure groups that, for the most part, are responsible for the pollution, shortage, and waste we seek to end.

Another way of stating where the nation stands in relation to its waters is to say that we are moving rapidly to solve *technical* problems, more slowly to solve *political* ones.

Stringent legislation and effective public and industrial cooperation have created one of the world's cleanest rivers in the highly industrialized Ruhr Valley of Germany. Yet, the Rhine, which flows through the heartland of the West German Federal Republic, is one of the world's most polluted waterways.

The paradox is explained by politics—international in this case. The Rhine is the busiest river in Europe. But its waters carry more tonnage in garbage and waste chemicals than the barges on its surface carry as freight. The Rhine is badly polluted because no effective authority governs the use of its waters. German experts say that more than 40 per cent of the wastes carried by the maltreated river originate in the potash mines of Alsace. France, Austria, and Switzerland have done little to abate Rhine pollution because they use the river only to serve their industries.

The same technology that keeps the Ruhr River clean is available to the Rhine. But the technical tools cannot be put to work in the absence of a policy and an effective authority to govern its waters. In the same way, failure to solve political problems—failure to develop a national policy—makes it impossible for the United States to utilize available technology fully.

Although they are interrelated, there are a number of reasons why no national commitment has been made to manage water resources.

One is the "do what was done last time" way of looking at the matter. Because our waters have been managed by state and local authorities—

with federal agencies participating only in traditional patterns—the task is not thought of as a national one. Only infrequently do we hear expressed a point of view like that of Seattle consulting economist H. Dwayne Kreager, who called the continuing water shortage in the populous Southwest a "national economic hazard," the pollution of Lake Erie a "national economic catastrophe," and the shortage of water for two years in the city of New York a "national embarrassment."

In his book *The Coming Water Famine*, Congressman Jim Wright of Texas called for a wider view of the value of water projects to the nation. He condemned the idea—hallowed by annual repetition in the press—that federal water developments are essentially gifts that members of Congress bear home to their constituents and said the term "pork barrel" is both "inappropriate and misleading."

It should be pointed out that airports as well as water projects are beneficial to local areas and that large doses of federal tax money go into building and improving them. They are not, however, referred to as "pork." They are recognized as valuable to the nation as well as to the communities in which they are built. One reason is that airport improvements are proposed in a National Airport Plan, which the Federal Aviation Agency issues every year. Water projects would gain in public esteem were they presented as units in a national program.

Strong opposition in principle to further federal involvement in water resources management is a second reason why no national commitment exists. Chapter II described the conference called by the U.S. Chamber of Commerce to protest the setting of federal water quality standards. The organization's president declared that there is "no national problem," and opposed the concept that the "problem can best be met in a national context." The Water Resources Planning Act reflected the state fears of federal domination in its requirement for unanimity before a river-basin plan can be adopted.

A third reason is that government agencies often prefer the *status quo*, as do the "client groups" that support them. In 1965, the American Waterways Operators released a memorandum from its Washington office warning members against the bill to move all federal natural resource agencies into one department.

"The future of navigation in the United States will be dim indeed if the Corps of Engineers loses its responsibility for civil works to a

282

282 THE WATER CRISIS

catch-all Department of Natural Resources," the memorandum declared. "The time to head off this transfer is now."

Another obstacle to adoption of a national policy is lack of recognition of the economic factors involved in providing water for the future. One of these factors is investment. This point was discussed in a paper titled "Economic Problems of Population Growth," which Oscar Harkavy presented at Georgetown University in 1964, and which was published in pamphlet form by the Ford Foundation. Harkavy said:

> Water demand and supply is very difficult to estimate far into the future. Assumptions must be made as to the extent of future investment in massive river development projects. Brackish water, even ocean water, can be demineralized with existing technology and will become increasingly economical as inexpensive sources of energy, such as solar energy, are developed. But these optimistic predictions assume timely investment of huge amounts of capital.

A corollary to the magnitude of needed investment is the fact that the water supplies of the future will be more expensive.

As has been pointed out frequently, most of the water that is easy to get at and inexpensive is already in use. Only costlier projects can put more to use. In the East and South, more treatment is required; this will raise costs. Growth of the large metropolitan centers of the West depends on more water; if, as hoped, it can be imported, the expense will far exceed that from the closer sources previously put to use.

It should be noted that a benefit to water management can be expected to accrue from rising water prices. More realistic pricing of water can lead to conservation. If users pay real costs, they will learn to ration when watering the lawn or recycling for industrial use, and to dump smaller quantities of industrial wastes into streams and lakes. The question of metering for domestic use in New York City is a case in point. Water is wasted—as is any other commodity—when it is free or when the price is very low.

Nevertheless, water supplies will cost more in the years ahead, and the cost will go much higher than necessary if haphazard development is permitted.

In sum, we have failed to fully comprehend the size and scope of the water management task. A century ago, water management meant the construction of dams, pipelines, and sewer systems. Later, it included treating municipal water supplies to kill disease germs. Meanwhile, rivers were improved for navigation, and dams constructed for electric power production. Subsequently, there came the building of flood control works and the protection of soils and watersheds against erosion. As more waste went into rivers and lakes, sewage treatment works became more common and more sophisticated. When pollution began to close beaches and spoil the wildlife environment of rivers, lakes, and estuaries, when building began to encroach on marshlands, it was seen that water management must include recreation and habitat conservation. After World War II, water management began to mean all of the above put together, and, by the 1960's, complete "multipurpose" use was the recognized goal.

For the future, water management must mean the reconciliation of all uses, preservation of water and related land resources, and provision of enough water for constantly expanding needs. This aim can be accomplished only through total planning of the water environment.

It has been a slow process, but the United States *is* moving toward acceptance of a national water policy. There were three significant straws in the wind in 1966. All fifty states officially informed the Secretary of the Interior that they would comply with the requirement that water quality standards on interstate streams be set by June 30, 1967. In the Clean Water Restoration Act of 1966, the Congress strengthened both the river-basin concept and federal-state cooperation in fighting pollution. By moving the Water Pollution Control Administration from the Department of Health, Education, and Welfare to the Department of the Interior, the President took a step in the direction of a natural resources department.

Also, in 1966, the Senate passed a bill to create a national water commission. It was introduced by Senator Henry M. Jackson, chairman of the Senate Committee on Interior and Insular Affairs. The fact that it stemmed from a proposal of the budget arm of the President—the Bureau of the Budget—indicated that concern for lack of unified water management extended to the highest levels of the executive branch.

As proposed, the commission would be composed of seven persons outside the federal government appointed by the President and confirmed by the Senate. It would report in five years. The group's task would be to review "present and anticipated national water resource problems. . . ." These included all the "alternative ways" of meeting the water requirements of the United States that have been discussed in this volume.

Although the House failed to pass the bill, it was reintroduced and passed by the Senate early in 1967. At this writing, it again awaits action by the House.

More than twenty federal commissions and committees have reviewed the nation's water problems during the past half century. Some were named from the executive departments by the President; others included representatives of the government and the general public. The most recent review body was the Senate Select Committee, which has been mentioned frequently in these pages.

A new national water commission could make a contribution of even greater value. It would come at a critical time. It would have a historic opportunity to demand a coherent national water policy and a vigorous national program. It could scarcely fail to exert enormous influence, since its recommendations would probably become the proposals of the national administration. Its prestige could be expected to override the objections of regional, economic, or agency interests.

The commission's great opportunity would lie in the capacity of such a body to take the long view of the national—and continental—water picture. An example of the need for such a view is the question of interbasin transfer. A body like Congress, made up of sectional representatives, finds it difficult to give fair consideration to such a question, especially one charged with emotion. This parochial approach has brought such results as the provision in the Planning Act that prohibits the National Water Resources Council from even considering diverting water from one basin into another. Federal agencies, too, are closely tied to regions, or industries, and cannot speak for the nation.

The proposed formation of such a commission—or its actual formation —must not be used as an excuse to "wait and see." Five years for a report means ten years before most recommendations could be in operation. The work of the Senate Select Committee cannot be described as anything but a success. Many forward steps in legislation were inspired by its findings and its proposals. But it reported in January, 1961, and, for example, urged river-basin planning. Five years later, legislation had been enacted, but only two river-basin authorities were actually in existence. It takes such organizations—or new departments that may be set up—many months to establish procedures, equip offices, and "staff up."

The condition of our waters will not permit delay of water resource programs. If water is to be provided and water resources protected for the many necessary uses, and if deterioration is to be stopped, we must go forward with watershed conservation, improved water use practices for industry, study of interbasin transfer, and research, including desalination and weather modification. Four considerations are of major significance:

The planning and construction of projects for water storage and flood control must be vigorously pursued.

The national clean water effort must be rapidly implemented to the full limits of the law.

A department of natural resources must be created promptly in the federal government.

The creation of river-basin authorities must be encouraged, with the goal of establishing effective planning agencies for all water resource regions.

These points constitute a minimum program for the end of the 1960's. America has run out of time in which to repair its water resources. With a gross national product approaching $800 billion a year, investment capital need not be a roadblock. Each day's delay adds to the cost, but cost is not the issue. The future of every American depends on water regardless of his income, profession, or station in life. No society can build material prosperity or spiritual health on the ruin of its physical environment.

Appendix

PRINCIPAL FEDERAL WATER RESOURCES LEGISLATION
1948–66

There are two general categories of legislation: authorization and appropriation. An authorization bill makes it lawful for a federal agency to conduct a program or build a project and for public funds to be spent on it. But the amount that can be spent in a particular fiscal year is listed in an appropriations bill. Frequently, amounts authorized are larger than those appropriated. This list of legislation refers to authorizations only. For clarity, the subject matter is presented in four divisions.

Table 1

WATER POLUTION

Year	*Title and Subject*	*Public Law No.*
1948	Water Pollution Control Act (provided a 5-year experimental pollution control program)	80–845
1950	Water Pollution Control Act Amendments (extending the 1948 act through 1956)	82–579
1956	Water Pollution Control Act Amendments (providing for federal grants to cities for sewage treatment plants, some federal enforcement powers, and research)	84–660
1961	*Water Pollution Control Act Amendments (extending federal enforcement powers, liberalizing construction grants program, accelerating research program)	87–88

* Senator Moss was a cosponsor of this bill.

Year	Title and Subject	Public Law No.
1965	*Water Quality Act (creating the Water Pollution Control Administration, authorizing larger appropriations and higher ceilings on construction grants, directing states to prepare quality standards by June 30, 1967)	89–234
1966	*Clean Water Restoration Act (greatly expanding federal grant funds, authorizing various studies and demonstration programs, providing a "bonus system" for state participation in financing construction of treatment plants and imposition of state-wide quality standards)	89–753

Table 2

WATER RESOURCES LEGISLATION

1952	Water Research and Development (establishing a program to demineralize sea water and brackish inland waters)	82–448
1953	Watershed Protection and Flood Prevention Act (assisting local organizations to plan and finance land treatment and construction of flood-control and agricultural water conservation structures)	83–566
1953	Water Conservation Facilities (extending to all states a water conservation program previously limited to arid states and authorizing federal loans for conservation activities)	83–597
1955	Saline Water Research (expanding the saline water research program)	84–111
1956	Small Reclamation Projects Act (providing federal assistance—principally loans—to states and organizations of water users for construction of small projects in the reclamation states)	84–984
1956	Watershed Protection and Flood Prevention Act Amendments (extending the program to nonagricultural uses of water and authorizing loans)	84–1018
1958	National Science Foundation Act Amendments (providing for a program of study and research on weather modification)	85–510
1958	Watershed Protection and Flood Prevention Act Amendments (authorizing federal cost sharing with states for fish and wildlife protection)	85–865
1958	Desalination Demonstration Plants (providing for construction of demonstration plants to produce sweet water from saline and brackish waters)	85–883

* Senator Moss was a cosponsor of these bills.

Year	Title and Subject	Public Law No.
1961	†Watershed Protection and Flood Prevention Act Amendments (making private, nonprofit water companies legal sponsors of projects under the act)	87–170
1961	*Saline Water Program Amendments (expanding saline water conversion program)	87–295
1964	*Water Resources Research Act (establishing water resources research centers and promoting a more adequate national program of water research)	88–379
1964	*Land and Water Conservation Fund Act (helping finance acquisition of outdoor land and water areas for recreation and helping pay state and federal recreation planning costs)	88–578
1965	Water Project Recreation Act (establishing uniform policies respecting recreation and fish and wildlife benefits and costs on federal multipurpose water projects)	89–72
1965	*Water Resources Planning Act (establishing water resources council and river-basin commissions and providing financial assistance to the states for water resources planning)	89–80
1965	*Saline Water (expanding and accelerating the saline water conversion program)	89–118
1965	*Rural Water Systems (assisting public, quasi-public, and nonprofit organizations to develop water systems for rural areas)	89–240
1966	*Water Resources Research Act Amendments (permitting use of additional types of institutions for federally financed water research)	89–404
1966	†Small Reclamation Projects Act Amendments (extending program to all states, altering interest formula, and expanding authorized amounts)	89–533

* Senator Moss was a cosponsor of these bills.
† Senator Moss was the principal sponsor of these bills.

Table 3

CIVIL WORKS PROJECTS
(Corps of Engineers)

Projects built by the Corps are not authorized in individual bills, but in
"omnibus flood control" bills generally passed once each year. This list includes those authorized in the last twenty years with a current estimated
federal cost of over $100 million each. Costs of land, easements, and rights-
of-way, as well as some water supply costs, are charged to local interests.

Year Authorized	Project	Federal Cost
1948, 1954, 1958 1960, 1962	Central and southern Florida (several streams)	$269,000,000
1950	The Dalles Lock and Dam, Columbia River, Oregon and Washington	$247,000,000
1950, 1965	John Day Lock and Dam, Columbia River, Oregon and Washington	$448,000,000
1950	Keystone Reservoir, Arkansas River, Oklahoma	$123,000,000
1950	Libby Reservoir, Kootenai River, Montana	$352,000,000
1954, 1960	Barkley Dam, Cumberland River, Kentucky and Tennessee	$142,000,000
1954	Inland Waterway from Delaware River to Chesapeake Bay, Delaware and Maryland	$104,429,000
1954, 1962	Kaysinger Bluff Reservoir, Osage River, Missouri	$196,000,000
1956	Great Lakes Connecting Channels, Michigan	$107,500,000
1958, 1962	Dworshak Reservoir, Clearwater River, Idaho	$243,000,000
1962	Illinois Waterway Duplicate Locks, Illinois River, Illinois	$167,000,000
1962	Tocks Island Reservoir, Delaware River, Pennsylvania, New York, New Jersey	$198,000,000
*1963	Mound City Lock and Dam, Ohio River, Illinois and Kentucky	$112,000,000
1965	Dickey Lincoln School Reservoirs, St. John River, Maine	$212,000,000
1965	Trinity River and tributaries, Texas	$763,500,000
1966	Knights Valley Reservoir, Franz-Maacama Creek drainage areas, Russian River Basin, California	$187,700,000
1966	Marysville Reservoir, Yuba River, California	$143,000,000

* Authorized by Secretary of Army under authority delegated by Congress in
the River and Harbor Act of 1909.

Table 4

WATER DEVELOPMENT PROJECTS
(Bureau of Reclamation)

Since 1947, seventeen projects costing more than $50 million each have been authorized for construction by the Bureau of Reclamation. The ten largest are listed here.

Year	Project	Total Estimated Cost	Public Law No.
1949	American River Division, Central Valley Project, California	$115,350,000	81–356
1949	Weber Basin Project, Utah	$105,077,000	81–273
1950	Sacramento Canals Unit, Central Valley Project, California	$135,404,000	81–839
1955	Trinity River Division, Central Valley Project, California	$256,974,000	84–386
1956	Colorado River Storage Project, Curecanti, Glen Canyon, Flaming Gorge, and Navajo Units, and Transmission Division	$688,000,000	84–485
1960	San Luis Unit, Central Valley Project, California	$599,371,000	86–488
1962	Fryingpan-Arkansas Project, Colorado	$182,581,000	87–590
1965	Garrison Diversion Unit, Missouri River Basin Project, North Dakota, South Dakota	$230,000,000	89–108
1965	Aburn Folsom South Unit, Central Valley Project, California	$424,670,000	89–161
1966	Third Powerplant, Grand Coulee Dam, Columbia Basin Project, Washington	$390,000,000	89–448

Bibliography

AMERICAN ASSOCIATION FOR THE ADVANCEMENT OF SCIENCE. *Water and Agriculture* (Publication No. 62, 1958); *Great Lakes Basin* (Publication No. 71, 1962); *Land and Water Use* (Publication No. 73, 1963). Baltimore, Md.: Horn-Shafer Co.

ASIMOV, ISAAC. *The New Intelligent Man's Guide to Science.* New York: Basic Books, 1965.

Big Load Afloat. American Waterways Operators (Washington, D.C.), 1965.

The Big Water Fight. League of Women Voters. Brattleboro, Vt.; Stephen Greene Press, 1966.

"Billions to Clean Up the Rivers," *Business Week,* April 24, 1965, pp. 50–58.

BREAK, GEORGE F. *Federal Lending and Economic Stability.* Washington, D.C.: Brookings Institution, 1965.

CARR, DONALD E. *Death of the Sweet Waters.* New York: W. W. Norton and Co., 1963.

CARSON, RACHEL. *Silent Spring.* Boston: Houghton Mifflin Co., 1962.

CAUDILL, HARRY M. *Night Comes to the Cumberlands.* Boston: Little, Brown & Co., 1963.

"Clean Air and Water" (Du Pont Publication No. 28). E. I. Du Pont de Nemours & Co. (Wilmington, Del.), 1965.

DAY, DOROTHY. *Loaves and Fishes.* New York: Harper & Row, 1963.

"Drought in Northeastern United States." Report of the Water Resources Council to the President, Washington, D.C., July 21, 1965.

DYMENT, ROBERT. "New York State Rolls Up Its Sleeves on Water Pollution," *Construction Craftsman* (Washington, D.C.), IV (May, 1965), 5–7.

ECKSTEIN, OTTO. *Water Resource Development.* ("Harvard Economic Studies," Vol. CIV.) Boston: Harvard University Press, 1961.

FEDERAL POWER COMMISSION. *National Power Survey Part I,* 1964; *National Power Survey Part II,* 1964; *Water Resources Appraisal for Hydroelectric Licensing,* 1964; *Planning and Status Reports,* 1965. Washington, D.C.: U.S. Government Printing Office.

GAFFNEY, MASON. "Diseconomies Inherent in Western Water Laws." Paper before Western Agricultural Economics Research Council at Tucson, Arizona, January 23, 1961.

GOLDBERG, ARTHUR J. *AFL-CIO Labor United.* New York: McGraw-Hill Book Co., 1956.

"Great Lakes Levels Study Requested." Report of International Joint Commission, December 9, 1964.

HAVEMAN, ROBERT H. *Water Resource Investment and the Public Interest.* Nashville, Tenn.: Vanderbilt University Press, 1965.

HODGE, CARLE. *Aridity and Man.* American Association for the Advancement of Science. Baltimore, Md.: Horn-Shafer Co., 1963.

HOLLIS, MARK D. "Water Pollution Today," *The Journal,* XXXVII (January, 1965), 1–7. Lancaster, Pa.: The Water Pollution Control Federation.

HOLLON, W. EUGENE. *The Great American Desert.* New York: Oxford University Press, 1966.

HOLUM, KENNETH. "Saline Water Conversion Program." Statement before House Irrigation Subcommittee, February 2, 1965.

"Hudson River Valley Commission Report to Governor Nelson A. Rockefeller and the Legislature of the State of New York," *The Hudson* (Iona Island, Bear Mountain, N.Y.), 1966.

KASSALOW, EVERETT M. *National Labor Movements in the Postwar World.* Evanston, Ill.: Northwestern University Press, 1963.

KENNEDY, HAROLD W. "Importance of Not Pricing Agriculture Out of the Water Picture." Speech at Convention of Irrigation Districts Association of Californa, Palm Springs, Calif., December 7, 1961.

————. "Quitting Title to Western Waters." Speech at National Association of Counties District Meeting, Las Vegas, Nev., December 13, 1962.

KERR, ROBERT S. *Land, Wood and Water.* New York: Fleet Publishing Corp., 1960.

KIERANS, T. W. "The Great Replenishment and Northern Development Canal." Presentation to Ontario Legislative Assembly, Toronto, May 5, 1965.

KUIPER, E. *Water Resources Development.* Washington, D.C.: Butterworth, 1965.

LANDSBERG, HANS H. *Natural Resources for U.S. Growth.* Baltimore, Md.: Johns Hopkins Press, 1964.

LANGBEIN, WALTER B., AND HOYT, WILLIAM G. *Water Facts for the Nation's Future.* New York: Ronald Press Co., 1959.

LEOPOLD, LUNA B., AND DAVIS, KENNETH S. *Water.* ("Life Science Library series.") New York: Time, Inc., 1966.

LEOPOLD, LUNA B., AND MADDOCK, T., JR. *The Flood Control Controversy.* New York: Ronald Press Co., 1954.

LLOYD, KENNETH M. "The Lake Erie–Ohio River Interconnecting Waterway." Statement by the Interconnecting Waterway, Inc., Columbus, Ohio, July, 1965.

MARRITZ, BOB. "A Visit to TVA–Resource Utopia," *Rural Electrification* (Washington, D.C.), No. 11 (August, 1965), 23–25.

McDONALD, ANGUS. "Natural Resources in the United States: 1965-2000." A survey by the National Farmers Union, Washington, D.C., September 15, 1965.

MILLER, D. W., *et al. Water Atlas of the United States.* Port Washington, N.Y.: Water Information Center, 1963.

NACE, RAYMOND L. "Global Thirst and the International Hydrological Decade," *The Science Teacher,* XXXII (January, 1965), 2–5.

"Nature's Constant Gift." TVA report on the water resource of the Tennessee Valley, June, 1966.

"The Niagara Keepsake," *The Journal of American History* (New York), VII (1913).

North American Water and Power Alliance Studies. Published by Ralph M. Parsons Co., Los Angeles, Calif., 1965.

NOSSITER, BERNARD D. *The Mythmakers.* Boston: Houghton Mifflin Co., 1964.

"Oregon's Water Problems and Future Needs." State Water Resources Conference, Salem, Oregon, December 10–11, 1964.

"Outdoor Recreation for America." Report to the President and the Congress by the Outdoor Recreation Resources Review Commission. Washington, D.C.: U.S. Government Printing Office, 1962.

"Nature's Constant Gift." TVA Report on the Water Resource of the Tennessee Valley, June, 1966.

PETERSON, DEAN F. "Man and His Water Resource." Faculty Honor Lecture, Utah State University, Logan, Utah, February, 1966.

POWERS, CHARLES F., AND ROBERTSON, ANDREW. "The Aging Great Lakes," *Scientific American,* Vol. CCV, No. 5 (November, 1966).

"Programs to Aid the Unemployed in the 1960's." W. E. Upjohn Institute (Kalamazoo, Mich.), January, 1965.

"Proposed Amistad Dam and Reservoir." Statement of the Rio Grande International Storage Dams Project, February 8, 1960.

"Report to Special Commission on Weather Modification." National Science Foundation, 1966.

THE RESOURCES AGENCY OF THE STATE OF CALIFORNIA. *The California State Water Project in 1964* (Bulletin No. 132–64, June, 1964); *North Coastal Area Investigation* (Bulletin No. 136, September, 1964).

———. Comments on the *Pacific Southwest Water Plan,* December, 1963.

"Restoring the Quality of Our Environment." Report of the Environmental Pollution Panel of the President's Science Advisory Committee. Washington, D.C.: U.S. Government Printing Office, 1965.

Save Our Water—The Peril to a Basic Resource." Switzerland: CIBA, 1963.

SHAPP, MILTON J. "Statement at White House Regional Conference," November 17, 1961.

SKINNER, ROOT A. "Southern California's Water Future," *INCO Magazine,* XXXI (Summer, 1966), 18–22.

STARNES, RICHARD. "Night Comes to Admiralty," *Field & Stream,* IV (August, 1965), 18–22.

UDALL, STEWART L. *The Quiet Crisis.* New York: Holt, Rinehart & Winston, 1963.

U.S. DEPARTMENT OF AGRICULTURE. *1955 Yearbook—Water.* Washington, D.C.: U.S. Government Printing Office, 1955.

U.S. DEPARTMENT OF HEALTH, EDUCATION, AND WELFARE. *National Conference on Water Pollution Proceedings,* December 12–14, 1960. Washington, D.C.: U.S. Government Printing Office, 1961.

————. *Conference on Pollution of the Interstate and Massachusetts Intrastate Waters of the Merrimack and Nashua Rivers, February 11, 1964.* Transcript of Conference.

U.S. DEPARTMENT OF THE INTERIOR. *Bureau of Sport Fisheries and Wildlife Report to Outdoor Recreation Resources Review Commission, ORRC Study Report No. 7.* Washington, D.C.: U.S. Government Printing Office, 1962.

————. *Garrison Diversion Unit.* Washington, D.C.: U.S. Government Printing Office, 1960.

————. *Principal Lakes of the United States.* Geological Survey Circular No. 476. Washington, D.C.: U.S. Government Printing Office, 1965.

————. *Water Resources Research Catalog,* Vol. I, February, 1965. Department of Water Resources Research. Washington, D.C.: U.S. Government Printing Office, 1965.

U.S. DEPARTMENT OF LABOR. *Fifty-second Annual Report, Fiscal Year 1964.* Washington, D.C.: U.S. Government Printing Office, 1964.

U.S. SENATE. Report No. 29 of Select Committee on National Water Resources, covering 90 studies pursuant to S. Res. 43 of 86th Congress, and committee prints listed below. Washington, D.C.: U.S. Government Printing Office, 1961.

No. 1   *Water Facts and Problems*
No. 2   *Reviews of National Water Resources During the Past 50 Years*
No. 3   *National Water Resources and Problems*
No. 4   *Surface Water Resources of the United States*
No. 5   *Population Projections and Economic Assumptions*
No. 6   *Views and Comments of the States*
No. 7   *Future Water Requirements for Municipal Use*

No. 8   Future Water Requirements for Principal Water-using Industries
No. 9   Pollution Abatement
No. 10   Electric Power in Relation to the Nation's Water Resources
No. 11   Future Needs for Navigation
No. 12   Land and Water Potentials and Future Requirements for Water
No. 13   Estimated Water Requirements for Agricultural Purposes and Their Effects on Water Supplies
No. 14   Future Needs for Reclamation in the United States
No. 15   Floods and Flood Control
No. 16   Flood Problems and Management in the Tennessee River Basin
No. 17   Water Recreation Needs in the United States 1960–2000
No. 18   Fish and Wildlife and Water Resources
No. 19   Water Resources of Alaska
No. 20   Water Resources of Hawaii
No. 21   Evapo-transpiration Reduction
No. 22   Weather Modification
No. 23   Evaporation Reduction and Seepage Control
No. 24   Water Quality Management
No. 25   River Forecasting and Hydrometeorological Analysis
No. 26   Saline Water Conversion
No. 27   Application and Effects of Nuclear Energy
No. 28   Water Resources Research Needs
No. 29   Water Requirements for Pollution Abatement
No. 30   Present and Prospective Means for Improved Reuse of Water
No. 31   The Impact of New Techniques on Integrated Multiple-purpose Water Development
No. 32   A Preliminary Report on the Supply of and Demand for Water in the United States as Estimated for 1980 and 2000.

SENATE PUBLIC WORKS COMMITTEE. Water Pollution Control. Hearings before Subcommittee on Flood Control on H.R. 3610 and S. 805, July 23, 1959. Washington, D.C.: U.S. Government Printing Office, 1959.
———. Water Pollution Control. Hearings by Subcommittee on Flood Control, May 8–9, 1961, on bills to amend the Federal Water Pollution Control Act. Washington, D.C.: U.S. Government Printing Office, 1961.

"Water—A Special Report," Power (New York), CX (June, 1966), 236 ff.
"The Water Crisis," Newsweek, LXVI (August 23, 1965), 48–52.
"Water in Industry." Published by the National Association of Manufacturers, New York, and the U.S. Chamber of Commerce, Washington, D.C., in cooperation with the National Task Committee on Industrial Wastes, January, 1965.
"Water on the Farm," Farm Quarterly, XX (Summer, 1965), 44–64.
WAYMAN, COOPER H. "A Hard Look at Soft Detergents," Bulletin of the Atomic Scientists, XXI (April, 1965), 22–26.

WHITE, GILBERT F. "The Facts About Our Water Supply," *Harvard Business Review* (Boston, Mass.), XXXVI (March–April, 1958), 87–94.

WOLF, LEONARD. "Cleaning Up the Merrimack," *Bulletin of the Atomic Scientists,* XXI (April, 1965), 16–22.

WRIGHT, JIM. *The Coming Water Famine.* New York: Coward-McCann, 1966.

Index